Explore s̶... ...dden gems

Scottish Gardens
open for charity

Contents

Scotland's **GARDENS** Scheme

Sponsored by

Investec

Tips & key to symbols

Top tips

By Arrangement

This is a great way to see a garden when it's quiet and Garden Owners will be delighted to hear from you to book a visit. Many gardens welcome visits from larger groups or clubs such as horticultural societies (regulations permitting), as well as individuals or couples. Do get in touch.

Photography

Most of our gardens are privately owned so any photographs taken must be for private use only. The Garden Owner's permission must be sought if images are to be included in publications. Our Volunteer Photographers may take photos on the open day. Please notify them if you don't wish to appear in our promotional materials.

Gardening Advice

Our Garden Openers love to chat about their gardens. If there's a bit of advice you're after, do ask!

Extra Assistance

Carers are offered free entry to our gardens and Assistance Dogs are always welcome.

Children & Families

Children are welcome with an accompanying adult, unless otherwise stated, but must be supervised at all times. Some openings offer children's activities – look for the children's activities symbol.

Group Visits

Many of our gardens are pleased to have groups visiting. Get in touch with the garden or contact the local District Organiser for more information.

Toilets

Private gardens do not normally have outside toilets. For security reasons, our Openers have been advised not to admit visitors into their homes.

Cancellations

All cancellations will be posted on our website, scotlandsgardens.org, under the garden listing.

Key to symbols

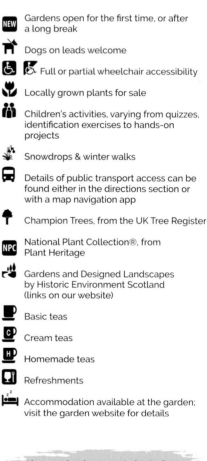

NEW Gardens open for the first time, or after a long break

Dogs on leads welcome

Full or partial wheelchair accessibility

Locally grown plants for sale

Children's activities, varying from quizzes, identification exercises to hands-on projects

Snowdrops & winter walks

Details of public transport access can be found either in the directions section or with a map navigation app

Champion Trees, from the UK Tree Register

NPC National Plant Collection®, from Plant Heritage

Gardens and Designed Landscapes by Historic Environment Scotland (links on our website)

Basic teas

Cream teas

Homemade teas

Refreshments

Accommodation available at the garden; visit the garden website for details

Always check our website before setting out, for any cancellations, last-minute changes to opening details or booking arrangements.

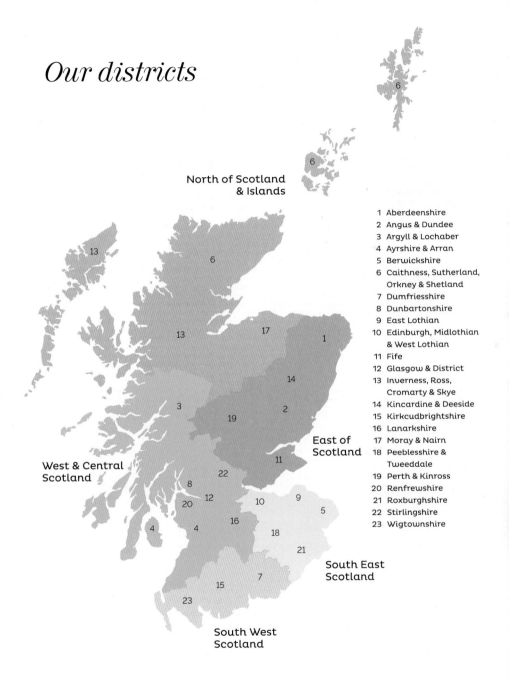

Our districts

North of Scotland
& Islands

East of
Scotland

West & Central
Scotland

South East
Scotland

South West
Scotland

1 Aberdeenshire
2 Angus & Dundee
3 Argyll & Lochaber
4 Ayrshire & Arran
5 Berwickshire
6 Caithness, Sutherland,
   Orkney & Shetland
7 Dumfriesshire
8 Dunbartonshire
9 East Lothian
10 Edinburgh, Midlothian
   & West Lothian
11 Fife
12 Glasgow & District
13 Inverness, Ross,
   Cromarty & Skye
14 Kincardine & Deeside
15 Kirkcudbrightshire
16 Lanarkshire
17 Moray & Nairn
18 Peeblesshire &
   Tweeddale
19 Perth & Kinross
20 Renfrewshire
21 Roxburghshire
22 Stirlingshire
23 Wigtownshire

Welcome

Welcome to a world of secret gardens, hidden gems and rare glimpses of the unique, the unusual and the exceptional.

Well, wasn't 2021 a rollercoaster? With the early season lockdown and many cancellations, it sometimes felt like a very dark time. But there really was a lot to celebrate in our 90th year, with most of our scheduled openings from June onwards going ahead as planned. We welcomed new visitors to our gardens and saw many happy reunions; we introduced takeaway teas; our plant sales were a hit. Most importantly, many charities were once again able to benefit from the funds raised at our open gardens.

Our gardens have been a great joy to so many of us this year and, once again, we thank the wonderful people who so generously throw open their gates to share their beautiful gardens, their enthusiasm and their gardening know how. We also applaud all our amazing network of volunteers around Scotland – our District Teams, who plan, organise and support so many garden openings around Scotland. It would not happen without them.

However – with a huge impact on our finances, this has been another challenging year for our charity and it will take us time to rebuild. To keep going, we need your help, so please get involved (contact details below):

- ✔ Donate to Scotland's Gardens Scheme to support our work

- ✔ Join one of our amazing District Teams

- ✔ Open your garden – if you love your garden, other people probably will too!

If you do just one thing, please spread the word about Scotland's Gardens Scheme. Enjoy your garden visits, chat to our garden owners, sample the famous tea and cakes and buy a plant or two to remind you of your visit – and don't forget to tell all your friends!

Liz Stewart
National Organiser

Front cover image: 2 Durnamuck © Andrea Jones

Back cover image: Temple Village

Editor: Liz Stewart

Artwork: Matt Armstrong, Serious Artworker, Daria Piskorz-Pronobis, Hazel Reid, Steven Ritchie

Maps: Alan Palfreyman Graphics

Contains OS Data © Crown Copyright and Database 2021

Printed by Belmont Press
ISBN13: 9780901549372

Scotland's Gardens Scheme Head Office

2nd Floor, 23 Castle Street

Edinburgh EH2 3DN

T: 0131 226 3714

E: info@scotlandsgardens.org

W: scotlandsgardens.org

Charity no: SC049866

FSC
MIX
Paper from responsible sources
FSC® C015185

Who's who

At the centre of Scotland's Gardens Scheme are hundreds of volunteers and garden owners all around Scotland who work tirelessly to organise and support garden openings. These amazing individuals are the heart and soul of our charity.

Scotland's Gardens Scheme is supported by our small team of Head Office staff and by our Board of Trustees, all of whom bring a range of specialist skills and interests. We are proud to have HRH The Duchess of Rothesay as our President and this year we are delighted to welcome a new Chairman, Dougal Philip, who will take over from David Mitchell in April. We would all like to say a special thank you to David for his many years of service to Scotland's Gardens Scheme and especially for his leadership through the challenges of the past two years.

Our staff and Trustees are pictured, left to right:

Peter Yellowlees (Honorary Treasurer), **Helen McMeekin** (Trustee), **David Buchanan-Cook** (Board Secretary), **Stephen McCallum** (Trustee), **Colin Crosbie** (Trustee), **Charlotte Hunt** (Honorary Vice President), **David Mitchell** (Chairman), **Charlotte Halliday** (Trustee), **Sarah Landale** (Deputy Chair), **Daria Piskorz-Pronobis** (Marketing Manager – Staff), **Emily Stair** (Trustee), **Hazel Reid** (Office Manager – Staff), **Liz Stewart** (National Organiser – Staff), **Steven Ritchie** (Communications Assistant – Staff), **Jonathan Cobb** (Trustee).

Chairman's message

Throughout life, if they are to grow and survive, individuals and communities must learn to adapt and change in response to new philosophies, opportunities, ideas or other challenges such as the climate and the pandemic.

Looking back over the past five years since I took the helm of this remarkable charity, I note that it has been a period of evolution and change like no other in our ninety-year history. Firstly we introduced the updated operating systems required to improve our effectiveness, outreach and ability to open gardens for charity, improving communication and resilience.

Next we strengthened and modernised our governance and reporting platform including becoming a SCIO, then as if that were not enough we had to rise to the challenges presented by Covid 19.

Throughout all of this, our community of Volunteers and Garden Openers has been a source of strength and inspiration to the Board and to myself as Chairman. The way in which they have supported our work with energy, dedication and a 'can do' attitude is admirable indeed.

You, our visitors, supporters and partners have also played a vital role in all of this, simply by being prepared to come to see our gardens, purchase plants and enjoy tea and cake.

The catalyst for all this effort is, I suggest, the 'life force' that we see in the gardens themselves. Year to year, despite the rigours of the variable Scottish climate, they bloom, grow, inspire, change and succeed in providing lessons for us all.

As I say welcome to the new trustees including the Chairman designate, Dougal Philip, I wish them well for the future and ask that you support them with their efforts to improve the quality of life for individuals and communities across Scotland. How can you do that?

Simply by visiting gardens in even greater numbers and by donating to the charity. Believe me, doing so will make you smile and feel better. Enjoy!

Thank you for your support.

Hugo Burnand ©

As President of Scotland's Gardens Scheme, it is a pleasure to introduce this year's guidebook and to have the opportunity to highlight the recent achievements of this wonderful organisation.

Firstly, and above all, I know that the garden openings across Scotland have provided an extremely welcome way for people to reunite with their friends and loved ones after the challenges of the last year. Your beautiful gardens have also been enjoyed by many who are new to the Scheme and who have been able to benefit from the accrued wisdom and experience of your slightly more seasoned gardening enthusiasts…

You have also raised a remarkable amount for charity, supporting, as you always do, a wide range of deserving causes and making a real difference to a great number of people throughout Scotland.

I should like to, as ever, express my warmest thanks to all your District Volunteers and Garden Openers, who have worked so hard and shown such determination, resilience, kindness and generosity.

May I wish you all good gardening and good weather for 2022!

Camilla

To plant a garden is to invest in tomorrow

At Investec Wealth & Investment we understand that growth doesn't happen by chance. That is why we have been sponsoring Scotland's Gardens Scheme, a source of beauty and inspiration, since 2009.

Like SGS, our heritage dates back over a century, providing exceptional levels of service to our clients. With offices in Edinburgh, Glasgow and across the UK, our local wealth experts can provide financial planning and tailor-made solutions to help you achieve your goals and secure your family's financial future.

With Investment Your Capital is at Risk.

Know where life can take you.

investecwin.co.uk

Our impact

Scotland's Gardens Scheme is a charity that supports the opening of gardens, mostly private, to the public, raising funds for other charities through garden gate tickets, plant sales and teas.

Did you know that 60% of funds raised through each garden opening, goes directly to support the owner's charity of choice? This means that in 2021, we supported over 250 good causes around Scotland from local, grassroots groups in the heart of communities, to national charities.

The remaining funds raised support our own charity to keep doing what we do, and also to make an annual donation to our three core beneficiaries, who we are immensely proud to support:

The Queen's Nursing Institute Scotland
dedicated to promoting excellence in community nursing to improve the health and well-being of people in Scotland

Maggie's
providing free cancer support and information in centres across the UK and online

Perennial
helping people who work in horticulture, and their families, when times get tough

Read more about our beneficiary charities on the following pages.

What we achieved together in 2021...

Over **750** volunteers gave an estimated **12,500** hours and their time, energy & enthusiasm, to organise...

Over **500** garden open days around Scotland

We welcomed an estimated **50,000** visitors to our open gardens

254 charitable causes supported and around **£300k** raised through garden openings (despite Covid cancellations!)

Most supported causes:

Healthcare & support services **34%**

Local communities (inc churches) **19%**

Wellbeing & community support **15%**

Exclusively yours...
for the day

Did you know that we have hundreds of gardens that are open to visitors by arrangement with the garden owner? This is your chance to arrange an exclusive visit!

BENEFITS OF ARRANGING A VISIT

Flexibility – arrange a time to suit you and the garden owner and last-minute bookings are often available

Privacy – see a garden away from the crowds

Enjoy a guided tour or freedom to wander

Small groups/couples or bigger groups welcome – just ask the owner or check the listing

HOW TO ARRANGE YOUR VISIT

Browse the guidebook or website and look for 'by arrangement' gardens in the opening details for each listing

Contact the garden owner to arrange a time – contact details or booking links will be in the book and website listing

Enjoy your visit!

Argyll and Lochaber, Dal an Eas © Nick Edgington

THE QUEEN'S NURSING INSTITUTE SCOTLAND

Scotland's Gardens Scheme was founded in 1931 to raise money for the Queen's Nursing Institute Scotland. Garden owners and visitors have been supporting nurses in Scotland's communities ever since.

Thank you.

Today, funding from Scotland's Gardens Scheme goes directly to helping the next generation of community nurses build a fairer, kinder, greener Scotland. We are two charities working together to enable Scotland's communities to flourish.

p: +44 (0)131 229 2333   **w:** www.qnis.org.uk   **e:** office@qnis.org.uk

Registered Scottish Charitable Incorporated Organisation SC005751

Go wild

One of the most commented-on points by garden visitors this year has been the number of gardens that now include a little bit of wild space to encourage biodiversity. The good news is that a laissez-faire approach to gardening can be a great way to let nature flourish. Here are some top tips inspired by our open gardens.

Don't mow the lawn – or at least, leave a little bit to grow long and see what happens. This creates a mini-jungle allowing shelter for all kinds of beneficial bug life. You'll be surprised at what comes up naturally, such as clover and daisies but you can also plant bulbs and wildflower plugs for naturalising and extending the feeding season for pollinators. Leave an area unmown for a month in the summer or why not dedicate a patch for the whole season and leave uncut until autumn. Clean mown edges around your long grass, or even a path through the middle, will make it look designed.

Unmowed patches at Skelbo House © Colin Gregory

Just add water – many of our gardens have wonderful ponds and water features, home to wildfowl, amphibians, dragonflies and other water-babies, but you don't need to go large to bring the benefits of water to your wild space. One of the most popular videos on our YouTube channel shows how to create a tiny pond out of a kitchen sink!

Cut out chemicals – to discourage hungry pests and beasties, try companion planting instead of reaching for the pesticide. Companion planting uses plants that are strongly scented to confuse pests seeking their host plant or can attract beneficial insects such as ladybirds to prey on aphids. Calendula, nasturtium, garlic chives and borage are just a few examples – find out more on the RHS website rhs.org.uk.

Grow and share! Boost your plant collection by having a go at propagating your own, either through cuttings or by collecting seeds in your garden to grow on yourself or swap with friends and neighbours. Have a look at the videos on our YouTube channel for tips to get you started.

Above all, talk to other gardeners! Gardeners have a wealth of knowledge, and everyone has their own top tips – and sometimes even plants – to share, so prepare to be inspired.

Find out top tips from our Garden Owners from our YouTube channel by scanning the QR code on the right.

How Perennial Helps

Perennial is the UK's only charity helping people in horticulture build and live better lives, but we can't provide our support for all those who look after our green spaces without your help. There are lots of ways to get involved. To find out more visit **perennial.org.uk**.

"Perennial's income has dropped dramatically due to Covid-19, yet the demand for their help continues to increase. Their partnership with Scotland's Gardens Scheme helps them to continue to deliver their frontline help and be confident to plan and launch new services."

Carole Baxter,
Perennial Trustee and Presenter of BBC Scotland Beechgrove TV programme.

How we helped Robert*

Life for self-employed gardener Robert has been tough over the last few years. A harsh Scottish winter in 2013 left him with no work, money worries and three teenage children to feed. More recently, ill health and relationship breakdown, has left him feeling vulnerable and scared about what the future will look like for him and his family.

But through it all Perennial's team have supported them, and now retired, Robert reflects on his relief at finding Perennial.

"I feel very lucky to have found Perennial – they totally transformed the lives of me and my children."

*Name changed to preserve anonymity and photo is a library photo.

Helping people in horticulture
Perennial

Donate now
0800 093 8792
perennial.org.uk/donate

Diana Macnab Award
for outstanding service

Each year we recognise a volunteer who has shown outstanding service to Scotland's Gardens Scheme. After the trials and tribulations presented by another extraordinary year, we decided to make two awards to recognise two exceptional people.

Margaret Gimblett

Margaret retired from her role as District Organiser for Perth & Kinross in summer 2021. She joined the Perth & Kinross committee in 2012 and became its chairman in 2013. Her enthusiasm, endless energy and fun leadership inspired everyone and injected a new purpose into her committee. In addition to keeping her District abreast of matters arising from Head Office, Margaret was also looking after nine gardens. Margaret has been instrumental in encouraging more small gardens and village gardens to open and this has been reflected in the District's annual takings. Margaret presided over their highest ever collection of funds in 2018.

She always sees the best in people and is always happy to help and encourage garden owners with advice and sometimes the odd cutting or two!

Margaret has been a tireless ambassador for Scotland's Gardens Scheme. She will be a hard act to follow!

Members of the Perthshire Team

Helen Rushton

Helen wears several hats for Scotland's Gardens Scheme. She is an Area Organiser for Aberdeenshire and opens her own Garden, Bruckhills Croft near Inverurie where she holds a National Plant Collection of snowdrops. Helen also manages the Scotland's Gardens Scheme Facebook page on a voluntary basis, writing literally hundreds of engaging posts through the year, reaching tens of thousands of people and keeping everyone up to date with garden news.

'I'm really pleased that Helen will be receiving the award. The amount she does for SGS, quietly behind the scenes, is just incredible. Her open days at Bruckhills Croft are expertly organised, and while she always seems completely relaxed, she is fully prepared to dash into the kitchen and whip up another sponge cake if stocks run low.' – *Verity Walters, District Organiser, Aberdeenshire.*

Find your way through cancer

Come to Maggie's

Maggie's offers the best possible psychological and emotional support for free to anyone with cancer and their families.

Built in the grounds of NHS hospitals, our centres are warm and welcoming places, with professional staff on hand to offer the support you need to find your way through cancer.

Our centres are open Monday to Friday, 9am – 5pm, and no referral is required. We are also online at maggies.org.

Maggie's centres across Scotland receive vital funds from every garden opening. Our heartfelt thanks go to everyone who supports Scotland's Gardens Scheme by opening their garden, volunteering or visiting a garden.

Scotland's
GARDENS
Scheme
OPEN FOR CHARITY

maggies.org

Maggie Keswick Jencks Cancer Caring Centres Trust (Maggie's) is a registered charity, no. SC024414

MAGGIE'S
Everyone's home of cancer care

East Lothian, Stobshiel House

We need your support

Scotland's Gardens Scheme is a charity, just like all the ones we support, and the past two years of cancellations and disruptions due to Covid have had a devastating impact on our own income.

Our small Head Office Team works hard to promote our participating gardens throughout the year. We are also dedicated to supporting our hundreds of volunteers to help them bring our garden open days to life and ensure a positive experience for everyone.

We know that our garden openings bring great enjoyment to garden owners and visitors alike, as well as providing valuable support to so many charities.

So, if you enjoy our garden openings and value our work, please do consider supporting our charity.

Dumfriesshire, Drumpark © Stuart Littlewood

Make a donation

Help to support our running costs, enabling us to give more funds to our beneficiary charities.

Leave a gift in your will

A legacy will help to support our operating costs enabling us to give more funds to our beneficiary charities. Indeed, without generous past legacies, we would have struggled to survive over the past two years.

To find out more about how to support our charity:

Visit our donations page **scotlandsgardens.org/donate/**
Call us on **0131 226 3714** or email **info@scotlandsgardens.org**
Write to us at **23 Castle Street, Edinburgh, EH2 3DN**

Thank you!

Photography Competition

New for 2022, to celebrate Visit Scotland's Year of Stories, we're inviting you to share the stories of your garden visits and open days through the year by entering our first ever photography competition!

Further details can be found on our website:

scotlandsgardens.org/photo-competition/

At Queen Victoria Park one's visitors always get a royal welcome.

Queen Victoria Park is an exclusive residential neighbourhood for the over 55s within a 100-acre garden paradise at Inchmarlo Retirement Village near Banchory in Aberdeenshire on Royal Deeside.

Queen Victoria Park is next to Inchmarlo Golf Centre and the River Dee, and comprises an active community of like-minded people with round-the-clock security and support services.

- 1 bed apartments with balconies from £85,000
- 2 bed apartments with balconies from £105,000

To find out more or to arrange viewings: please call Fenella Scott on 01330 824981 or email fenella.scott@inchmarlo-retirement.co.uk

Where Gracious Living
Comes Naturally

inchmarlo-retirement.co.uk

Discover how Queen Victoria Park might be just your type of place.

Join in and make a difference

Scotland's Gardens Scheme is an amazing charity which brings people together to share their love of gardens, all while supporting hundreds of charities each year.

And the good news is, there are lots of different ways to get involved. We're always looking for new gardens of all shapes, sizes and designs to join in and we'd love to hear from you!

Love your garden? Why not open it for charity!

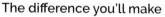

Lizzie and Malcolm Schofield opened their garden for the first time in 2021

The difference you'll make

It's a great way to support the work of hundreds of charities each year and inspire visitors by sharing your love of gardening.

The support you'll receive

Your garden will be promoted in the Yellow Book, online and in the press. You'll also receive advice and support from our Head Office and volunteer District Teams and you'll meet loads of like-minded people!

Become a volunteer

Volunteers are the heart and soul of our organisation, and we are proud to be 98% volunteer led. We are always keen to welcome new people to get involved at all levels and in all areas around Scotland. We have different roles to suit your time, interest and availability, so please do browse our website for current opportunities.

You could be an Area Organiser and help to find new gardens to join us, or a District Treasurer helping with finance; you could volunteer to help out on open days, by selling garden gate tickets or helping with baking and teas; you could even share your photography and social media skills. You'll meet new friends and visit beautiful gardens, all while helping to raise valuable funds for charity.

To find out more, please email **info@scotlandsgardens.org** or visit **scotlandsgardens.org/join-in/**

Scotland's Gardens Scheme Fife © David Buchanan-Cook

East Lothian: Stobshiel © Delia Ridley-Thomas

Scottish Gardens
open for charity

Welcome to our gardens

We do hope you enjoy exploring the gardens on the following pages and planning your visits for the year ahead.

A few things to remember before you set out:

- **Plan ahead**

  Check our website for any last-minute changes to opening details or booking arrangements.

- **Be a responsible visitor**

  Make sure you follow any Scottish Government guidance or restrictions that may be in place.

- **Arrange a visit**

  Did you know that many of our gardens are open by arrangement?

  Contact the garden owner to plan a visit – contact details can be found in the garden listing.

Enjoy your visits and we look forward to seeing you in the garden.

Snowdrops &
winter walks

Yellow snowdrops at Bruckhills Croft, Aberdeenshire

*'Galanthophile
an enthusiastic collector or lover of snowdrops'*

We missed our 2021 Snowdrop openings but are so pleased to be back for 2022 with a range of magical winter walks for you. It's always such a thrill to see the first of the snowdrops peeping through the leaves, then emerging into carpets of white as far as the eye can see.

So, wrap up warm and head outdoors to explore these beautiful snowdrop and winter gardens. Many welcome dogs on leads and some even provide homemade teas to keep you warm.

Find a winter wonderland near you

© Andy Leonard

Find your winter wonderland in the listings below; more details in the following pages and on our website. Look out for the snowdrop icon for gardens with snowdrop displays.

For more places to visit as part of the Scottish Snowdrop Festival, visit **discoverscottishgardens.org.**

Aberdeenshire

- Bruckhills Croft
- Laundry Cottage

Angus & Dundee

- Dunninald Castle
- Lawton House

Dumfriesshire

- Craig

East Lothian

- Shepherd House

Fife

- Auchtertool House
- Millfield Garden

Kincardine & Deeside

- Ecclesgreig Castle

Kirkcudbrightshire

- Barholm Castle

Lanarkshire

- Cleghorn

Moray & Nairn

- 10 Pilmuir Road West

Peeblesshire & Tweeddale

- Kailzie Gardens
- Kirkton Manor House

Perth & Kinross

- Braco Castle
- Cloan
- Fingask Castle
- Princeland House

Wigtownshire

- Craichlaw

Cleghorn, Lanarkshire © Alistair McNeill

New gardens for 2022 NEW

It's always a thrill when the owner of a potential new garden gets in touch, keen to share their beloved garden. We know that our visitors are always excited to see what new gardens we have in store for you.

We're proud to present some fantastic new gardens for you this year. Remember, they are all raising funds for charity so please do lend your support and make their open day a special experience.

We would like to thank all of our garden owners, new and old, for throwing open their garden gates to share with you. If you'd like to join in by opening your own garden, we would love to hear from you.

Ayrshire: 25 Stoneyholm Road

Perth & Kinross: Princeland House © Graham Wood

Edinburgh: Clermont © Yerbury Studio

Fife: Coul House © David Buchanan-Cook

Glasgow: Heart of Scotstoun Community Gardens

Dumfriesshire: Craigieburn

Lanarkshire: Auchlochan Walled Garden

East Lothian: A Blackbird Sings

Lanarkshire: Little Sparta © Andrew Lawson

Stirlingshire: Tillicoultry Parish Church Community Garden

Skye: Armadale Castle © Armadale Castle, Gardens and Museum

Berwickshire: Anton's Hill Walled Garden ©Andrew McCarthy

New gardens by district

Aberdeenshire

- Upper Third Croft

Angus & Dundee

- Colliston Castle
- The Old Schoolhouse

Argyll & Lochaber

- Achamore Gardens

Ayrshire & Arran

- 25 Stoneyholm Road
- 29 Scaur O'Doon Road
- The Garden at Carbieston

Berwickshire

- Anton's Hill Walled Garden
- Broomhill Villa

Dumfriesshire

- Craigieburn
- Garden Cottage, Knockhill

East Lothian

- A Blackbird Sings
- Gifford Bank*

Edinburgh, Midlothian & West Lothian

- Claremont House
- Finlay's Wee Garden

Fife

- Auchtertool House
- Coul House
- Millfield Garden
- Strathkinness Community Garden and Orchard

Glasgow & District

- Braehead House
- Heart of Scotstoun Community Gardens

Inverness, Ross, Cromarty & Skye

- 7 Braes of Conon
- Ar Dachaigh
- Armadale Castle, Gardens & Museum
- Paabay House Woodland Garden
- Raasay Walled Garden

Kincardine & Deeside

- The Old Farmhouse

Kirkcudbrightshire

- Clonyard Farm

Lanarkshire

- Auchlochan Walled Garden
- Lindsaylands
- Little Sparta

Peeblesshire & Tweeddale

- Carolside*

Perth & Kinross

- Princeland House

Renfrewshire

- No 14 – A Village Garden
- Perch Corner

Stirlingshire

- Tillicoultry Parish Church Community Garden

Wigtownshire

- Aldouran Wetland Garden
- Glasnick Smithy/House on Stilts
- The Old Manse

*Returning after a break of over five years

Scotland's Gardens 🌷 Scheme plant sales

Each year we hold a number of big plant sales across the country, run by our District Teams and Garden Owners, with plants that have been lovingly propagated by our volunteers. Locally grown plants are often well suited to your

growing conditions and it's a great way to boost your borders with a range of interesting plants.

Best of all, you will find plenty of volunteers who are happy to answer your plant queries and share their gardening know how.

As well as our major plant sales listed below, many garden openings include a range of lovely plants for sale. Keep an eye out for the Plants for Sale icon on the following pages and on our website.

© Camelia Hudema

Aberdeenshire
Leith Hall Plant Sale
Huntly, AB54 4NQ
Saturday 28 May, 10am – 3pm

Angus & Dundee
Angus Plant Sale
Logie Walled Garden, DD8 5PN
Saturday 6 August, 2 – 5pm

Dunbartonshire
4 Cairndhu Gardens Plant Sale
Helensburgh, G84 8PG
Sunday 19 June, 2 – 5pm

Glenarn Plant Sale
Rhu, G84 8LL
Sunday 21 August, 2 – 5pm

James Street Community Garden
Plant Sale
Helensburgh, G84 8EY
Sunday 4 September, 12 – 4pm

Edinburgh, Midlothian & West Lothian
Redcroft
Edinburgh EH12 6EP
Saturday/Sunday, 14/15 May, 2pm - 5pm

Fife
Cambo Spring Plant & Garden Market
Kingsbarns, KY16 8QD
Sunday 10 April, 11am – 3pm

SGS Plant Sale
at St Andrews Botanic Garden
St Andrews, KY16 8RT
Sunday 2 October, 11am – 3pm

Peeblesshire & Tweeddale
Lamancha Community Hub Plant Sale
(NEW)
Old Moffat Road, Lamancha, EH46 7BD
Sunday 5 June, 10am – 1pm

Renfrewshire
SGS Kilmacolm Plant Sale
Outside Kilmacolm Library,
Kilmacolm, PA13 4LE
Saturday 30 April, 10am – 12noon

Stirlingshire
Kilbryde Castle (NEW)
Dunblane FK15 9NF
Sunday 22 May, 11am – 5pm
New for 2022, this opening will include a plant sale with local nurseries – check the Scotland's Gardens Scheme website for further information nearer the time

ARGYLE®
CONSULTING LIMITED

Expert financial
solutions tailored
to you.

argyleconsulting.co.uk

Financial
Planners

Chartered

Garden groups & village adventures

Group and village openings are amongst our most loved events and provide the opportunity to see a wonderful range of gardens, all on the same day. From tiny, sculptural urban courtyards to cottage gardens brimming with colour and frothing with insects, our garden owners are eager to share their much loved spaces with you.

Find out more about our group and village openings on the following page and do check our website for updates and new additions.

Would you like to join in with a group of friends and neighbours to share your gardens? We would love to hear from you. Please contact **info@scotlandsgardens.org**

Edinburgh: Even More Gardens of the Lower New Town

Credit @iangblack

Aberdeenshire

- Hatton of Fintray Village Gardens*

Angus & Dundee

- Brechin Gardens in June*
- Brechin Gardens in July*
- Trio of Gardens on Glamis Drive*

Argyll & Lochaber

- Ardverikie with Aberarder

Ayrshire & Arran

- Dundonald Village Gardens*

Berwickshire

- Coldstream Open Gardens
- Duns Open Gardens
- Marlfield Gardens

Caithness, Sutherland, Orkney & Shetland

- Old Granary Quoy and The Quoy of Houton*

Dunbartonshire

- Hillcroft with Stonecroft*

East Lothian

- Dirleton Village
- Inveresk Village
- Stenton Village
- Tyninghame House and The Walled Garden

Edinburgh

- Broomieknowe Gardens*
- Dean Gardens
- Even More Gardens of the Lower New Town
- Moray Place and Bank Gardens
- Pentland Crescent Gardens*
- Silverburn Village
- Spring Temple Gardens

Fife

- Blebo Craigs Village Gardens
- Boarhills Village Gardens*
- Crail: Gardens in the Burgh
- Newburgh – Hidden Gardens
- Pittenweem: Gardens in the Burgh

Glasgow & District

- Kilsyth Gardens
- The Gardens of Milton of Campsie*

Inverness, Ross, Cromarty & Skye

- Kiltarlity Gardens

Kirkcudbrightshire

- Four Gardens in Anwoth*

Peeblesshire & Tweeddale

- Gattonside Village Gardens
- West Linton Village Gardens

Roxburghshire

- Morebattle Village Gardens*
- Yetholm Village Gardens

Stirlingshire

- Bridge of Allan Gardens

Wigtownshire

- Damnaglaur House with Amulree and Rawson Garden
- Damnaglaur House with The Homestead and Mid Curghie*

*Includes new gardens; check the listing for details

Champion trees 🌳

Cedar of Lebanon, Helensbank Garden

Champion Trees are recognised by the Tree Register as being the UK's tallest, oldest, widest or rarest examples of their species and you can find examples of these venerable trees in our gardens, listed below. Take a moment to breathe in their history and imagine all the events and lives that have passed under their boughs over many centuries. Look out for the Tree icon in the book and do ask the garden owners to tell you about their tree treasures.

● Aberdeenshire
Cruickshank Botanic Garden
Quercus ilex, Acer griseum and a tri-stemmed Nothofagus obliqua

● Angus & Dundee
Colliston Castle (NEW)
Wellingtonia, Copper Beech

● Argyll & Lochaber
Ardkinglas Woodland Garden
The mightiest conifer in Europe and others

Benmore Botanic Garden
Many rare trees and giant conifers

● Caithness & Sutherland
Amat
Abies Procera, Noble Fir

● East Lothian
Gullane House
Elm, Oak

Tyninghame House and The Walled Garden
Two British and seven Scottish

● Fife
Helensbank
The garden has a 'notable' Cedar of Lebanon - 2nd largest in Fife

● Inverness, Ross, Cromarty & Skye
House of Aigas and Field Centre
Douglas fir, Atlas cedar and Sequoiadendron giganteum

Dundonnell House
Yew and holly

Old Allangrange
Yew and sweet chestnut

● Kirkcudbrightshire
Threave Garden
Acer platanoides 'Princeton Gold'; Carpinus caroliniana; X Cuprocyparis leylandii 'Picturesque' and a further 25 Scottish Champion Trees

● Peeblesshire & Tweeddale
Dawyck Botanic Garden
Numerous

Kailzie Gardens
Larch planted 1725

● Perthshire
Megginch Castle
Acer palmatum

Fingask Castle
Pinus wallichiana (Bhutan Pine) and the handsome remnants of what was the largest walnut in Scotland

● Wigtownshire
Castle Kennedy and Garden
95 in total; including 12 British, 30 Scottish, 44 for Dumfries and Galloway and 9 trees described as 'otherwise remarkable'

Logan Botanic Garden
Polylepis and Eucalyptus

Logan House Gardens
7 British and 11 Scottish

Did you know...
The Douglas fir can live for 500 years and grow up to 60m tall in Britain.
The Cercidiphyllum japonicum is often known as the 'Candyfloss Tree' as its turning leaves release the smell of burnt sugar in autumn.
Giant redwoods can live for over 3,000 years as the tannin in their bark helps to boost their resistance to pests and diseases.

Looks like you need more square feet.

Our experienced sales and lettings teams have a proven track record of achieving the best possible outcome for our clients. We pride ourselves on our local knowledge and connections and provide a personal and bespoke service to property owners throughout Scotland.

RETTIE

PROPERTY WITH CHARACTER

0131 220 4160

rettie.co.uk

National Plant Collections

National Plant Collections ® (NPCs) are registered collections of plants – usually based on botanic groupings – which are cultivated with the aim of preserving them for future generations. As such, they play an important role in the conservation work of the accrediting body, Plant Heritage.

The process for becoming the holder of an NPC is very challenging and the holder must demonstrate in-depth knowledge of the collection, as well as maintaining comprehensive plant records, accurate labelling, evidence of ongoing research and a plan for succession. All collections must be accessible to the public.

For further information, visit **plantheritage.org.uk**

We are proud to share the following collections with you through Scotland's Gardens Scheme. Do take the opportunity to speak to the garden owner about their National Collection – you will find them fascinating! Find more openings details on the following pages and on our website.

Helen Rushton achieved National Plant Collections ® status in 2021 for her *Galanthus* collection at Bruckhills Croft

● Aberdeenshire
Bruckhills Croft
Galanthus (NEW)
Open by arrangement 25 January - 11 March for Snowdrops and Winter Walks. Also open Sunday 3 July, 12pm - 5pm

● Argyll & Lochaber
Benmore Botanic Garden
Abies, South American temperate conifers, Picea
Open for Scotland's Gardens Scheme on Sunday 2 October, 10am - 5pm*

● Fife
Cambo Spring Plant & Garden Market
Galanthus
Sunday 10 April, 11am – 3pm*

Helensbank
Portland Roses
Open by arrangement 1 June - 30 September

● Peeblesshire & Tweeddale
Carolside
Pre 19th century Gallica Roses
Saturday 9 July, 11am – 5pm*

Dawyck Botanic Garden
Larix spp. and Tsuga spp
Sunday 9 October, 10am – 5pm*

● Perth & Kinross
Megginch Castle
Scottish cider apples, Scottish Heritage apples and pears
Sunday 10 April, 12pm – 4pm

● Stirlingshire
Milseybank
Meconopsis
Open by arrangement 1 May - 31 May

● Wigtownshire
Amulree
Nicotiana species
Saturday/Sunday, 16/17 July 10am - 4pm

Logan Botanic Garden
Gunnera, Leptospermum, Griselinia, Clianthus and Sutherlandia
Sunday 22 May, 10am – 5pm*

*Also open on other dates through the season – check the garden's website.

Visit four Botanic Gardens to see one of the richest plant collections on Earth

Edinburgh
Arboretum Place and Inverleith Row,
Edinburgh EH3 5LR
Tel 0131 248 2909 | rbge.org.uk
Open every day from 10 am (except 1 January
and 25 December)
Garden entry is free

Logan
Port Logan, Stranraer,
Dumfries and Galloway DG9 9ND
Tel 01776 860231 | rbge.org.uk/logan
Open daily 1 March to 15 November
Admission charge applies

Benmore
Dunoon, Argyll PA23 8QU
Tel 01369 706261 | rbge.org.uk/benmore
Open daily 1 March to 31 October
Admission charge applies

Dawyck
Stobo, Scottish Borders EH45 9JU
Tel 01721 760254 | rbge.org.uk/dawyck
Open daily 1 February to 30 November
Admission charge applies

Become a Friend and help us to explore, conserve
and explain the world of plants for a better future.
Call **0131 552 5339** or visit **rbge.org.uk/membership**

Royal
Botanic Garden
Edinburgh

Aberdeenshire

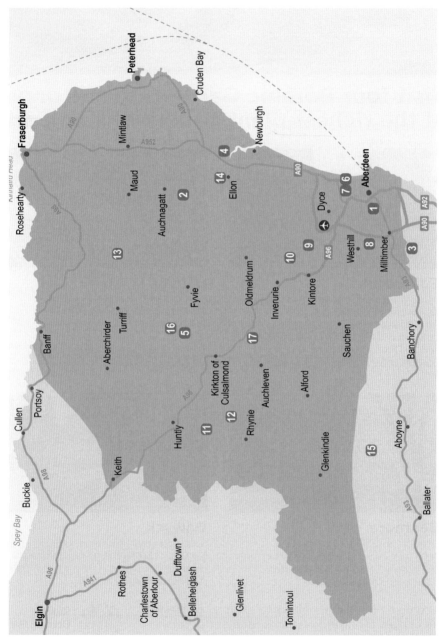

Aberdeenshire

OUR VOLUNTEER ORGANISERS

District Organiser:	Verity Walters	Tillychetly, Alford AB33 8HQ E: info@scotlandsgardens.org
Area Organisers:	Gill Cook Anne Fettes Jennie Gibson Anne Lawson Helen Rushton	 6 The Chanonry, Old Aberdeen AB24 1RP Asloun, Alford AB33 8NR Bruckhills Croft, Inverurie AB51 8YB
District Photographer:	Andy Leonard	Parkvilla, 47 Schoolhill, Ellon AB41 9AJ
Treasurer:	Ann Doyle	South Cottage, Inverurie AB51 8YS

GARDENS OPEN ON A SPECIFIC DATE

Westhall Castle, Oyne, Inverurie	Sunday, 10 April
Auchmacoy, Ellon	Sunday, 10 April
Cruickshank Botanic Garden, 23 St Machar Drive, Aberdeen	Saturday, 14 May
Leith Hall Plant Sale, Huntly	Saturday, 28 May
Airdlin Croft, Ythanbank, Ellon	Fri/Sat/Sun, 3/4/5 June
Heatherwick Farm, Kintore, Inverurie	Sunday, 19 June
Hatton of Fintray Village Gardens, Hatton of Fintray Village Hall	Sunday, 26 June
Heatherwick Farm, Kintore, Inverurie	Sunday, 26 June
Altries, Maryculter, Aberdeenshire	Sunday, 26 June
Bruckhills Croft, Rothienorman, Inverurie	Sunday, 3 July
Easter Ord Farm, Easter Ord, Skene, Westhill	Fri/Sat/Sun, 8/9/10 July
5 Woodlands Gardens, Cults, Aberdeen	Sunday, 17 July
Parkvilla, 47 Schoolhill, Ellon	Saturday/Sunday, 30/31 July
Easter Ord Farm, Easter Ord, Skene, Westhill	Fri/Sat/Sun, 19/20/21 August
Heatherwick Farm, Kintore, Inverurie	Sunday, 4 September
Tarland Community Garden, Tarland, Aboyne	Saturday, 24 September

GARDENS OPEN BY ARRANGEMENT

Laundry Cottage, Culdrain, Gartly, Huntly	1 January - 31 December
Bruckhills Croft, Rothienorman, Inverurie	25 January - 11 March
Chaplains' Court, 20 The Chanonry, Old Aberdeen, Aberdeen	1 April - 30 September
Upper Third Croft, Rothienorman, Inverurie	1 June - 31 August
Middle Cairncake, Cuminestown, Turriff	1 June - 31 August

Aberdeenshire

 5 WOODLANDS GARDENS
Cults, Aberdeen AB15 9DU
Keith Thornton

A two-thirds of an acre plot planted out in 2008 and specialising in more unusual trees and shrubs. The collection of Magnolia trees has reached flowering size, and includes *sprengeri* 'Diva', *sargentiana* 'Star Wars' and *Michelia doltsopa*. The rhododendron borders include early flowers, scented species and scented azaleas. Old roses feature with a collection of scented heritage French varieties, including *centifolia de peinte*, 'cabbage' roses and Pemberton musk roses. There is a small orchard of apple, pear and plum trees, and a large outdoor peach in the courtyard garden. Soft fruit and vegetable plots are laid out.

Open: Sunday 17 July, noon - 5pm, admission £5.00, children free.

Directions: From the A90, take Milltimber junction A93 to Cults. At lights turn left up Kirk Brae, then right to Friarsfield Road. At top of hill, turn right into Woodlands housing estate, first left then first left again into Woodlands Gardens. From the A92 take the A93 to Braemar, after 200m turn right to Craigton Road, follow this for one mile, then Woodlands estate is on the left. The nearest bus stop is *Baird's Brae* on routes 19 or 201, then about an 18-minute walk.

Opening for: Scottish SPCA: Drumoak Branch, The New Arc & Annie's Trust

AIRDLIN CROFT
Ythanbank, Ellon AB41 7TS
Richard and Ellen Firmin
T: 01358 761491 E: rsf@airdlin.com
W: www.airdlin.com

Since 1983 the garden has been developed to be both attractive to wildlife and horticulturally interesting, while also providing fruit and vegetables. Polytunnels with figs, peaches and pumpkins in one and a collection of hostas, wrestling for space with seed-grown rhododendrons, in the other. Native trees form the backbone of the woodland garden, providing shelter for a range of shrubs and herbaceous plants from around the world. In the new windswept garden, an embryonic shelterbelt is struggling to protect recent plantings. We are avid propagators and there is always an interesting range of plants available for sale.

Open: Friday/Saturday/Sunday, 3/4/5 June, 1pm - 5pm, admission £5.00, children free.

Directions: From the A948, three miles north of Ellon, take the left turn towards *Drumwhindle*. After another couple of miles take the second left towards *Cairnorrie*. Proceed for nearly a mile, ignoring the first Airdlin Croft at Coalmoss, and turn left at the first bend, go down our 300 yard track, parking is in the field at the bottom.

Opening for: Fauna & Flora International

Aberdeenshire

3 ALTRIES
Maryculter, Aberdeenshire AB12 5GD
Mr and Mrs Melfort Campbell

The Altries garden has been redesigned to give a feeling of space and to let in the light. The house itself is surrounded by a terraced area, borders and lawns. There is an exceptional view looking west up the River Dee; a woodland walk; a slate sphere sculpture using the original slates of the house following the refurbishment; a striking ten-foot wall making use of the down-takings of the house; a small new greenhouse with rose arbour path and further use of granite; and the original walled garden which has vegetables, fruit, and a picking garden. Each area of the garden has its own feeling of being a separate destination. Beautiful mature beech trees surround the area, giving a great sense of privacy.

Open: Sunday 26 June, 2pm - 5pm, admission £5.00, children free. Disabled parking at the house.

Directions: From Bridge of Dee, follow the South Deeside road, B9077. Half a mile after Maryculter House Hotel, turn left at yellow *SGS* sign, and follow signs to car park. For SatNav follow AB12 5GJ.

Opening for: River Dee Trust

4 AUCHMACOY
Ellon AB41 8RB
Mr and Mrs Charles Buchan
E: sharon@buchan.co.uk

Auchmacoy House's attractive policies feature spectacular displays of thousands of daffodils.

Open: Sunday 10 April, 1pm - 4pm, admission £4.00, children free. Please, NO dogs.

Directions: A90 from Aberdeen. Turn right to Auchmacoy/Collieston.

Opening for: The Royal British Legion: Ellon Branch

5 BRUCKHILLS CROFT
Rothienorman, Inverurie AB51 8YB
Paul and Helen Rushton
T: 01651 821596 E: helenrushton1@aol.com

An informal country cottage garden extending to three-quarters of an acre with a further acre as wildflower meadow and pond. There are several distinct areas which include a white border; a butterfly alley; kitchen garden with polytunnel; greenhouse and fruit cage; an orchard and a blue and yellow border. Relax on one of the many seats in the garden and soak up the atmosphere. Awarded National Collection status for Galanthus (snowdrops) in 2021. National Plant Collection: Galanthus.

Open: by arrangement 25 January - 11 March for Snowdrops and Winter Walks. Also open Sunday 3 July, noon - 5pm. Admission £5.00, children free.

Directions: From Rothienorman take the B9001 north for two-and-a-half miles. On the S-bend turn left. Take the second left *Bruckhills* sign. At the farmyard turn sharp right (opposite farmhouse), and the croft is at the end of the lane.

Opening for: Befriend A Child Ltd

Aberdeenshire

6 CHAPLAINS' COURT

20 The Chanonry, Old Aberdeen, Aberdeen AB24 1RQ
Irene Wischik
T: 01224 491675 E: irene@wischik.com

This historic walled garden has a long, well-stocked herbaceous border offering a succession of vivid colour from early spring to winter. It is divided by an ornamental pergola, a perfect place to sit and enjoy the garden. Large trees of ash, beech, horse chestnut, oak and sycamore give this garden a mature feel. A specimen Camperdown elm sits in the centre of the lawn, which in spring is covered in a carpet of crocuses, snowdrops and scilla. Vegetables and herbs produce plentiful crops, together with newly planted espalier and fan trained apple and pear trees.

Open: by arrangement 1 April - 30 September, admission £5.00, children free.

Directions: Bus 1 or 2 from Aberdeen city centre to St Machar Drive, and head towards St Machar Cathedral. Or drive down St Machar Drive, turn into The Chanonry and drive down until the junction with Don Street.

Opening for: SSAFA Forces Help

Chaplains' Court

7 CRUICKSHANK BOTANIC GARDEN

23 St Machar Drive, Aberdeen AB24 3UU
Cruickshank Botanic Garden Trust, Aberdeen University
W: www.abdn.ac.uk/botanic-garden

A tour is offered by the Curator, Mark Paterson. The garden is 4.5 hectares, and comprises a rock garden built in the 1960s complete with cascading water and pond system; a long double-sided herbaceous border; a formal rose garden with drystone walling and an arboretum. It has a large collection of flowering bulbs and rhododendrons, and many unusual shrubs and trees. It is sometimes known as 'Aberdeen's best kept secret'.
Champion Trees: *Quercus ilex, Acer griseum* and a tri-stemmed *Nothofagus obliqua.*

Aberdeenshire

Open: Saturday 14 May, 1pm - 3pm, admission £5.00, children free. Open for a tour which will start shortly after the annual spring plant sale held by the Friends of Cruickshank Botanic Garden. Plant Sale: 10:30am – noon, next to herbaceous border.

Directions: Come down St Machar Drive over the four-way junction, just before the first set of traffic lights turn left into the Cruickshank Garden car park. The pedestrian garden entrance is off The Chanonry. Limited parking available for this day only in the Cruickshank car park – AB24 3UU.

Opening for: Friends Of The Cruickshank Botanic Garden

8 EASTER ORD FARM
Easter Ord, Skene, Westhill AB32 6SQ
Catherine Fowler
T: 01224 742278 E: catherine.a.fowler@gmail.com

A one-acre mature cottage garden with year-round interest. The garden has an open aspect with views towards Lochnagar. It is made up of 'rooms'. There is a fruit garden, large herbaceous borders, lawn areas, small wildlife pond, vegetable garden and mini-orchard with wildflowers.

Open: Friday/Saturday/Sunday, 8/9/10 July, 2pm - 4pm. Also open Friday/Saturday/Sunday, 19/20/21 August, 2pm - 4pm. Admission £5.00, children free. Just drop in, no need to book!

Directions: Two miles from Westhill and can be reached using full postcode on Sat Nav. From Aberdeen take A944 towards Westhill. At the traffic lights before Westhill take the slip road on to the B9119 then immediately left towards Brotherfield. After one mile turn right at the T junction. After 350 yards turn left into the lane. Garden is first entrance on right.

Opening for: Aberdeen Royal Infirmary Roof Garden

9 HATTON OF FINTRAY VILLAGE GARDENS
Hatton of Fintray Village Hall AB21 0YG
Fintray Gardening Club
W: www.fintray.chessck.co.uk/fintraygardeningclub

A trail around an historic rural estate village, 11 miles from Aberdeen City. The village has maintained its historic centre, along with the remains of a 17th century church and extensive tree-lined avenues. On view are a number of richly planted private gardens in a variety of styles from cottage gardens to more contemporary, along with small front gardens and vegetable patches. Hosted by the Fintray Gardening Club, there is a chance to see work undertaken by the community to diversify and enhance the village green spaces, including a community orchard. There are also a number of wildflower areas planted for pollinators.

Open: Sunday 26 June, 12:30pm - 4:30pm, admission £5.00, children free. Tickets and maps will be available at the Fintray Village Hall. The majority of the gardens are within easy walking distance of the village centre. Entry ticket includes tea and home baking at the village hall.

Directions: On the B977 – Fintray is three miles from Kintore, or five miles from Dyce on the B979 (off the A96) – Fintray is three miles from Blackburn. Unfortunately there is no bus service. Car parking will be signposted and is available at the Lairds Park Recreation Area just next to the village hall. Cycle racks are available at the village hall and the recreation area.

Opening for: Hatton of Fintray Community

Aberdeenshire

10 HEATHERWICK FARM
Kintore, Inverurie AB51 0UQ
Lucy Narducci

This old farmhouse garden of one and a half acres has been regenerated over the past eight years and continues to evolve and develop. It has an open, spacious feel and new landscaping with additional planting has created distinct areas. The garden includes a formal square front lawn with perennial borders, a kitchen garden surrounded by orchard and a recently added native grass and wildflower meadow.

Open: Sunday 19 June & Sunday 26 June, 1pm - 5pm. Also open Sunday 4 September, 1pm - 5pm. Admission £5.00, children free.

Directions: From Inverurie centre, take the B9001 southwards. At the corner of St Mary's Place and St James's Place follow signs for *Keithhall*. Then follow signs for *Balbithan*. Heatherwick is signposted and on the left after Hogholm Stables. It is three miles from the centre of Inverurie.

Opening for: Myeloma UK

Heatherwick Farm

11 LAUNDRY COTTAGE
Culdrain, Gartly, Huntly AB54 4PY
Judith McPhun
T: 01466 720768 E: judithmcphun@icloud.com

An informal cottage-style garden of about one and a half acres by the river Bogie. Two contrasting steep slopes make up the wilder parts. The more intensively gardened area around the cottage includes a wide variety of herbaceous plants, shrubs and trees, an orchard area and fruit and vegetable plots, making a garden of year-round interest.

Open: by arrangement 1 January - 31 December. Admission £5.00, children free. Snowdrops during February and March.

Directions: Four miles south of Huntly on the A97.

Opening for: Amnesty International UK Section Charitable Trust

Aberdeenshire

12 LEITH HALL PLANT SALE

Huntly AB54 4NQ
The National Trust for Scotland
T: 01464 831148
W: www.nts.org.uk/visit/places/leith-hall

The west garden was created by Charles and Henrietta Leith-Hay in the Arts and Crafts style during Edwardian times. In summer, the magnificent serpentine herbaceous and catmint borders provide a dazzling display and the kitchen garden produces heritage fruit and vegetables for sale. The carefully reconstructed rock garden is currently being replanted.

Open: Saturday 28 May, 10am - 3pm, admission £3.50, children free.

Directions: On the B9002 one mile west of Kennethmont.

Opening for: The National Trust for Scotland: Leith Hall Garden

13 MIDDLE CAIRNCAKE

Cuminestown, Turriff AB53 5YS
Nick and Penny Orpwood
T: 01888 544432 E: orpwood@hotmail.com

Situated in rolling farmland, the shape of our park has resulted in seven small gardens, each with its own character, but with some plants repeated to provide continuity. In addition, there is a large kitchen garden which makes us self-sufficient for most of the year. Lawns with heather beds complete the garden. Many plants are grown from seed saved, or cuttings propagated, and we are making minor changes which will mean easier maintenance. We try to garden sustainably without the use of chemicals and with due regard for wildlife. Visitors can make their own way round the garden or have a guided tour.

Open: by arrangement 1 June - 31 August, admission £5.00, children free. Homemade teas at additional charge.

Directions: Middle Cairncake is on the A9170 between New Deer and Cuminestown. It is clearly signposted.

Opening for: Scotland's Gardens Scheme SCIO

14 PARKVILLA

47 Schoolhill, Ellon AB41 9AJ
Andy and Kim Leonard
T: 07786 748296 E: andy.leonard@btinternet.com

A south-facing Victorian walled garden, lovingly developed from a design started in 1990 to give colour and interest all year. Enjoy densely planted herbaceous borders, pause under the pergola clothed in clematis, honeysuckle and rambling roses, continue on to the bottom of the garden where three ponds and wildflower beds reflect a strong focus on wildlife. This is a hidden gem of a garden that has won awards including *Ellon Best Garden* and with plants rarely seen in north east Scotland.

Open: Saturday/Sunday, 30/31 July, 2pm - 5pm, admission £5.00, children free.

Directions: From centre of Ellon head north towards Auchnagatt. Schoolhill is third left. From Auchnagatt head into Ellon along Golf Road, Schoolhill is first right after the golf course. Limited on-street parking, car parks in Ellon (five minutes walk) and Caroline's Well Wood. Public toilets in Ellon town centre.

Opening for: St Mary On The Rock Episcopal Church Ellon, Alzheimer Scotland & Ellon Men's Shed

Aberdeenshire

15 TARLAND COMMUNITY GARDEN
Tarland, Aboyne AB34 4ZQ
The Gardeners of Tarland

Tarland Community Garden opened in 2013 and is a Tarland Development Group project. It provides an inclusive and accessible community growing space for local residents. It has indoor (polytunnel) and outdoor raised beds for rent, plus communal planting areas including a soft fruit cage, fruit trees and a herb garden. It is a place for members to grow produce, learn, share and have fun.

Open: Saturday 24 September, noon - 4pm, admission £3.00, children free.

Directions: Take the B9094 from Aboyne or the A96 and B9119 from Aberdeen. Arriving at the village square the gardens will be clearly signposted.

Opening for: Tarland Development Group

16 UPPER THIRD CROFT
Rothienorman, Inverurie AB51 8XY
Lois Thompson and John W. Graham
T: 01464 871032 or 0776 550 1775 E: upperthirdgardens@gmail.com

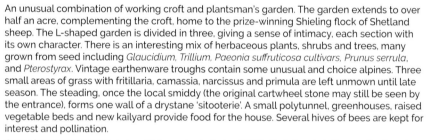

An unusual combination of working croft and plantsman's garden. The garden extends to over half an acre, complementing the croft, home to the prize-winning Shieling flock of Shetland sheep. The L-shaped garden is divided in three, giving a sense of intimacy, each section with its own character. There is an interesting mix of herbaceous plants, shrubs and trees, many grown from seed including *Glaucidium, Trillium, Paeonia suffruticosa cultivars, Prunus serrula,* and *Pterostyrax.* Vintage earthenware troughs contain some unusual and choice alpines. Three small areas of grass with fritillaria, camassia, narcissus and primula are left unmown until late season. The steading, once the local smiddy (the original cartwheel stone may still be seen by the entrance), forms one wall of a drystane 'sitooterie'. A small polytunnel, greenhouses, raised vegetable beds and new kailyard provide food for the house. Several hives of bees are kept for interest and pollination.

Open: by arrangement 1 June - 31 August, admission £5.00. Unfortunately the garden is not suitable for dogs, children or wheelchairs.

Directions: Take the B9001 north through Rothienorman towards Largue. Approximately three miles from Rothienorman turn up left signposted *Logie Newton, Fisherford* and *Wells of Ythan.* The croft entrance is the second farm entrance on the left (sign on field gate), half-a-mile from the junction. Follow the farm track round to park at the garden entrance.

Opening for: Mrs Murray Home For Stray Dogs & Cats

Aberdeenshire

17 **WESTHALL CASTLE**
Oyne, Inverurie AB52 6RW
Mr Gavin Farquhar
T: 01224 214301 E: enquiries@ecclesgreig.com

Set in an ancient landscape in the foothills of the impressive and foreboding hill of Bennachie, is a circular walk through glorious daffodils with outstanding views. This interesting garden is in the early stages of restoration, with large groupings of rhododendrons and specimen trees. Westhall Castle is a 16th-century tower house, incorporating a 13th-century building of the bishops of Aberdeen. There were additions in the 17th, 18th and 19th centuries. The castle is semi-derelict, but stabilised from total dereliction. A fascinating house encompassing 600 years of alteration and additions.

Open: Sunday 10 April, 11am - 4pm, admission £5.00, children free.

Directions: Marked from the A96 at Old Rayne and from Oyne Village.

Opening for: Bennachie Guides

Westhall Castle

Angus & Dundee

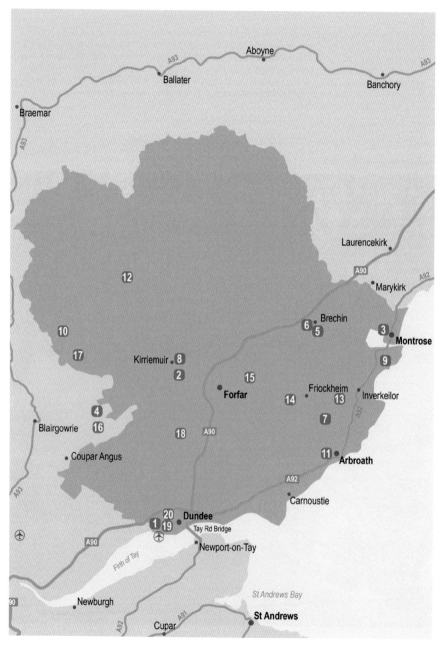

Angus & Dundee

OUR VOLUNTEER ORGANISERS

District Organisers:	Pippa Clegg	Easter Derry, Kilry, Blairgowrie PH11 8JA
	Terrill Dobson	Logie House, Kirriemuir DD8 5PN
Area Organisers:	Debbie Butler	Top Croft, Arniefoul, Angus DD8 1UD
	Moira Coleman	Templeton House, Arbroath DD11 4QP
	Jan Crow	Lower Duncraig, 2 Castle St, Brechin DD9 6JN
	Frances Dent	12 Glamis Drive, Dundee DD2 1QL
	Jeanette Ogilvie	House of Pitmuies, Guthrie DD8 2SN
	Donna Orton	33 High Street, Edzell DD9 7TE
	Kate Robinson	23 Old Shore Head, Arbroath DD11 1BB
	Frances Shepherd	Windyridge, 10 Glamis Drive DD2 1QL
	Claire Tinsley	Ethie Mains, Inverkeilor DD11 5SN
Treasurer:	James Welsh	Dalfruin, Kirktonhill Road, Kirriemuir DD8 4HU

GARDENS OPEN ON A SPECIFIC DATE

Lawton House, Inverkeilor, by Arbroath	Thursday - Sunday, 10-13 March
Inchmill Cottage, Glenprosen, near Kirriemuir	Thursday, 7 April
10 Menzieshill Road, Dundee	Saturday/Sunday, 16/17 April
Colliston Castle, Colliston, Arbroath	Saturday/Sunday, 30 April/1 May
Inchmill Cottage, Glenprosen, near Kirriemuir	Thursday, 5 May
Balhary Walled Garden, Balhary, Alyth, Blairgowrie	Friday/Saturday, 13/14 May
10 Menzieshill Road, Dundee	Saturday/Sunday, 14/15 May
Dalfruin, Kirktonhill Road, Kirriemuir	Sunday, 22 May
Trio of Gardens on Glamis Drive, 3, 10 & 12 Glamis Drive, Dundee	Saturday/Sunday, 28/29 May
Inchmill Cottage, Glenprosen, near Kirriemuir	Thursday, 2 June
The Doocot, Kinloch, Meigle, Blairgowrie	Sunday, 12 June
Balhary Walled Garden, Balhary, Alyth, Blairgowrie	Friday/Saturday, 17/18 June
Torwood, Milton of Ogilvie, Glenogilvy, Glamis by Forfar	Saturday/Sunday, 18/19 June
Brechin Gardens in June, Locations across Brechin	Sunday, 26 June
The Old Schoolhouse, Kilry	Saturday/Sunday, 2/3 July
Inchmill Cottage, Glenprosen, near Kirriemuir	Thursday, 7 July
The Doocot, Kinloch, Meigle, Blairgowrie	Sunday, 10 July
Arwin House, 17 Renny Crescent, Montrose	Sat/Sun, 16/17 July
Easter Cammock, Glenisla, Blairgowrie	Saturday, 30 July
Brechin Gardens in July, Locations across Brechin	Sunday, 31 July
Inchmill Cottage, Glenprosen, near Kirriemuir	Thursday, 4 August
Angus Plant Sale, Logie Walled Garden, Kirriemuir	Saturday, 6 August
Balhary Walled Garden, Balhary, Alyth, Blairgowrie	Fri/Sat, 19/20 August
Hospitalfield Gardens, Hospitalfield House, Westway, Arbroath	Saturday, 20 August
Inchmill Cottage, Glenprosen, near Kirriemuir	Thursday, 1 September
Balhary Walled Garden, Balhary, Alyth, Blairgowrie	Fri/Sat, 23/24 September
Westgate, 12 Glamis Drive, Dundee	Sat/Sun, 15/16 October

Angus & Dundee

GARDENS OPEN REGULARLY

Dunninald Castle, Montrose	1 - 28 February (Suns, Mons & Tues) and 1 May - 31 August (Suns, Mons & Tues, except July open daily)
Pitmuies Gardens, House of Pitmuies, Guthrie, by Forfar	1 April - 30 September
Primula Garden at Reswallie, Reswallie, Forfar	Tuesdays/Thursdays, 5 April - 30 June

GARDENS OPEN BY ARRANGEMENT

Inchmill Cottage, Glenprosen, near Kirriemuir	1 April - 30 September
Primula Garden at Reswallie, Reswallie, Forfar	1 April – 30 June
10 Menzieshill Road, Dundee	18 April - 13 May

Dunninald Castle © John Carracher

Angus & Dundee

1 10 MENZIESHILL ROAD
Dundee DD2 1PW
Frances Tait
T: 01382 665719

On a sloping site facing the river, No 10 is home to one of the nine wells in this part of the west end of Dundee. At one time, the well provided drinking water for a nearby farmhouse and two cottages. It was also the first and last water available to carriers' horses on their way to and from Dundee. Now it feeds rhododendrons and camellias, many of which came from the Rothschilds' garden at Exbury, Hampshire. Of particular interest are magnolia 'Manchu Fan' and rhododendrons 'Loderic King George' and 'Lady Chamberlain'. More recently, an area near the well has been given over to bulbs and small herbaceous plants, various irises and primulas.

Open: Saturdays & Sundays, 16/17 April and 14/15 May, 2pm - 5pm. Also open by arrangement 18 April - 13 May. Admission £4.00, children free.

Directions: Turn off A85/Riverside Avenue at the roundabout towards the Dundee Botanic Garden. Pass the Botanics and the road bears left and becomes Perth Road. Take a right on to Invergowrie Drive and then first left on Menzieshill Road. Buses 5 and 9 to the foot of Glamis Road and walk west to Invergowrie Drive.

Opening for: Friends of Dundee University Botanic Garden

10 Menzieshill Road © Camelia Hudema

2 ANGUS PLANT SALE
Logie Walled Garden, Kirriemuir DD8 5PN
SGS Angus & Dundee Organisers
E: angusdundee@scotlandsgardens.org.uk

Please join us for our annual plant sale. We will offer a good, interesting selection, sourced from private gardens and with some donations from our local nurseries. It's advisable to come promptly and bring boxes and trays. Donations of plants either before or during sales will always be welcome.

Open: Saturday 6 August, 2pm - 5pm, admission £3.00, children free.

Directions: From the A90, take A926 towards Kirriemuir. Just after Maryton, take a left into Logie Business Park and then take second left onto the single track road. Then take the first left onto a beech tree lined drive and follow signs to *The Walled Garden*.

Opening for: SGS and Beneficiaries

Angus & Dundee

3 ARWIN HOUSE
17 Renny Crescent, Montrose DD10 9BW
Trish and Andy Winton

We moved here nine years ago and created our garden from a building site! With careful planning and design the garden has evolved. The emphasis was to create different 'rooms' offering peace, harmony and tranquility, with various specimen plants, herbaceous borders, vegetable plot and a greenhouse. A highlight feature is a memorial garden with an Asian theme in memory of our late son. We were fortunate to feature on *The Beechgrove Garden* in 2019. We look forward to welcoming you and hope you enjoy your visit.

Open: Saturday/Sunday, 16/17 July, 11am - 5pm, admission £5.00, children free. There are coffee shops and restaurants nearby.

Directions: From Northesk Road, turn left onto Brechin Road, past Lidl then first right and immediately turn left onto Renny Crescent.

Opening for: Alzheimer Scotland

Arwin House

Angus & Dundee

4 BALHARY WALLED GARDEN
Balhary, Alyth, Blairgowrie PH11 8LT
Teri and Paul Hodge-Neale
W: www.facebook.com/balharywalledgarden

This two-acre working walled garden is being lovingly restored back to full production with the development of the 'no dig' method to grow many varieties of vegetables with impressive results. The maturing herbaceous borders have the space to encourage drifts of colour and interest throughout the seasons. The walls that surround the garden give microclimate conditions, allowing for the culture of heritage and new varieties. Paul and Teri also have their own private Therapy Garden which is a beautiful space with serene water features, statuary, stonework and unusual plants, and available to visit at specific times.

Open: Fridays & Saturdays, 13/14 May, 17/18 June, 19/20 August and 23/24 September, 2pm - 5pm. Admission £5.00, children free. Paul will give seasonal talks each day in the garden from 3pm - 4pm explaining 'no dig' and other aspects of gardening at Balhary and swapping ideas with visitors. Note that the Therapy Garden will be open to visitors on Saturdays only.

Directions: Situated between Alyth and Meigle on the B954 opposite the sign to *Jordanstone.*

Opening for: Perennial

---

5 BRECHIN GARDENS IN JUNE
Locations across Brechin DD9 6AW
The Gardeners of Brechin

10 Dalhousie Street (NEW) Brechin DD9 7BU (Sari and Douglas Hill): A mature, sloping south-facing garden reflecting the owners' passion for plants.
9 Pearse Street Brechin DD9 6JR (James Mackie): Opening in memory of its creator Irene Mackie, the well-known plantswoman whose love of plants is reflected in every inch of this beautiful tranquil garden.
Bishops Walk 11A Argyll St, Brechin DD9 6JL (Steff and Mike Eyres): A hidden walled garden planted with scented climbing and shrub roses, lavenders, perennials and evergreen shrubs and conifers including an established Woolemi.
Gardeners Cottage (NEW) Fern, Brechin DD8 3FF (Nick and Michelle Tonge): Surrounded by a listed wall this two-acre garden, neglected for many years, is now a labour of love for the new owners.
Hoodston House (NEW) Findowrie DD9 6RF (Kat and Aaron Robertson): A work-in-progress family garden and wildlife haven created from scratch within last two years on a tight budget.
Kirkton Cottage (NEW) Aberlemno DD8 3PE (George Henry and Susan Norris): Nestled in a dip beside a stream, this country cottage garden is packed with plants.
Latchlea 17A North Latch Road, Brechin DD9 6LE (Pamela Stevens): A new garden begun as a way of coping with bereavement. Inspired by the Queen saying that 'everyone should plant as many trees as possible'.
Rosehill West 15C North Latch Road, Brechin DD9 6LF (Robert and Jenny Martin): An acre of newly planted garden, formerly a field, featuring mature original trees, herbaceous areas, fruit trees (quince and crab apple), and a path through recently planted trees.
Smiddyhill (NEW) 23 Dalhousie Street, Brechin DD9 7BB (Ian and Morag Wood): A beautifully tended town garden full of surprises including a New Zealand type weather indicator!

Open: Sunday 26 June, noon - 5pm, admission £5.00, children free. Tickets and teas available at Gardner Memorial Church Hall, St Ninians Square, Brechin DD9 6AW.

Directions: Gardens are located around the town of Brechin. Look for the SGS yellow arrows.

Opening for: The Dalhousie Centre Day Care For The Elderly & Gardner Community Association

Angus & Dundee

6 **BRECHIN GARDENS IN JULY**
Locations across Brechin DD9 6AW
The Gardeners of Brechin

10 Dalhousie Street (NEW) Brechin DD9 7BU (Sari and Douglas Hill): A mature, sloping south-facing garden reflecting the owners' passion for plants.
15 Dalhousie Street (NEW) Brechin DD9 7BB (Ross Henderson and Damien Douglas): New to gardening, the owners have created a bijoux container garden in their south-facing front garden.
17 Dalhousie Street (NEW) Brechin DD9 7BB (Sarah Lloyd and Murray Skinner): Garden designer Sarah and Murray have, in only two years, created their town garden, divided into rooms.
2 Park Grove (NEW) Brechin DD9 7AJ (Phyllis MacLennan): A mature, secluded garden with different areas for relaxing among colourful borders, shrubberies and mature trees.
75 Park Road (NEW) Brechin DD9 7AP (Ewan and Wilma Haggart): An attractive medium sized corner plot divided into areas of special interest.
24 North Latch Road DD9 6LE (Alistair and Mary Gray): Learn how the owners grow and show vegetables and how these can be a spectacular display of colourful bedding-full greenhouses.
Bishops Walk 11A Argyll Street DD9 6JL (Steff and Mike Eyres): A hidden, walled garden planted with scented climbing and shrub roses, lavenders, perennials and evergreen shrubs and conifers including an established Wollemi.
Brechin Cathedral Allotments Chanory Wynd, Brechin DD9 6EU (Brechin Cathedral Allotments Gardeners): Eleven varied plots reflect the interests and personalities of each plot-holder and include fruit, vegetables and herbs. A unique feature is the historical 'College Well' used by medieval monks.
Dalhousie Estate Allotments (NEW) Brechin Bridge, Arbroath Road, Brechin DD9 6TJ (George Garden): Fourteen varied plots in a beautiful setting making much use of reclaimed materials including a wind powered generator, raised beds and sheds of all shapes and sizes!
Kirkton Cottage (NEW) Aberlemno DD8 3PE (George Henry and Susan Norris): Nestled in a dip beside a stream this country cottage garden is packed with plants.
Open: Sunday 31 July, noon - 5pm, admission £5.00, children free. Tickets and teas available at Gardner Memorial Church Hall, St Ninians Square, Brechin DD9 6AW.

Directions: Gardens are located around the town of Brechin. Look for the SGS yellow arrows.

Opening for: The Dalhousie Centre Day Care For The Elderly & Gardner Community Association

7 **COLLISTON CASTLE**
Colliston, Arbroath DD11 3RS
Susan and John Lansley

Sixteenth-century 'z plan' castle, built by Cardinal Beaton with a later Victorian addition. The gardens, neglected in past years, have been attacked and the overgrown wilderness has regained some form. The garden is in its infancy with a new small walled garden and the beginnings of a formal garden with box hedging and a rose bed. The rest of the ten acres is mostly parkland with large specimen trees including a Wellingtonia. Large rhododendrons survive from the castle's previous gardens with an abundance of daffodils.
Champion Trees: Wellingtonia, Copper Beech.
Open: Saturday 30 April & Sunday 1 May, 2pm - 5pm, admission £5.00, children free. Tours of the castle can be booked on arrival.

Directions: A933 from Arbroath towards Friockheim. Drive through Colliston Village, continue past the church. Approximately 500 metres on the right, take the road signposted *West Mains of Colliston*. Follow this past the farm and around to the left, the castle gates are on your right.

Opening for: Church of St Mary the Virgin

Angus & Dundee

8 **DALFRUIN**
Kirktonhill Road, Kirriemuir DD8 4HU
Mr and Mrs James A Welsh

A well stocked connoisseur's garden of about a third of an acre situated at the end of a short cul-de-sac. There are many less common plants like varieties of trilliums, meconopsis (blue poppies), tree peonies (descendants of ones collected by George Sherriff and grown at Ascreavie), dactylorhiza and codonopsis. There is a scree garden and collection of ferns. The vigorous climbing rose, Paul's Himalayan Musk, grows over a pergola. Interconnected ponds encourage wildlife.

Open: Sunday 22 May, 2pm - 5pm, admission £4.00, children free.

Directions: From the centre of Kirriemuir turn left up Roods. Kirktonhill Road is on the left near top of the hill. Park on Roods or at St Mary's Episcopal Church. Disabled parking only in Kirktonhill Road. Bus 20 (from Dundee) getting off at either stop on the Roods.

Opening for: Kirriemuir Day Care Ltd

9 **DUNNINALD CASTLE**
Montrose DD10 9TD
The Stansfeld family
T: 01674 672031 E: estateoffice@dunninald.com
W: www.dunninald.com

We welcome our visitors to explore our 100 acres of woods, wild garden, policies and a walled garden. From January to May, the main interest is the wild garden and policies where snowdrops in January are followed by daffodils and finally bluebells in May. In June, the emphasis turns to the walled garden, rich in interest and colour throughout the summer. Situated at the bottom of the beech avenue, the walled garden is planted with rose borders, traditional mixed borders, vegetables, herbs, soft fruits and fruit trees and there is a greenhouse.

Open: 1 February - 28 February (Sundays, Mondays & Tuesdays), 1pm - 4:30pm for Snowdrops and Winter Walks. Also open 1 May - 30 June (Sundays, Mondays & Tuesdays), 1 July - 31 July (everyday) & 1 August - 31 August (Sundays, Mondays & Tuesdays), 1pm - 5pm. Admission £5.00, children free. See website for Castle Tours.

Directions: Three miles south of Montrose, ten miles north of Arbroath, signposted from the A92.

Opening for: Donation to SGS

Angus & Dundee

10 EASTER CAMMOCK
Glenisla, Blairgowrie PH11 8PF
June and John Browning
T: 01575 582222

Panoramic views of Glenisla and a large variety of wildflowers in July are a highlight of Easter Cammock. Large pond surrounded by water plants, perennial and annual wild flowers and many relatively young plants. Established woodland area, rockery, herbaceous borders. Access by farm track.

Open: Saturday 30 July, 2pm - 5pm, admission £4.00, children free.

Directions: From Perth take A94 through Coupar Angus to just before Meigle. Take B954 and follow signs to Glenisla. From Dundee take A923 to Muirhead, then B954, turn right just after Meigle and follow signs to Glenisla as above. Continue on B954 Glenisla road until it meets the B951 from Kirriemuir at Backwater crossroads. Turn left towards Glenisla on B951. Approx two miles on, turn left at *Easter Cammock* sign opposite red postbox. Up farm track, bend left at T-junction, drive through farm and follow road for half mile to Easter Cammock. Ample parking.

Opening for: Hot Chocolate Trust & Scotland's Charity Air Ambulance

11 HOSPITALFIELD GARDENS
Hospitalfield House, Westway, Arbroath DD11 2NH
Hospitalfield Trust
E: info@hospitalfield.org.uk
W: www.hospitalfield.org.uk

In 2021 the walled garden at Hospitalfield was comprehensively redeveloped to a design by celebrated garden designer and plantsman, Nigel Dunnett. The new garden tells the 800-year horticultural story of this extraordinary site from its monastic origins in the 13th century through to the Victorian passion for ferns. You will be able to explore the garden in its second year as it continues to grow into its inspirational design; full of diverse textures and striking colours. The house that overlooks the garden was remodelled in the 19th century by Elizabeth Allan-Fraser and her husband, the artist Patrick Allan-Fraser, who designed their home in the Arts and Crafts style. Their fernery, which sits within the walled garden, has been restored and re-planted with ferns from all over the world and will also be open for visitors. For more information about Hospitalfield and its international cultural programme rooted in contemporary visual arts please visit the website.

Open: Saturday 20 August, 11am - 4pm, admission £6.00, children free. Admission is for the walled garden and fernery and Angus residents will receive an annual pass with their admission. The new glass house café offers excellent refreshments and there will also be a sale of plants propagated and grown by our Garden Club volunteers.

Directions: Comprehensive directions can be found on the website at www.hospitalfield.org. uk/visit/location

Opening for: Donation to SGS

Angus & Dundee

12 INCHMILL COTTAGE

Glenprosen, near Kirriemuir DD8 4SA
Iain Nelson
T: 01575 540452

This is a long, sloping and terraced garden at over 800 feet in the Braes of Angus, developed to be a garden for all seasons. Half is dominated by bulbs, rhododendrons, azaleas, primulas, meconopsis and clematis. The other half is mainly later summer bulbs, herbaceous plants and roses. There is also a rockery/scree and fernery.

Open: Thursdays 7 April, 5 May, 2 June, 7 July, 4 August and 1 September, 2pm - 5pm. Also open by arrangement 1 April - 30 September. Admission £4.00, children free.

Directions: Please DO NOT use SatNav. From Kirriemuir take the B955 (signposted *The Glens*) to Dykehead (about five miles). From there follow the *Prosen* sign for about five miles. Inchmill is the white-fronted cottage beside the phone box. Car parking beside the church (50 yards away) and by the village hall opposite.

Opening for: The Archie Foundation

13 LAWTON HOUSE

Inverkeilor, by Arbroath DD11 4RU
Katie and Simon Dessain

Woodland garden of beech trees, carpeted with snowdrops, aconites and crocuses in spring, set around a 1755 house. There is also a walled garden planted with fruit trees and vegetables. The property was owned for many years by Elizabeth and Patrick Allan-Fraser who built Hospitalfield House in Arbroath.

Open: Thursday - Sunday, 10 - 13 March, 10am - 5pm for Snowdrops and Winter Walks, admission £4.00, children free.

Directions: Take B965 between Inverkeilor and Friockheim, turn right at sign for *Angus Chain Saws*. Drive approximately 200 metres, then take first right.

Opening for: Siobhan's Trust

Lawton House

Angus & Dundee

14 **PITMUIES GARDENS**
House of Pitmuies, Guthrie, by Forfar DD8 2SN
Jeanette and Ruaraidh Ogilvie
T: 01241 828245 E: ogilvie@pitmuies.com
W: www.pitmuies.com

Two renowned semi-formal walled gardens adjoin an 18th-century house and steading, sheltering long borders of herbaceous perennials, superb old-fashioned delphiniums and roses, together with pavings rich with violas and dianthus. An extensive and diverse collection of plants, interesting kitchen garden, spacious lawns, and river, lochside and woodland walks beneath fine trees. A wide variety of shrubs with good autumn colour and a picturesque turreted doocot and a 'Gothick' wash house. Myriad spring bulbs include carpets of crocus following massed snowdrops and daffodils.

Open: 1 April - 30 September, 10am - 5pm, admission £5.00, children free.

Directions: From Forfar take A932 east for seven miles and gardens are signposted on the right. From Brechin take A933 south to Friockheim and turn right onto A932; then gardens are signposted on the left after one-and-a-half miles.

Opening for: Donation to SGS

15 **PRIMULA GARDEN AT RESWALLIE**
Reswallie, Forfar DD8 2SA
Colin Gair
T: 07747 688402 E: colingair161@btinternet.com

The garden started as a wedding gift of primula to Colin and his wife Iris in 1971. Colin moved to Reswallie in 2011 after Iris died, and he maintains and expands her collection as a tribute. Space was created to expand the original garden by the collapse of trees, the removal of *Rhododenron ponticum*, excavations in search of a family dog and the destruction of a rabbit warren. Today there are 45 species of primula, including rare ones, each with a sign including name, country of origin, flower colour and flowering season. These are planted among meconopsis, miniature rhododendron, hostas, various bulbs and many other plants. The garden is also in memory of David Lloyd-Jones and Helen Lloyd-Jones who died after the garden had started. The garden has been extended with more plantings and footpaths for 2022.

Open: 5 April - 30 June (Tuesdays & Thursdays), 2pm - 5pm. Also open by arrangement 1 April - 30 June. Admission £4.00, children free. There will be a substantial variety of primula plants for sale.

Directions: Take the A932 from Forfar and signposted to *Arbroath*. Continue about three miles and turn left signposted to *Reswallie*. Take the second right down the hill.

Opening for: Marie Curie & Macmillan Cancer Support

Angus & Dundee

16 **THE DOOCOT**
Kinloch, Meigle, Blairgowrie PH12 8QX
Liz and George McLaren

The house and garden sit in a two-acre site with views to the Sidlaws and Grampians. The house is a converted 18th century steading with a large doo'cot tower, completed in 2009. Garden development began in 2013 with several flowering cherries and two small herbaceous beds, and expanded in 2014 with the creation of a parterre rose garden, and the addition of shrub, herbaceous beds and areas of heather and hard planting including rhododendrons, azaleas and a variety of trees. In 2019 the garden was further developed to create seated areas and themed beds. A wildlife pond is being added for the 2022 season.

Open: Sunday 12 June, 2pm - 5pm. Also open Sunday 10 July, 2pm - 5pm. Admission £5.00, children free.

Directions: Approximately two miles west of Meigle on the A94 (towards Coupar Angus). Just before the hamlet of Longleys there is a turning to the right with a small lodge with red eaves on the roadside. Turn up that tarmac road and The Doocot is 400 metres on the right.

Opening for: Glamis, Inverarity and Kinnettles Parish Church of Scotland: Ladies Guild (Sunday 12 June) & Ardler Kettins & Meigle Parish Church of Scotland: Ladies Guild (Sunday 10 July)

Primula Garden at Reswallie

Angus & Dundee

17 THE OLD SCHOOLHOUSE
Kilry PH11 8HU
Carol & Richard Till

The garden extending to two-thirds of an acre comprises two distinct areas. Firstly, the original cottage-style garden with lawn and borders of mixed shrubs, perennials and annuals, enhanced by a variety of trees. The second area is a recently acquired paddock which is home to a polytunnel, a fruit cage, a Finnish BBQ hut with decking and a riverside deck on the bank of Kilry Burn which runs along the southern edge of the garden.

Open: Saturday/Sunday, 2/3 July, 2pm - 5pm, admission £4.00, children free.

Directions: From Perth take A94 to Coupar Angus and just before Meigle take the B954 and follow signs to Glen Isla and then to Kilry, signed to the left. Follow road past Kilry Church then downhill, past former Kilry Primary School and continue for half a mile until reaching The Old School on the left. From Dundee take the A923 to Muirhead and then B954 to Meigle, turn right up B954 towards Glen Isla and then follow signs as above.

Opening for: Willows Animal Sanctuary & British Heart Foundation

The Old Schoolhouse

18 TORWOOD
Milton of Ogilvie, Glenogilvy, Glamis by Forfar DD8 1UN
John Gordon
T: 07988 010418 E: j.gordon.82@btinternet.com
W: www.gardendisplays.co.uk

A small, attractively laid-out country garden striving towards year-round interest, enjoyment and relaxation through association and succession planting of trees, shrubs, herbaceous, ornamental grasses, perennials and bulbs. John's aim for his gardening is to focus on ecologically-based, wildlife-friendly planting schemes, guided by natural and semi-natural habitats. This approach is demonstrated beautifully in his garden, separated into rooms focusing on different colour schemes and styles, including a small woodland area, mixed borders and prairie-style planting.

Angus & Dundee

Open: Saturday/Sunday, 18/19 June, 11am - 4pm, admission £5.00, children free.

Directions: Take A928 between Kirriemuir turnoff on A90 or Glamis turnoff on A94. Follow road signposted *Glenogilvy, Handwick, Dryburn*. Torwood is second house from the end on the left.

Opening for: Alzheimer Scotland

 ### 19 TRIO OF GARDENS ON GLAMIS DRIVE
3, 10 & 12 Glamis Drive, Dundee DD2 1QL
Elaine Lowe, Frances Shepherd and Frances & John Dent

A charming collection of neighbouring gardens on Glamis Drive.
Greengaites (NEW) 3 Glamis Drive, Dundee DD2 1QG (Elaine Lowe): A cottage-style garden with small trees, herbaceous borders and rockery. Interest throughout the seasons with magnolia blossom and bulbs in the spring, moving into summer with wisteria, clematis and roses growing up the walls of this pretty 1920s house. The herbaceous borders and rockery provide colour throughout summer and autumn.
Westgate 12 Glamis Drive, Dundee DD2 1QL (John and Frances Dent): This established garden with mature trees occupies a half-acre, south-facing site overlooking the River Tay and Fife hills. The tennis court lawn has herbaceous borders. The woodland area includes hidden features, garden ornaments and a miniature topiary garden and bower. A small rose garden, a fountain and two oriental-themed water gardens complete the tour.
Windyridge 10 Glamis Drive DD2 1QL (Frances M. Shepherd): Approximately half an acre on a south facing site, Windyridge overlooks the River Tay towards the hills of Fife. The garden, set out in the 1920s, comprises different areas; a terrace at the top looks over a central lawn with a sundial in the middle and is flanked on both sides with wide herbaceous borders. An arbour divides this area with the orchard containing several old and some new fruit trees. Passing under the covered beech hedge at the bottom takes one into the vegetable area. This garden is a work in progress and has many established plants and mature trees.

Open: Saturday/Sunday, 28/29 May, 2pm - 5pm, admission £6.00, children free. Teas at Westgate and Windyridge and plant stall at Greengaites.

Directions: Buses 5, 22 or 73 from Dundee city centre. Please note there is no roadside parking on Glamis Drive. Limited disabled parking available at the houses.

Opening for: Maggie Keswick Jencks Cancer Caring Centres Trust (Dundee)

20 WESTGATE
12 Glamis Drive, Dundee DD2 1QL
John and Frances Dent

This established garden with mature trees occupies a half-acre south-facing site overlooking the River Tay and Fife hills. The tennis court lawn has herbaceous borders. The woodland area includes hidden features, garden ornaments and a miniature topiary garden and bower. A small rose garden, a fountain and two oriental-themed water gardens complete the tour.

Open: Saturday/Sunday, 15/16 October, 4pm - 8pm, admission £5.00, children free. Children's activities, Indian-themed refreshments and a variety of floodlighting effects. Torches recommended.

Directions: Buses 5, 22 or 73 from Dundee city centre. Please note there is no roadside parking on Glamis Drive. Limited disabled parking available at the house.

Opening for: Dr Graham's Homes Kalimpong (UK)

Argyll & Lochaber

Sponsored by

⊕ Investec

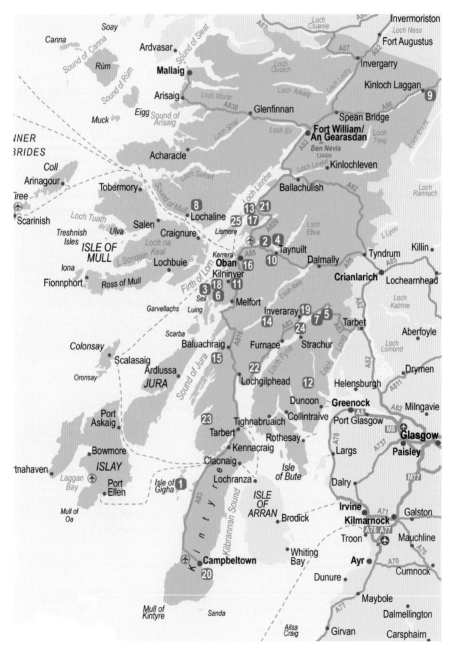

Argyll & Lochaber

OUR VOLUNTEER ORGANISERS

District Organiser:	Minette Struthers	Camasmaddy, Ardmaddy, by Oban PA34 4QY
		E: info@scotlandsgardens.org
Area Organisers:	Grace Bergius	Craignish House, by Lochgilphead PA31 8QN
	Shian Carlow	Balliemore, Loch Striven, Dunoon PA23 8RH
	Mary Lindsay	Dal an Eas, Kilmore, Oban PA34 4XU
District Photographer:	Maurice Wilkins	Dunrobian, Laurel Road, Oban PA34 5EA
Treasurer:	Shelagh Cannon	Kames Bay, Kilmelford PA34 4XA

GARDENS OPEN ON A SPECIFIC DATE

Knock Newhouse, Lochgair	Saturday/Sunday, 14/15 May
Strachur Flower & Woodland Gardens, Strachur	Sunday, 15 May
Achamore Gardens, Isle of Gigha	Saturday, 21 May
Ardno, Cairndow	Sunday, 22 May
Braevallich Farm, by Dalmally	Sunday, 22 May
Strachur Flower & Woodland Gardens, Strachur	Sunday, 22 May
Ardverikie with Aberarder, Kinloch Laggan, Newtonmore	Sunday, 5 June
Braevallich Farm, by Dalmally	Sunday, 19 June
Benmore Botanic Garden, Benmore, Dunoon	Sunday, 2 October

GARDENS OPEN REGULARLY

Ardkinglas Woodland Garden, Cairndow	1 January - 31 December
Ardmaddy Castle, by Oban	1 January - 31 December
Ardtornish, by Lochaline, Morvern	1 January - 31 December
Barguillean's 'Angus Garden', Taynuilt	1 January - 31 December
Druimneil House, Port Appin	1 January - 31 December
Achnacloich, Connel, Oban	1 January - 31 December (Sats only)
Kinlochlaich Walled Garden, Appin	3 March - 31 October
Inveraray Castle Gardens, Inveraray	28 March - 31 October
Ardchattan Priory, North Connel	1 April - 31 October (Weds only)
An Cala, Ellenabeich, Isle of Seil	1 April - 31 October
Crinan Hotel Garden, Crinan	1 May - 31 August

Argyll & Lochaber

GARDENS OPEN BY ARRANGEMENT

Berandhu, Appin, Argyll	1 April - 31 October
Dal an Eas, Kilmore, Oban	1 April - 30 September
Ormsary House, Ormsary, Lochgilphead, Argyll	1 April - 31 October
Barochreal, Kilninver, Oban, Argyll	1 May - 30 September
The Secret Garden, Isle of Lismore, Oban, Argyll	1 May - 1 October
Eas Mhor, Cnoc-a-Challtuinn, Clachan Seil, Oban	1 May - 31 October
Kildalloig, Campbeltown	1 May - 31 October

Ardmaddy Castle

Argyll & Lochaber

1 ACHAMORE GARDENS

Isle of Gigha PA41 7AD
The Isle of Gigha Trust
E: gardens@gigha.org.uk
W: www.gigha.org.uk

Created by Colonel Sir James Horlick with the assistance of Gardener Kitty Lloyd Jones in 1944, Achamore Gardens is the home of Horlick's renowned rhododendron and camellia collection. Flourishing in Gigha's warm microclimate, the 54-acre gardens host many notable and unusual plants and trees from around the world. The woodland walks with rhododendrons, azaleas, camellias, New Zealand tree ferns, hydrangeas and fuchsias complement the walled garden's tender exotics, herbaceous borders and bamboo maze. The garden viewpoint has stunning views over to Islay and Jura while the pond area offers a secluded oasis. After years of decline, The Isle of Gigha Heritage Trust is now actively working to restore and develop Achamore Gardens.

Open: Saturday 21 May, 10am - 4pm, admission £7.00, children free. The garden is also open to visitors through the season.

Directions: Access to Gigha is via CalMac ferry. Gigha can be explored by foot or bicycle so you can choose to leave your vehicle for free at the Tayinloan ferry car park and help to avoid congestion of traffic on Gigha's single track roads. The garden is three-quarters of a mile from the ferry.

Opening for: Gigha Village Hall

2 ACHNACLOICH

Connel, Oban PA37 1PR
Mr T E Nelson
T: 01631 710223 E: charlie_milne@msn.com

The 20-acre woodland garden, overlooking Loch Etive, has been planted over the last century with a wide range of trees and shrubs from Asia, China, Japan, North America, Chile and New Zealand. Many have grown to considerable size. The light woodland canopy consists of native oaks and a number of magnificent 150-year-old Scots pines and European larch. Amongst these are open glades, carpeted with bluebells and numerous other bulbs. Two ponds and streams are planted with primulas, iris species, lysichitum, and astilbes. The woodland contains innumerable species of rhododendron and azalea, of which the triflorums and yunnanense are outstanding. Amongst these are species of acer, betula, camellia, cercidiphyllum, cornus, crinodendron, drimys, embothrium, enkianthus, eucryphia, hoheria, magnolia, malus, nothofagus, pieris, sorbus, stewartia, telopea and viburnum. Beside the house is a giant Douglas fir from Douglas' original introduction. One of the first Dawyck beeches stands beside the drive. Fine autumn colours.

Open: 1 January - 31 December (Saturdays only), 2pm - 4pm, admission £5.00, children free.

Directions: On the A85 two miles east of Connel. The car park is at the bottom of the drive.

Opening for: Macmillan Cancer Support

Argyll & Lochaber

3 AN CALA
Ellenabeich, Isle of Seil PA34 4RF
Mrs Sheila Downie
W: www.gardens-of-argyll.co.uk/view-details.php?id=447

A wonderful example of a 1930s designed garden, An Cala sits snugly in its horseshoe shelter of surrounding cliffs. A spectacular and very pretty garden with streams, waterfall, ponds, many herbaceous plants as well as azaleas, rhododendrons and cherry trees in spring. Archive material of Thomas Mawson's design was found recently and is available to visitors.

Open: 1 April - 31 October, 10am - 6pm, admission £5.00, children free.

Directions: Proceed south from Oban on Campbeltown Road for eight miles, turn right at the *Easdale* sign, a further eight miles on the B844; the garden is between the school and the village. Bus Oban - Easdale.

Opening for: Cancer Research UK

An Cala © Maurice Wilkins

4 ARDCHATTAN PRIORY
North Connel PA37 1RQ
Mrs Sarah Troughton
T: 01796 481355 E: admin@ardchattan.co.uk
W: www.ardchattan.co.uk

Overlooking Loch Etive, Ardchattan Priory Garden has a mature rockery, extensive herbaceous and rose borders to the front of the house. On either side of the drive, shrub borders, numerous roses and ornamental trees, together with bulbs, give colour throughout the season. The Priory, founded in 1230, is now a private house. The ruins of the chapel and graveyard are in the care of *Historic Environment Scotland* and open with the garden.

Open: 1 April - 31 October (Wednesdays only), 9:30am - 5:30pm, admission £5.00. Children under 16 free.

Argyll & Lochaber

Directions: Oban 10 miles. From north, turn left off the A828 at Barcaldine onto the B845 for six miles. From east or from Oban on the A85, cross Connel Bridge and turn first right, proceed east on Bonawe Road.

Opening for: Donation to SGS

Ardchattan Priory © Nick Edgington

5 | ARDKINGLAS WOODLAND GARDEN
Cairndow PA26 8BG
Ardkinglas Estate
T: 01499 600261
W: www.ardkinglas.com

In a peaceful setting overlooking Loch Fyne, the garden contains one of the finest collections of rhododendrons and conifers in Britain. This includes the mightiest conifer in Europe - a silver fir, as well as many other Champion Trees. There is a gazebo with a unique scriptorium based around a collection of literary quotes. The garden has a Fairy Trail and a Gruffalo Trail. It is a *VisitScotland* 3-star garden.
Champion Trees: The mightiest conifer in Europe and others.

Open: 1 January - 31 December, dawn - dusk, admission £5.00, children over three years old £2.00.

Directions: Entrance through Cairndow village off the A83 Loch Lomond/Inveraray road.

Opening for: Donation to SGS

Argyll & Lochaber

6 ARDMADDY CASTLE
by Oban PA34 4QY
Mr and Mrs Archie Struthers
T: 01852 300353 E: minette@ardmaddy.com
W: www.ardmaddy.com/places-visit

The gardens lie in a most spectacular setting in the centre of a horseshoe valley sheltered by mixed mature woodlands and the elevated castle standing on a volcanic mound to seaward. The walled garden is full of magnificent rhododendrons, a collection of rare and unusual shrubs and plants, the Clock Garden with its cutting flowers, the Crevice Garden, a new border with grasses and coastal theme, fruit and vegetables grown with labour saving formality, all within dwarf box hedging. Beyond, a woodland walk, with its 60-foot *Hydrangea petiolaris*, leads to the Water Garden which in spring has a mantle of bluebells and daffodils and in early summer a riot of *Primula candelabra*, irises, rodgersias and other damp-loving plants and grasses. Lovely autumn colour. A plantsman's garden for all seasons.

Open: 1 January - 31 December, 9am - dusk, admission £5.00, children free. Holiday cottages available sleeping 4 - 12. Find out more at www.ardmaddy.com

Directions: Take the A816 south of Oban for eight miles. Turn right onto the B844 to Seil Island/ Easdale. Four miles on, turn left on to Ardmaddy Road (signposted) for a further two miles.

Opening for: Donation to SGS

7 ARDNO
Cairndow PA26 8BE
Kate How
T: 01499 302304/ 02072 211996 E: ardnokate@gmail.com

From the rich varied landscape, a romantic garden has been created from scratch over the past 25 years. Visitors can stroll in the walled garden near the house, or explore the old oak wood planted with many interesting shrubs. These are growing up fast, adding shape and colour. Across the burn is the gorge and a wonderful waterfall. The woodland garden ends in the meadow, planted with irises and a collection of unusual trees, which continues down to the beach and a magnificent huge rock. My garden is a place to be peaceful in. Come and enjoy but be prepared - as some of the paths are steep with lots of steps!

Open: Sunday 22 May, 10am - 4pm, admission £5.00, children free.

Directions: Situated at the top end of Loch Fyne between Cairndow and St Catherines, off the A815.

Opening for: To be confirmed

8 ARDTORNISH
by Lochaline, Morvern PA80 5UZ
Mrs John Raven
W: www.ardtornish.co.uk

Ardtornish Estate spreads out around Loch Aline, a huge, wooded, U-shaped bay, a natural haven. Wonderful gardens of interesting mature conifers, rhododendrons, deciduous trees, shrubs and herbaceous, set amid magnificent scenery. Much of the garden is covered by native birch, alongside extensive planting of exotic species, under mature groups of larch, firs and pine, whose strong form and colour complement the pink sandstone towers and gables of Ardtornish House.

Open: 1 January - 31 December, 10am - 6pm, admission £5.00, children free.

Directions: Three miles from Lochaline along the A884.

Opening for: Donation to SGS

Argyll & Lochaber

9 ARDVERIKIE WITH ABERARDER
Kinloch Laggan, Newtonmore PH20 1BX
The Feilden family, Mrs P Laing and Mrs E T Smyth-Osbourne
T: 01528 544300

Ardverikie Kinloch Laggan, Newtonmore PH20 1BX (Mrs P Laing and Mrs E T Smyth-Osbourne).
Lovely setting on Loch Laggan with magnificent trees. Walled garden with large collection of acers, shrubs and herbaceous plants. Architecturally interesting house (not open) featured in *Monarch of the Glen* and *The Crown*.

Aberarder Kinloch Laggan, Newtonmore PH20 1BX (The Feilden family).
The garden has been laid out over the last 20 years to create a mixture of spring and autumn plants and trees, including rhododendrons, azaleas and acers. The elevated view down Loch Laggan from the garden is exceptional.

Open: Sunday 5 June, 2pm - 5:30pm, admission £5.50, children under 16 free.

Directions: On the A86 between Newtonmore and Spean Bridge.
Ardverikie House entrance is at the east end of Loch Laggan via the bridge by Gatelodge.
Aberarder Lodge entrance is about 200 meters west of the Ardverikie entrance, next to the small cottage.

Opening for: Laggan Parish Church & Highland Hospice

10 BARGUILLEAN'S 'ANGUS GARDEN'
Taynuilt PA35 1HY
The Josephine Marshall Trust
T: 01866 822333 E: info@barguillean.co.uk
W: www.barguillean.co.uk

Nine-acre woodland garden around an 11-acre loch set in the Glen Lonan Hills. Spring-flowering shrubs and bulbs, extensive collection of rhododendron hybrids, deciduous azaleas, conifers and unusual trees. The garden contains a large collection of North American rhododendron hybrids from famous contemporary plant breeders. Some paths can be steep. Three marked walks from 30 minutes to one-and-a-half hours.

Open: 1 January - 31 December, 9am - dusk, admission £5.00, children free. Coach tours by appointment.

Directions: Three miles south off the A85 Glasgow/Oban road at Taynuilt, road marked *Glen Lonan*, three miles up a single track road, turn right at the sign.

Opening for: SSAFA Forces Help

Argyll & Lochaber

11 BAROCHREAL

Kilninver, Oban, Argyll PA34 4UT
Nigel and Antoinette Mitchell
T: 01852 316151 E: antoinettemitchell1946@gmail.com
W: www.barochreal.co.uk

The garden was started in 2006. Fencing and stone walling define it from the rest of Barochreal land. Every year an area has been added, resulting in the gardens you will see today. There are rhododendron banks, a water feature, waterfalls and burns, a pond, a walled rose garden, active beehives (now housed in a purpose built bee shelter built in 2021), tiered areas, a greenhouse and wild garden across the burn. Maintained walking tracks in the fields lead to viewpoints. Biodiversity studies revealed that rare butterflies inhabit the small glen by the waterfall, there are forty different species of moths including rare micro moths and over seventy species of wildflowers in the fields, including three types of wild orchids. There is an abundance of wildlife including red squirrels, pine martens and a wide range of birds can be seen. This garden is a haven of tranquility.

Open: by arrangement 1 May - 30 September, admission £5.00, children free. Visiting by arrangement allows the owners to personally show visitors around if they wish, and explain the history around Barochreal, a village in the 1700s before Oban existed.

Directions: Fifteen minutes south of Oban. On the main A816 Oban to Lochgilphead road just to the south of the village of Kilninver on the left-hand side of the road. Bus Oban - Lochgilpead stops at Kilninver School, short walk after. Please disregard SatNav and use what3words address instead www.w3w.co/albums.forest.tinned.

Opening for: Scottish SPCA

Barochreal © Maurice Wilkins

Argyll & Lochaber

12 BENMORE BOTANIC GARDEN

Benmore, Dunoon PA23 8QU
A Regional Garden of the Royal Botanic Garden Edinburgh
T: 01369 706261 E: benmore@rbge.org.uk
W: www.rbge.org.uk

Benmore's magnificent mountainside setting is a joy to behold. Its 120 acres boast a world-famous collection of plants from the Orient and Himalayas to North and South America, as well as an impressive avenue of giant redwoods, one of the finest entrances to any botanic garden. Established in 1863, these majestic giants stand over 150 foot high. Seven miles of trails throughout lead to a restored Victorian Fernery and a dramatic viewpoint at 420 feet looking out to surrounding mountains and Holy Loch. There are also traditional Bhutanese and Chilean pavilions and the magnificent Golden Gates. Keep an eye out for red squirrels and other wildlife as you explore the garden.
Designed Landscape: http://portal.historicenvironment.scot/designation/GDL00056.
National Plant Collection: Abies, South American Temperate Conifers, Picea.

Open: Sunday 2 October, 10am - 5pm, admission details can be found on the garden's website. Also see website for details of regular opening times - www.rbge.org.uk.

Directions: Seven miles north of Dunoon or 22 miles south from Glen Kinglass below Rest and Be Thankful pass. On the A815. Bus service is limited.

Opening for: Donation to SGS

13 BERANDHU

Appin, Argyll PA38 4DD
John and Fiona Landale
T: 01631 730585 mobile 07900 377 414 E: johnllandale@gmail.com

A sheltered one-and-a-half acre coastal garden in a scenic setting offering fabulous views over Loch Laich to Loch Linnhe, Castle Stalker and the Morvern hills beyond. Craggy limestone abounds on the undulating site, some of which forms natural rockeries. Native trees mix with introduced firs and conifers. A variety of rhododendrons and azaleas provide spring and early summer colour. A mix of limestone overlaid with peat gives an unusual mix of wild flowers. This well-tended garden also has lovely wild areas of bog garden and woodland.

Open: by arrangement 1 April - 31 October, admission £5.00, children free.

Directions: In Appin turn off the A828 Connel to Ballachulish road at Gunn's Garage signposted for *Port Appin*. After one mile when the road turns uphill, first entrance on the right, half way up the hill.

Opening for: The Appin Village Hall & Alzheimer Scotland

Argyll & Lochaber

14 BRAEVALLICH FARM
by Dalmally PA33 1BU
Mr Philip Bowden-Smith
T: 01866 844246 E: philip@brae.co.uk

Discover two gardens, one at the farm and the upper garden further up the hill. The former is approximately one-and-a-half acres and developed over the last 40 years. Its principal features include dwarf rhododendron, azaleas (evergreen and deciduous), large drifts of various primula and meconopsis and bluebells, and mixed herbaceous perennials/shrubs; there is also quite a serious kitchen garden. The second garden has been developed over the last 30 years out of a birch and sessile oak wood and is a traditional West Coast glen garden intersected by two pretty burns with waterfalls. The garden has been extended over the last few years and now covers nearly ten acres with extensive new paths, and a suspension bridge over the ravine. Whilst the plants are important, many say that it is the topography with its differing vistas which make this garden such a peaceful and special place. The bud-set for 2022 appears to be truly exceptional so it should be a spectacular year - frosts allowing!

Open: Sunday 22 May & Sunday 19 June, 12pm - 5:30pm, admission £5.00, children free. There will be a wide selection of plants, principally rhododendrons, for sale on our plant stall. Dogs must be on leads.

Directions: South-east of Loch Awe on the B840, 15 miles from Cladich, seven miles from Ford.

Opening for: Mary's Meals

15 CRINAN HOTEL GARDEN
Crinan PA31 8SR
Mrs N Ryan
T: 01546 830261 E: nryan@crinanhotel.com
W: www.crinanhotel.com

Small rock garden with azaleas and rhododendrons created in a steep hillside over a century ago; with steps leading to a sheltered, secluded garden with sloping lawns, herbaceous beds and spectacular views of the canal and Crinan Loch.

Open: 1 May - 31 August, dawn - dusk, admission by donation. Raffle of signed, limited edition fine art print by Frances Macdonald. Tickets available at the coffee shop, art gallery and hotel.

Directions: Take the A83 to Lochgilphead, then the A816 to Oban, then the A841 Cairnbaan to Crinan. Daily bus.

Opening for: Feedback Madagascar

16 DAL AN EAS
Kilmore, Oban PA34 4XU
Mary Lindsay
T: 01631 770246 E: dalaneas@live.com

An informal country garden with the aim of increasing the biodiversity of native plants and insects while adding interest and colour with introduced trees, shrubs and naturalised perennials. There is a structured garden round the house and beyond there are extensive flower-filled 'meadows' with five different species of native orchid. Grass paths lead to waterfalls, vegetable plot, woodland garden, views and ancient archaeological sites.

Open: by arrangement 1 April - 30 September, admission by donation. Teas on request.

Argyll & Lochaber

Directions: From Oban take the A816 to Kilmore three-and-a-half miles south of Oban. Turn left on road to Barran and Musdale. Keep left at junction for Connel. Dal an Eas is approximately one mile on the left before the big hedges.

Opening for: Mary's Meals & RNLI

Dal An Eas © Nick Edgington

 17 ## DRUIMNEIL HOUSE
Port Appin PA38 4DQ
Mrs J Glaisher (Gardener: Mr Andrew Ritchie)
T: 01631 730228 E: druimneilhouse@btinternet.com

Large garden overlooking Loch Linnhe with many fine varieties of mature trees and rhododendrons and other woodland shrubs. Nearer the house, an impressive bank of deciduous azaleas is underplanted with a block of camassia and a range of other bulbs. A small Victorian walled garden is currently being restored. Owner, Janet Glaisher, is the winner of the Diana Macnab Award 2020. She has opened Druimneil House for Scotland's Garden Scheme for a remarkable 38 years.

Open: 1 January - 31 December, dawn - dusk, admission by donation. Teas normally available. Lunch by prior arrangement.

Directions: Turn in for Appin off the A828 (Connel/Fort William Road). After two miles take a sharp left at Airds Hotel and it's the second house on the right.

Opening for: The Queen's Nursing Institute Scotland & The Appin Village Hall

Argyll & Lochaber

18 EAS MHOR
Cnoc-a-Challtuinn, Clachan Seil, Oban PA34 4TR
Mrs Kimbra Lesley Barrett
T: 01852 300469 E: kimbra1745@gmail.com

All the usual joys of a west coast garden plus some delightful surprises! A small contemporary garden on a sloping site - the emphasis being on scent and exotic plant material. Unusual and rare blue Borinda bamboos (only recently discovered in China) and bananas. The garden is at its best in mid to late summer when shrub roses and sweet peas fill the air with scent. The delightful, sunny deck overlooks stylish white-walled ponds with cascading water blades. Recent additions include a 20-foot citrus house, Chinese pergola walk and peony border.

Open: by arrangement 1 May - 31 October, admission £5.00, children free.

Directions: After arranging a visit and agreeing a time, you will be met at the Tigh An Truish Car Park by the Atlantic Bridge, Isle of Seil. Or if travelling by bus, you will be met off the bus and taken to Eas Mhor. Please inform Mrs Barrett the time of your arrival. The bus stops at the bottom of Cnoc-a-Challtuinn Road.

Opening for: Small Paws Rescue: Oban

19 INVERARAY CASTLE GARDENS
Inveraray PA32 8XF
The Duke and Duchess of Argyll
T: 01499 302203 E: manager@inveraray-castle.com
W: www.inveraray-castle.com

The castle gardens are a blaze of yellows with varieties of narcissus in the spring followed by bluebells in May. Rhododendrons and azaleas abound and flower from April to June and the newly restored rose garden is a mass of pinks in late June and July. Very fine specimens of Cedrus deodara, Sequoiadendron giganteum (Wellingtonia), Cryptomeria japonica, Taxus baccata and others thrive in the damp climate. The Flag-Borders on each side of the main drive with paths in the shape of Scotland's national flag, the St Andrew's Cross, are outstanding in spring with Prunus 'Ukon' and P. subhirtella and are under planted with rhododendrons, eucryphias, shrubs and herbaceous plants giving interest all year.
Designed Landscape: http://portal.historicenvironment.scot/designation/GDL00223

Open: 28 March - 31 October, 10am - 5pm, admission £7.00, children under five free. Tearoom and Shop on site. Free parking with castle and garden entrance. Pre-booking via website recommended. Tours with the Head Gardener can be arranged in advance. Only assistance dogs within the castle and garden. Please check the website for current opening days and times, further information and accessibility. www.inveraray-castle.com

Directions: Inveraray is 60 miles north of Glasgow and 45 miles from Oban. Regular bus services from Glasgow, Oban and Campbeltown. SatNav PA32 8XF.

Opening for: Donation to SGS

20 KILDALLOIG
Campbeltown PA28 6RE
Mr and Mrs Joe Turner
T: 07979 855930 E: kildalloig@gmail.com

Coastal garden with some interesting and unusual shrubs including Australasian shrubs and trees, climbing roses and herbaceous perennials. There is a woodland walk and a pond garden with aquatic and bog plants.

Argyll & Lochaber

Open: by arrangement 1 May - 31 October, admission £5.00, children free. Group visits must be pre-booked.

Directions: Take the A83 to Campbeltown, then three miles south east of town past Davaar Island.

Opening for: Marie Curie & Macmillan Cancer Support

21 KINLOCHLAICH WALLED GARDEN

Appin PA38 4BD
Miss F M M Hutchison
T: 07881 525754 E: fiona@kinlochlaich.plus.com
W: www.kinlochlaichgardencentre.co.uk

Octagonal walled garden incorporating a large Nursery Garden Centre with a huge variety of plants growing and for sale. Bluebell woodland walk and spring garden. Many rhododendrons, azaleas, trees, shrubs and herbaceous plants, including many unusual ones such as embothrium, davidia, stewartia, magnolia, eucryphia and tropaeolum. A quarter of the interior of the walled garden is borders packed with many unusual and interesting plants, espaliered fruit trees, and with an ancient yew in the centre, and another quarter is vegetable growing.

Open: 3 March - 31 October, 10am - 4pm, admission £3.00, children free. Winter by appointment - we are generally about.

Directions: On the A828 in Appin between Oban, 18 miles to the south, and Fort William, 27 miles to the north. The entrance is next to the police station. Infrequent bus Oban to Fort William - request stop.

Opening for: The Appin Village Hall & Down's Syndrome Scotland: West of Scotland Branch

22 KNOCK NEWHOUSE

Lochgair PA31 8RZ
Mrs Hew Service
T: 01546 886628 E: corranmorhouse@aol.com

Like all good gardens, our woodland garden has evolved over time. It is centered on a 250 foot lochan, a small waterfall and lily pond. The first trees and rhododendrons were planted in the 60s, with major additions in the 90s. A variety of cut leaf and flowering trees were added after the storms of 2011/12. As a result the garden now has a wide range of specimen trees, camellias, hoheria, eucryphia, stewartia to name a few in addition to the azaleas and rhododendrons. January flowering is followed with spring flowers and bluebells and then into the autumn with spectacular colours. I am delighted to welcome visitors at any time so please let me know when you would like to visit.

Open: Saturday/Sunday, 14/15 May, 1pm - 5:30pm, admission £5.00, children free. Plants for sale. Tours and groups must be pre-booked.
Directions: On the A83. The house is not visible from the road. From Lochgilphead, half-a-mile south of Lochgair Hotel and on the left-hand side of the road, and from Inveraray on the right-hand side of the road half-a-mile after the Lochgair Hotel; the drive opening is marked and enters the woods. Bus Route - Inveraray to Lochgilphead

Opening for: St Columba's - Poltalloch & Cancer Research UK

Argyll & Lochaber

23 ORMSARY HOUSE
Ormsary, Lochgilphead, Argyll PA31 8PE
Lady Lithgow
T: 01880 770738 E: mclithgow@ormsary.co.uk

Ormsary is on the shore of Loch Caolisport looking across to Islay and Jura. The house policies are resplendent in spring with bluebells and daffodils under fine oak trees. There are woodland gardens with azaleas, rhododendrons and a collection of trees and shrubs. The walled garden, which has evolved over a couple of centuries, is on two levels. The top half is a kitchen garden producing plants, fruit and vegetables for the house; a winter garden and 'Muscat of Alexandria' vinery have been heated by hydroelectric power for 100 years. A magnificent *Polylepis australis* beckons to the lower Secret Garden with its lawn, roses, magnolias and long mixed border. It opens onto the banks of Ormsary Water. There are also woodland walks accessed via the upper woodland garden.

Open: by arrangement 1 April - 31 October, admission £5.00, children free.

Directions: Take the A83 road from Lochgilphead towards Campbeltown for four miles, then take the B8024 signposted to *Kilberry*, travel ten miles and follow signs to the *Estate office* for directions to the garden.

Opening for: SGS and Beneficiaries

Ormsary House

24 STRACHUR FLOWER & WOODLAND GARDENS
Strachur PA27 8BX
Sir Charles and Lady Maclean

The flower garden is sheltered by magnificent beeches, limes, ancient yews and Japanese maples. There are herbaceous borders, a burnside rhododendron and azalea walk, rockery, tulips and spring bulbs. Enjoy the old woodland of Strachur Park, laid out in 1782, and the wildlife rich lochan.

Argyll & Lochaber

Open: Sunday 15 May & Sunday 22 May, 1pm - 5pm, admission £5.00, children free.

Directions: Turn off the A815 at Strachur House Farm entrance. Park in farm square. Bus Dunoon - Inveraray. From Edinburgh/Glasgow take the ferry from Gourock to Dunoon.

Opening for: British Red Cross

25 THE SECRET GARDEN
Isle of Lismore, Oban, Argyll PA34 5UL
Eva Tombs
T: 01631 760128 E: eva.tombs@gmail.com

A unique garden at the centre of a biodynamic farm on the Island of Lismore in the Inner Hebrides. The garden created from a field has a strong geometric layout that reflects the ecclesiastical history of the island. It has a vegetable garden, a tree nursery, a physic garden, an orchard and a polytunnel. The garden is a haven for wildflowers, birds, bees and butterflies. Standing stones, meadows, new woodlands, mountains and the sea encompass the whole. A herd of rare breed Shetland cattle, chickens, ducks and friendly cats.

Open: by arrangement 1 May - 1 October, admission £5.00, children free. Plants, seeds, fruit and vegetables, flowers, meat and eggs for sale. No dogs please, there are lots of animals around. Refreshments by arrangement.

Directions: Please telephone for directions. Approximately two miles from Port Appin ferry.

Opening for: SGS and Beneficiaries

The Secret Garden © Mairi Fleck

Ayrshire & Arran

Sponsored by

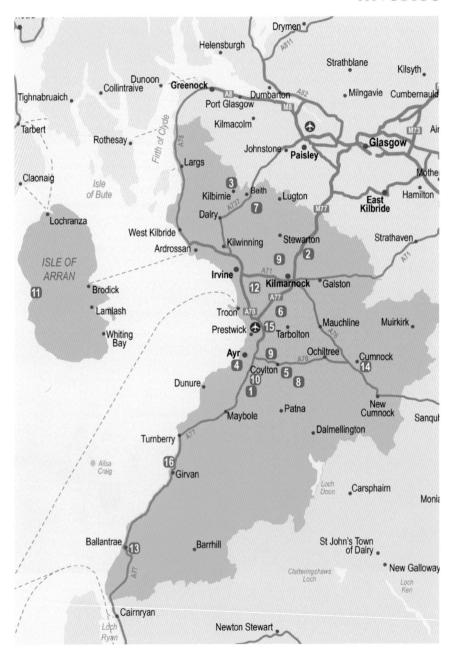

Investec

Ayrshire & Arran

OUR VOLUNTEER ORGANISERS

District Organisers:	Rose-Ann Cuninghame	45 Towerhill Avenue, Kilmaurs KA3 2TS E: r.cuninghame@btinternet.com
	Lavinia Gibbs	Dougarie, Isle of Arran KA27 8EB
Area Organisers:	Kim Donald MBE	19 Waterslap, Fenwick KA3 6AJ T: 07836 583546
	Pattie Kewney	
	Fiona McLean	
	Rosie Pensom	
	Wendy Sandiford	
	Sue Veitch	
	Linda Vosseler	
District Photographers:	David Blatchford	
	Rob Davis	
Treasurers:	Lizzie Adam	Bayview, Pirnmill, Isle of Arran KA27 8HP
	Carol Freireich	18 Netherblane, Blanefield, Stirling G63 9JW

GARDENS OPEN ON A SPECIFIC DATE

Netherthird Community Garden, Craigens Road, Netherthird	Saturday, 14 May
29 Scaur O'Doon Road, Ayr	Friday - Monday, 10 - 13 June
Barrmill Community Garden, Barrmill Park and Gardens	Sunday, 12 June
Dundonald Village Gardens, Dundonald, Kilmarnock	Saturday, 18 June
Barnweil Garden, Craigie, near Kilmarnock	Sunday, 19 June
Underwood Lodge, Craigie, Kilmarnock, South Ayrshire	Saturday/Sunday, 25/26 June
Carbieston House, Coylton, Ayr	Saturday/Sunday, 2/3 July
Dougarie, Isle of Arran	Tuesday, 5 July
Whitewin House, Golf Course Road, Girvan	Sats and Suns, 16 July - 14 August
19 Waterslap, Fenwick	Sunday, 24 July
25 Stoneyholm Road, Kilbirnie	Sunday, 24 July

GARDENS OPEN REGULARLY

Dalrymple Community Garden, Barbieston Road, Dalrymple	1 January - 31 December

GARDENS OPEN BY ARRANGEMENT

Glenapp Castle, Ballantrae, Girvan	1 January - 31 December
Burnside, Littlemill Road, Drongan	1 April - 31 August
Auldbyres Farm Garden, Coylton	10 April - 30 September
Barnweil Garden, Craigie, near Kilmarnock	15 May - 17 July & 10 - 20 October
1 Burnton Road, Dalrymple	1 June - 31 August
Whitewin House, Golf Course Road, Girvan	1 July - 31 August

Ayrshire & Arran

1 1 BURNTON ROAD
Dalrymple KA6 6DY
David and Margaret Blatchford
T: 01292 561988 E: d.blatchford273@btinternet.com

A tiny slice of jungle nestled within a small triangular plot. To the front of the house are two beds planted with nectar-secreting plants. In a larger bed, a sea of *Stipa tenuissima* is studded with perennials. To the rear, a small patio is home to some bonsai, a collection of potted terrestrial ferns and stone troughs hold tender and hardy succulents. A serpentine path meanders through dense planting of palms, bamboos, bananas and tree ferns. Of particular note, is the use of hardy and tender bromeliads and a collection of aroids such as *Arisaemia, Alocasia* and *Colocasia*. Flower highlights are provided by lilies (species and cultivars) and later in the season, cannas and hardy gingers such as *Hedychium* and *Roscoea*. A large specimen of *Schefflera taiwaniana* cloaks the side of a summer house and rare *Cordyline indivisa* is staging a modest resurgence after the winter of 2021.

Open: by arrangement 1 June - 31 August, admission £5.00, children free.

Directions: From the north take the A77 Ayr to Stranraer. At the roundabout, turn left onto the A713 and follow the road past the hospital to the junction with B742, turn right into the village and park in the White Horse car park at the T junction. The garden is on the corner of Burnton and Barbieston Roads. From the south take the A77 towards Ayr, turn right onto the B7034. Follow into the village, at Kirkton Inn junction turn left onto Barbieston Road. Bus 52 from Ayr.

Opening for: Dalrymple, Skeldon and Hollybush Project

2 19 WATERSLAP
Fenwick KA3 6AJ
Mrs Kim Donald
T: 07836 583546 E: kd581@aol.com

This south facing garden began life in 2015 with only four mature chestnut, lime and willow trees. A challenging site, the owner has designed it to give year-round colour. Traditional hedging provides shelter for this contemporary cottage garden, planted with a wide variety of now well established trees, shrubs, perennials, roses and many clematis. Snowdrops, daffodils and hellebores are planted in abundance for spring interest. For summer, herbaceous borders and shrubberies frame a lawn. Paths link raised vegetable beds, greenhouse, cold frames, fruit trees, beds and a small woodland area. The burn on the southside inspired the flow of the garden, the banks of which are planted with water loving trees, shrubs and gunnera, giving welcome shelter from frosts and winds. The garden remains a work in progress.

Open: Sunday 24 July, 1pm - 5pm, admission £6.00, children free. Advance tickets can be purchased from Kim Donald or on-line, check the SGS website. Tickets are also available on the day. Sorry no dogs.

Directions: M77 from the south take J8 signed *Fenwick*. Into village, past coffee shop turn right into Waterslap. From north take J7 signed *Fenwick*, down Main Road, at bottom turn left into Waterslap.

Opening for: The Brain Tumour Charity

Ayrshire & Arran

3 **25 STONEYHOLM ROAD**
Kilbirnie KA25 7DT
Gillian and James Sharp

The house itself was built in 1887, but when we moved in over 10 years ago, the garden was a jungle. We removed 12 trees, many of them self-seeded trees, discovered a sunken garden and had to fill it with 20 tonnes of topsoil. Therefore, starting from this blank canvas and a love of gardening, we divided the garden into rooms to add interest, including a parterre, herbaceous border, patio and lots of different seating areas, including one by Nigel Bialy, to take advantage of the sun at various times of the day.

Open: Sunday 24 July, 2pm - 5pm, admission £5.00, children free.

Directions: On the main road as you come into Kilbirnie from Lochwinnoch. Parking is just off the main road at the side of the house on Dipple Road, the garden is on a corner. Alternate parking can be found past the house, through the traffic lights and left at the roundabout. Public bus service runs to the Cross in Kilbirnie, with a five-minute walk from there to the garden. For details go to Traveline Scotland www.travelinescotland.com

Opening for: The Royal Air Force Benevolent Fund

4 **29 SCAUR O'DOON ROAD**
Ayr KA7 4EP
Mr C Tucker
T: 01292 443206 E: clivet72@gmail.com

And in the beginning (1975) there was sand...and wind...and salt...and small children so it took around 20 years to establish shelter-belts of shrubs in key locations and these in turn determined the layout and development of the garden. This has now evolved into four separate gardens, each with its own characteristics. The exotic garden boasts magnolia, olive, fig, choisya, callistemon and desfontania amongst many others. The woodland garden contains inter alia ilex, copper beech, laburnum and includes a spectacular Sole Grande specimen. The most recent development has been the terraced garden with several varieties of hebe, cistus, spirea, plus various sedums and herbaceous plants but is still very much a work in progress. The hanging garden is potentially a major attraction and an artificial bog is under construction, along with the development of a kitchen garden. Over the years, soil has been imported and incorporated in the ground but the main source of humus and body has been seaweed, with a plentiful supply just beyond the front entrance and compost, annual production of which is now over one cubic metre per annum. The garden has been described as one of surprise and this accords with the basic philosophy behind it.

Open: Friday to Monday, 10/11/12/13 June, 2pm - 5pm, admission £5.00, children free. Visitors should note that some paths are quite narrow and not advised for anyone dependent on walking aids. These are highlighted in the garden plan. If telephoning, evenings are preferred.

Directions: On the A77 bypass approaching the town follow the signs for Stranraer until the far end until you come to the turning for Alloway. Doonfoot and Heads of Ayr are on the right. Follow the road, keeping left at the roundabout, for about half-a-mile to the T junction at the Burns Centre and turn left. After crossing over the bridge turn right into Longhill Avenue and carry straight on across the roundabout and down Earls Way. Turn right at the T junction and then into the seafront car park. The entrance to the garden is at the end of the cul-de-sac. Use the well signed car park. Buses 9 and 361 from the centre of town.

Opening for: Clydesdale Parkinson's Group

Ayrshire & Arran

5 AULDBYRES FARM GARDEN
Coylton KA6 6HG
Marshall and Sue Veitch
E: su.pavet@btinternet.com

Surrounded by a working farm, this compact, established garden has mature shrubs, wildlife pond, bog garden and stream. Stunning views towards Ayr and Arran 'borrow' the countryside panorama. The crispness of spring borders, with woodland gems, gives way to a riot of summer perennial favourites. A 'Pot Theatre' of containers brightens the farmyard with seasonal displays. Personal tour and tea/coffee on request. Family walks, through farm woods and Hannahston community woodland, are recommended - dogs on leads welcome.

Open: by arrangement 10 April - 30 September, admission £5.00, children free.

Directions: In Coylton take road signposted *B742*, past Coylton Arms Pub in Low Coylton, *Auldbyres* signposted on left after half-a-mile.

Opening for: Beatson West of Scotland Cancer Centre

6 BARNWEIL GARDEN
Craigie, near Kilmarnock KA1 5NE
Mr and Mrs Ronald W Alexander
E: ronaldwalexander@btinternet.com

The garden, now approaching 50 years in its development, surrounds an 18th century farmhouse with a large lawn on the south side, flanked by herbaceous borders with a soft colour palette of blue, pink, purple and white. The whole is surrounded by woodland walks featuring Oscar's ditch and lined with foliage plants including rodgersias, regal and ostrich ferns, red and white candelabra primulas, black iris and the rarely seen *Peltiphyllum peltatum* and *Smilacina*. Elsewhere in the woodland there is a fine gunnera stand and the Golden Glade with golden acer, philadelphus and other golden leaved shrubs and underplantings. On the north side of the house are rectangular borders flanking the view from the big arched window to Ben Lomond 60 miles away. On each side of these borders are long rose borders, backed by beech hedges. The roses, mostly David Austin, should be well into their first flush. In the autumn it is mainly about leaf colour with the acers and American oaks being particularly good and the last flush of the roses, with asters, sedums and gentians, still bringing colour to the borders.

Open: Sunday 19 June, 2pm - 5pm. Also open by arrangement 15 May - 17 July and 10 - 20 October. Admission £6.00, children free.

Directions: Two miles from Craigie. Right off the B730, two miles south of the A77 heading to Tarbolton.

Opening for: Tarbolton Parish Church of Scotland & The Ridley Foundation

7 BARRMILL COMMUNITY GARDEN
Barrmill Park and Gardens KA15 1HW
The Barrmill Conservation Group
T: 07920 098171

This large woodland garden is carved from a 19th-century whinstone quarry and situated within an 1890s parkland, once known for the quoiting green provided for the village thread mill and ironstone pit workers of that time. Enhancement of the gardens began in 2010 by volunteers, with assistance from *The Beechgrove Garden*. Features include enchanted woodland walks, the Vale Burn, views of the Dusk Water, a restored 19th-century cholera pit

Ayrshire & Arran

aka 'the Deid Man's Plantin', wish trees, wishing wells, doors to the Elfhame, guided walks, nature trail and traditional Ayrshire quoits game. The woodland backdrop is complemented by an understorey of natural planting throughout.

Open: Sunday 12 June, 2pm - 5pm, admission £4.00, children free.

Directions: From Stewarton take the A735 to Dunlop, go left down Main Street B706 to Burnhouse, over at crossroads to Barrmill B706. From Lugton south on the A736, right at Burnhouse, B706 to Barrmill. From Glasgow on the M8 take J28a signposted *Irvine*, on Beith bypass take left B706 to Barrmill.

Opening for: Barrmill and District Community Association

---

8 BURNSIDE

Littlemill Road, Drongan KA6 7EN
Sue Simpson and George Watt
T: 01292 592445 E: suesimpson33@btinternet.com

This maturing and constantly changing six-and-a-half acre garden began in 2006. There is a wide range of plants from trees to alpines, giving colour and variability all year. Next to the road flows the Drumbowie Burn, parallel to which is a woodland border with snowdrops, erythroniums, hellebores, trilliums, rhododendrons and acers. Near the house are a raised bed and large collection of troughs, with an interesting range of alpines. The garden boasts herbaceous beds, ericaceous garden, screes, three alpine glasshouses with award-winning plants, polytunnel, pond and arboretum - underplanted with daffodils, camassia, fritillaries and crocus. With a view towards matrimonial harmony, there are two sheds which may be of interest.

Open: by arrangement 1 April - 31 August, admission £6.00, children free. Hot drinks and baking available on request from £2.50. Visit the website for additional openings

Directions: From A77 Ayr bypass take A70 Cumnock for five-and-a-quarter miles, at Coalhall, turn onto B730 Drongan (south) for two-and-a-half miles. Burnside entrance is immediately adjacent to a black/white parapeted bridge. Ordnance survey grid ref: NS455162.

Opening for: IFDAS : at River Garden Auchincruive

Burnside © David Blatchford

Ayrshire & Arran

9 CARBIESTON HOUSE
Coylton, Ayr KA6 5JU
Wilma Wilson

Carbieston has a walled garden containing apple trees underplanted with peonies, salvias, daylilies and other species divided by rows of ophiopogons and cardoons combining to bring a sense of rhythm to the planting. The central sections continue to function as a bountiful kitchen garden thanks to the hard work and dedication of Alan who grows everything from seed. A cutting garden has recently been included in this walled area with many colourful dahlias. Other parts of the garden feature rose beds and a newly developed area has been planted with plants mainly from Asia. This is definitely a garden in progress, the current focus being on creating woodland areas full of hellebores and hydrangeas, again propagated by Alan who seems to manage to grow anything.

Open: Saturday/Sunday, 2/3 July, 2pm - 5pm, admission £5.00.

Directions: Take the A70 from Ayr. Just before Sundrum Caravan Park opposite Carbieston Byres Farm, turn left on to Uplands Road. At the top of the hill turn left through the white gate. Signed on the A70 from the roundabout on the A77 and from Coylton.

Opening for: ACCBSG & Ramsbury School Development Trust

10 DALRYMPLE COMMUNITY GARDEN
Barbieston Road, Dalrymple KA6 6DY
Dalrymple Community Landscape Project

Opened in September 2019, the garden, situated opposite the shops in Barbieston Road, is run by a dedicated team of volunteers; part of the Dalrymple, Skeldon and Hollybush Project. A large central lawn is surrounded by extensive areas of original meadow turf and already we have seen the appearance of wildflowers, with a concomitant increase in insect diversity, and the appearance of butterflies associated with wild grasses. Damselflies and amphibians have begun to visit the two ponds. We have planted several thousand spring bulbs including snake's head fritillaries and camassias and as the new year progresses we will be adding willows and other native shrubs to provide a richer habitat.

Open: 1 January - 31 December, dawn - dusk.

Directions: From the north take the A77 Ayr to Stranraer. At the A713 junction take the left turn and follow the road past the hospital to the B742 junction, turn right into the village and park behind the shops in the centre of the village. From south of the A77, take the B7034 and turn right. Bus 52 from Ayr.

Opening for: Dalrymple, Skeldon and Hollybush Project

Ayrshire & Arran

11 DOUGARIE
Isle of Arran KA27 8EB
Mrs S C Gibbs
E: office@dougarie.com

A most interesting terraced garden in a castellated folly built in 1905 to celebrate the marriage of the 12th Duke of Hamilton's only child to the Duke of Montrose. Good selection of tender and rare shrubs and herbaceous border. Small woodland area with trees including azara, abutilon, eucryphia, hoheria and nothofagus.

Open: Tuesday 5 July, 2pm - 5pm, admission £4.00, children free.

Directions: Five miles from Blackwaterfoot. Regular ferry sailing from Ardrossan and Claonaig (Argyll). Information from Caledonian MacBrayne, Gourock, T: 01475 650100. Parking is free.

Opening for: Pirnmill Village Association

12 DUNDONALD VILLAGE GARDENS
Dundonald, Kilmarnock KA2 9HG
The Gardeners of Dundonald

Glenfoot House (NEW) 58 Main Street KA2 9HG (Helen Press): This mature but evolving garden is south facing for the most part, wrapping round the old village manse. The garden looks across farmland and the historic woodland of Dundonald Glen. Divided into sections including shady woodland, vegetable and cut flower garden, newly restored greenhouse and large lawned area enclosed by herbaceous borders. The planting comprises mature shrubs, old fashioned roses and hardy perennials in a romantic cottage garden style of loose planting.
Kirk Style (NEW) 53 Main Street KA2 9HH (Gillian Meldrum): Originally part of the old smithy for Dundonald, this modestly sized enclosed family garden runs the length of the lane from the church to the village church hall. A haven for pollinators and wildlife, the garden is zoned for family life with a custom-built gazebo and zones for relaxation, play and greenhouse. A mature magnolia generously underplanted with hellebores, astrantia and other lovers of dappled shade divides the garden. Chickens are at the heart of this organic garden, which includes maturing apple, mirabelle and birch trees. Planting is informal cottage style with a wide variety of plants, colour and texture.
The Coach House (NEW) 58a Main Street KA2 9HG (Sheila Payne): The Coach House was the stable block for the original manse. The small gravel garden faces south-west overlooking the church glebe, ancient Dundonald Woods and the historic castle. Interesting shrubs and small trees, attractive for their flowers, complement herbaceous planting with old-fashioned roses, climbers and peonies.

Open: Saturday 18 June, 2pm - 5pm, admission £5.00, children free. Dundonald Parish Church will be open on the day. Maps, tickets, cake stall and cream teas will be available in the church hall and plants for sale in the church grounds.

Directions: Five miles south of Kilmarnock/north of Prestwick. Take the left off the A77 onto the B730. Follow signs to *Dundonald and castle.*
Glenfoot House is directly opposite the Auchens pub at the end of the drive.
Kirk Style is directly opposite the church at the top of Main Street by a gate on the right-hand side.
The Coach House is at the end of the small right-hand drive directly opposite the Auchens pub.

Opening for: Dundonald Parish Church

Ayrshire & Arran

13 GLENAPP CASTLE
Ballantrae, Girvan KA26 0NZ
Mr Paul Szkiler
T: 01465 831212 E: info@glenappcastle.com
W: www.glenappcastle.com

The 36-acre grounds at Glenapp Castle are secluded and private. Many rare and unusual plants and shrubs can be found, including magnificent specimen rhododendrons. Paths meander round the azalea pond, through established woodland leading to the wonderful walled garden with a 150-foot Victorian glasshouse. Fresh herbs and fruit from the garden are used every day in the castle kitchen. Much of the gardens were designed by Gertrude Jekyll (1843-1932), the world-famous garden designer, applying the principles of the Arts and Crafts Movement, who worked in collaboration with Edwin Lutyens. A new walk has been created opening up the Glen, where Glenapp's Champion Trees will be found.
Champion Trees: *Abies cilicica*, *Cercidiphyllum japonicum* and *Picea likiangensis*.

Open: by arrangement 1 January - 31 December.

Directions: From the north take the A77 south. Pass through Ballantrae, crossing the River Stinchar as you leave. Take the first turning on the right, 100 yards beyond the river (not signposted). From the south take the A77 north, turn left 100 yards before the bridge over Stinchar at Ballantrae. The castle gates are one mile along this road.

Opening for: Donation to SGS

14 NETHERTHIRD COMMUNITY GARDEN
Craigens Road, Netherthird, Cumnock KA18 3AR
Netherthird Community Development Group
E: jamielor@aol.com W: facebook.com/Netherthird-Community-Development-Group-174476469271910

Netherthird Community Garden will be opening with a 'Wildlife for Families Theme' to suit all ages. Follow our nature trail with wild orchids. See our long cottage border bursting with shrubs, perennials and annuals, vegetable beds and polytunnels where we grow tomatoes and plants. The striking wooden gazebos were funded by the Prince's Trust for outdoor lessons. Visit the vast sandpit and take part in a treasure hunt and fancy dress class for young dog owners. All run by, and for, volunteers and the local community.

Open: Saturday 14 May, 2pm - 5pm, admission £3.00, children free.

Directions: Driving south on the A76 Cumnock Bypass, look for the roundabout signposted *B7083*. Take this exit which heads to Cumnock and after a few hundred yards take a right turn into Craigens Road. Netherthird Primary School is on the right and parking is available there. The Community Garden is nearby. There is disabled parking at the garden.

Opening for: Netherthird Community Development Group

15 UNDERWOOD LODGE
Craigie, Kilmarnock, South Ayrshire KA1 5NG
Marilyn Badman
T: 01563 830439 E: mbadman1@sky.com

Underwood Lodge has a secluded garden surrounded by farmland and woodland which give some protection and adds to the ambience. The main structure of the garden has been in place for 19 years, however significant remodelling has taken place in the last three years. The one acre-garden comprises a variety of mature trees, shrubs, herbaceous and wall grown

Ayrshire & Arran

plants. A woodland garden is at an embryonic stage with the construction of a woodland path, the planting of some semi-mature rhododendrons and some underplanting of woodland plants. The planting within all areas of the garden demonstrates an understanding of form and texture of plants, which adds to its enjoyment.

Open: Saturday/Sunday, 25/26 June, 12pm - 5pm, admission £5.00, children free. Visitors should make contact in advance and will be given a timed slot during the open days.

Directions: Southbound on the A77, pass Hansel Village and take the next left signposted Underwood/Ladykirk. Northbound on the A77 take the exit to Symington then first right, to join the Southbound Carriageway. Take the Underwood/Ladykirk turning. At the stone bridge, turn left and Underwood Lodge is the first house on the left.

Opening for: Annbank Parish Church Of Scotland

Underwood Lodge © David Blatchford

16 WHITEWIN HOUSE
Golf Course Road, Girvan KA26 9HW
Linda Finnie and Graeme Finnie
T: 01465 712358 M: 07855 269247 E: lafinnie@hotmail.com

Historic Whitewin House was built for Baronet Henry Tate of Tate and Lyle. The House stands in one acre of formal Victorian Garden redesigned over a five-year period, in the form of an English Manor House Garden which, of course, comes with its challenges because of its coastal location. The rockeries, beautiful scalloped lawns and the plethora of statuary, all complement the use of authentic Victorian bedding plants, trees and shrubs, ideally mirroring the ambience and grandeur of the house interior. Whitewin House is fortunate in having the prime position in Golf Course Road, having been the first house built there, standing majestically overlooking the Firth of Clyde, Ailsa Craig, Arran and the Kintyre Peninsula.

Open: Saturdays and Sundays, 16/17, 23/24, 30/31 July and 6/7, 13/14 August. Also open by arrangement 1 July - 31 August. Admission £5.00, children free.

Directions: Approaching Girvan from the north on the A77 the turning to Golf Course Road is on the right hand side of the road before the town centre. Follow signs for the *Golf Course*. From the south on the A77 come through Girvan, turn left at the lights, then first left and follow the signs for the *Golf Course*. Entrance to the property will be signposted.

Opening for: SGS and Beneficiaries

Berwickshire

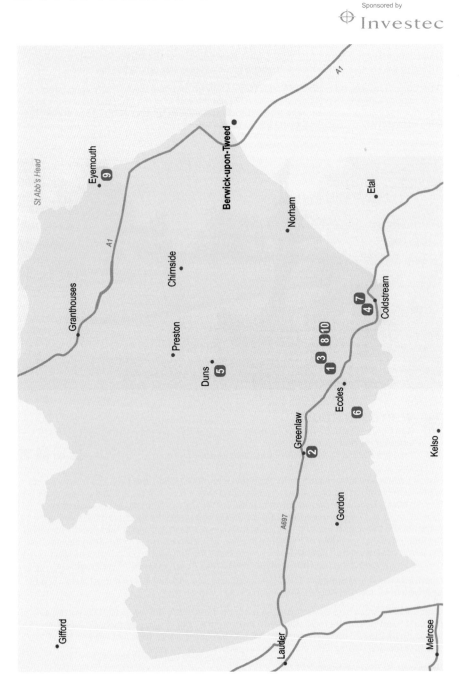

Berwickshire

OUR VOLUNTEER ORGANISERS

District Organiser:	Christine McLennan	Marlfield, Coldstream TD12 4JT E: info@scotlandsgardens.org
Area Organisers:	Christine Johnson Candy Philip Susan Vassallo	 34 Trinity Park, Duns TD11 3HN 4 Lambton Green, Coldstream TD12 4EN
District Photographers:	Kenneth Patterson Malcolm Ross	3 Yarrow Close, East Ord TD15 2YE 2 Dall Hollow, North Berwick EH39 5FN
Treasurer:	Forbes McLennan	Marlfield, Coldstream TD12 4JT

GARDENS OPEN ON A SPECIFIC DATE

Harlaw Farmhouse, Eccles near Kelso	Sunday, 17 April
Broomhill Villa, 4 Edinburgh Road, Greenlaw	Sunday, 15 May
Ruthven House, Coldstream	Sunday, 26 June
Netherbyres, Eyemouth	Sunday, 3 July
Coldstream Open Gardens, Coldstream	Sunday, 10 July
Marlfield Gardens, Coldstream	Sunday, 31 July
Duns Open Gardens, Volunteer Hall, Langtongate	Sunday, 21 August

GARDENS OPEN REGULARLY

Bughtrig, near Leitholm, Coldstream	1 June - 1 September

GARDENS OPEN BY ARRANGEMENT

Ruthven House, Coldstream	1 January - 30 September
Marlfield Gardens, Coldstream	1 January - 30 September
Lennel Bank, Coldstream	1 May - 30 September
Netherbyres, Eyemouth	1 May - 31 August
Broomhill Villa, 4 Edinburgh Road, Greenlaw	1 June - 31 July
Anton's Hill Walled Garden, Leitholm, Coldstream	7, 9, 14 & 16 July

Berwickshire

1 ANTON'S HILL WALLED GARDEN
Leitholm, Coldstream TD12 4JD
Andrew McCarthy and Graham Ward
T: 01890 840449 / 07713 063426 E: andyjomcc123@gmail.com

Popular in previous years, Anton's Hill Walled Garden is opening again with Scotland's Garden Scheme and with new owners. The garden was lovingly restored by the previous owners over 25 years and has appeared on *BBC Beechgrove* in addition to other TV programmes. Managed on organic principles, it contains an important collection of over 200 apple, pear and plum varieties, as well as an extensive vegetable garden, herbaceous borders, ponds, lawns, nuttery, specimen trees and a small beech and oak woodland.

Open: by arrangement 7, 9, 14 and 16 July. Admission £5.00, children free.

Directions: The garden will be signposted off the B6461, approximately half-a-mile west of Leitholm.

Opening for: Donation to SGS

Anton's Hill Walled Garden © Andrew McCarthy

2 BROOMHILL VILLA
4 Edinburgh Road, Greenlaw TD10 6XF
Tatyana Aplin
T: 07957 288557 E: aplin848@btinternet.com

Broomhill garden is on the northern side of Greenlaw comprising half-an-acre of spring colour nestled between village and farmland. The garden is maintained by a passionate plant collector featuring narcissuses, tulips, meconopses, and hundreds of other flowers. The collection has been developed along informal lines with treats at every turn. A radiant display of blooms that changes through the year intended not only for the visual pleasure of the garden but also for the house with cut flower arrangements as well as produce for the table and larder.

Open: Sunday 15 May, 1pm - 5pm. Also open by arrangement 1 June - 31 July. Admission £5.00, children free.

Directions: On the A697 at the northern end of Greenlaw Village

Opening for: Cancer Research UK

Berwickshire

3 BUGHTRIG
near Leitholm, Coldstream TD12 4JP
Mr and Mrs William Ramsay
E: ramsay@bughtrig.co.uk

A traditional hedged Scottish family garden with an interesting combination of sculpture, herbaceous plants, shrubs, annuals and fruit. It is surrounded by fine specimen trees, which provide remarkable shelter.

Open: 1 June - 1 September, 11am - 5pm, admission £5.00, children free.

Directions: Quarter-of-a-mile east of Leitholm on the B6461.

Opening for: Donation to SGS

4 COLDSTREAM OPEN GARDENS
Coldstream Community Centre, High Street, Coldstream TD12 4EN
The Gardeners of Coldstream

Historic Coldstream. Scotland's first true border town. Situated on the River Tweed which forms a natural boundary between Scotland and England. There will be a rich variety of gardens open for the enthusiast to explore, many open for the first time. All the garden openers will be delighted to share their garden triumphs and interests with you.

Open: Sunday 10 July, 1pm - 5pm, admission £5.00, children free. Tickets, teas, route maps, plant sales and facilities available at the Community Centre on the High Street.

Directions: Coldstream is on the A697, equidistant between Kelso and Berwick-upon-Tweed. The Community Centre (an old church building) is in the west end of town. There is ample parking on the street and in nearby car parks.

Opening for: Macmillan Cancer Support

Broomhill Villa

Berwickshire

5 DUNS OPEN GARDENS
Volunteer Hall, Langtongate, Duns TD11 3AF
The Gardeners of Duns
E: theold.stables@btinternet.com

Duns, formerly the county town of Berwickshire, lies approximately 12 miles north of the border between Scotland and England and still retains a thriving market square reminiscent of an ancient Scottish Burgh. It is home to an award-winning motor sport museum depicting the life and career of Formula 1 Champion, Jim Clark OBE, as well as Duns Castle Estate with its numerous paths to explore. There are extensive green areas in and around the town offering delightful walks all year round. After a hugely successful first year of opening our gardens in 2021, we are delighted to be able to do so again this year. Our gardens are lovingly tended by enthusiastic gardeners, happy to share them with like-minded people. They offer a wonderful variety of size, layout and planting, ensuring that there is something for everyone. We are sure you will enjoy your time in Duns, meeting and chatting with other garden lovers and sharing ideas and plans for future garden projects.

Open: Sunday 21 August, noon - 5pm, admission £5.00, children free. Teas/coffees/home-baking available to purchase at the Volunteer Hall where you can also purchase tickets and route maps. Locally grown plants for sale. There are a number of other eateries in and around the Market Square for anyone who would like to make a day of it and enjoy a leisurely lunch or snack.

Directions: Duns is situated on the crossroads of the A6112 and A6105, approximately 14 miles west of Berwick upon Tweed and is easily accessible from the A1 onto the A6112 and from the A68/697 onto the A6105.

Opening for: AHFD: A Heart for Duns

6 HARLAW FARMHOUSE
Eccles near Kelso, Roxburghshire TD5 7RA
Jean Wood
T: 07479 357999 E: jean.greenfingers@gmail.com

Harlaw is set in a one-acre garden surrounding a typical Berwickshire farmhouse, in a truly rural setting with lovely Border views. The owner has spent many years building up a collection of over 65 varieties of named daffodils and narcissus, naturalised throughout the garden. It has a mature nuttery with several highly productive walnut, hazel and gingko biloba trees and an orchard with apple, pear and plum trees. In the summer there is a large cutting garden and vegetable patch. There are two greenhouses with a large cactus collection. The gardener is a keen plantswoman, propagating most of her own stock.

Open: Sunday 17 April, 1pm - 5pm, admission £5.00, children free.

Directions: From the east drive through Eccles village then take the first turning on the right signposted *Loan Knowe*. Continue to the *cycle route* sign, turn left and the house is one mile on the left. From Ednam, go through the village, take the left turn to Hume, go to the T junction, turn right and continue to the white cottage, take the right fork *cycle route* and Harlaw is half-a-mile on the right.

Opening for: Border Womens Aid

Berwickshire

7 | LENNEL BANK

Coldstream TD12 4EX
Mrs Honor Brown
T: 01890 882297 E: honor.b.brown@gmail.com

Lennel Bank is a terraced garden overlooking the River Tweed, consisting of wide borders packed with shrubs and perennial planting, some unusual. The water garden, built in 2008, is surrounded by a rockery and utilises the slope, ending in a pond. There is a small kitchen garden with raised beds in unusual shapes. Different growing conditions throughout the garden from dry, wet, shady and sunny, lend themselves to a variety of plants and enhance interest in the garden.

Open: by arrangement 1 May - 30 September, admission £5.00, children free.

Directions: On the A6112 Coldstream to Duns road, one mile from Coldstream.

Opening for: British Heart Foundation

Harlaw Farmhouse © Christopher Jones

Berwickshire

8 MARLFIELD GARDENS
Coldstream TD12 4JT
Christine and Forbes McLennan, Ron Whittaker, Max and Kate Lowe
T: 01890 840700 M: 07717 237357 E: forbes.mclennan@gmail.com

Marlfield, previously a traditional 80 acre farm, now a quiet hamlet with three lovely gardens:
Marlfield Farmhouse (Christine and Forbes McLennan) – this two acre garden has been open for the past three years with extensive lawns, specimen trees, herbaceous borders and a large raised bed allotment style vegetable garden.
West Cottage (Max and Kate Lowe) – a beautiful cottage garden, intensively planted with herbaceous borders, mixed shrubberies, vegetable and fruit plot.
The Lodge (Ron Whittaker 07766 296453) – newly re-designed, this half-acre garden, with fine views of the surrounding countryside, is a lovely mix of lawns, herbaceous borders, wild flower meadow, vegetables and fruit. A chance to observe a lovely garden in development.

Open: Sunday 31 July, 1pm - 5pm. Also open by arrangement 1 January - 30 September. Admission £5.00, children free.

Directions: Four miles north of Coldstream on the old Duns road. Half-a-mile off the main road.

Opening for: Macmillan Cancer Support

Marlfield Gardens © Kay Slater

9 NETHERBYRES
Eyemouth TD14 5SE
Col S J Furness
T: 01890 750337

An unusual elliptical walled garden, dating from 1740, with a mixture of flowers, fruit and vegetables. A very old pear tree, possibly dating from the 18th century, and the largest rose in Berwickshire, *Rosa filipes* 'Kiftsgate'. A wide variety of roses and herbaceous borders.

Open: Sunday 3 July, 1pm - 5pm. Also open by arrangement to parties of four or more 1 May - 31 August. Admission £5.00, children free.

Directions: Half-a-mile south of Eyemouth on the A1107 to Berwick.

Opening for: Sovereign Order of St. John Charitable Trust

Berwickshire

10 RUTHVEN HOUSE

Coldstream TD12 4JU
Keith and Karen Fountain
T: 01890 840680 E: ruthvenhouse@btconnect.com

The three acres of Ruthven's garden have lovely views towards the Cheviots. The garden's central feature is two ponds joined by a winding stream. The garden is composed of various differing areas, herbaceous borders, woodland areas, a gravel garden, a knot garden, rockeries, an orchard laid to meadow, a kitchen garden, a nuttery, a small lavender field and, adjacent to the house, a formal rose garden. Much of the work to create the garden from the original few small beds around the house has only been undertaken in the last few years, so the garden has not yet reached complete maturity. The latest projects involve the development of a new herbaceous border on the rear lawn, a quadrant bed for azaleas in the spring and dahlias and chrysanthemums later in the year, adjacent to the drive; and ornamental grass beds on the rear lawn. The small fold of Highland cattle in the adjacent field complete the scene.

Open: Sunday 26 June, 1pm - 5pm. Also open by arrangement 1 January - 30 September. Admission £5.00, children free. Groups and individuals are welcome.

Directions: Four miles north of Coldstream on the old Duns road.

Opening for: Macmillan Cancer Support (Sunday 26 June) & Scottish Association For Mental Health (1 January - 30 September)

Berwickshire Ruthven House © Malcolm Ross

Caithness, Sutherland, Orkney & Shetland

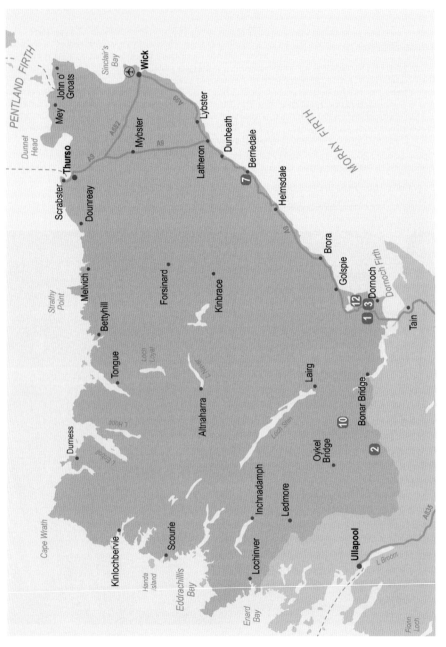

Caithness, Sutherland, Orkney & Shetland

Sponsored by
Investec

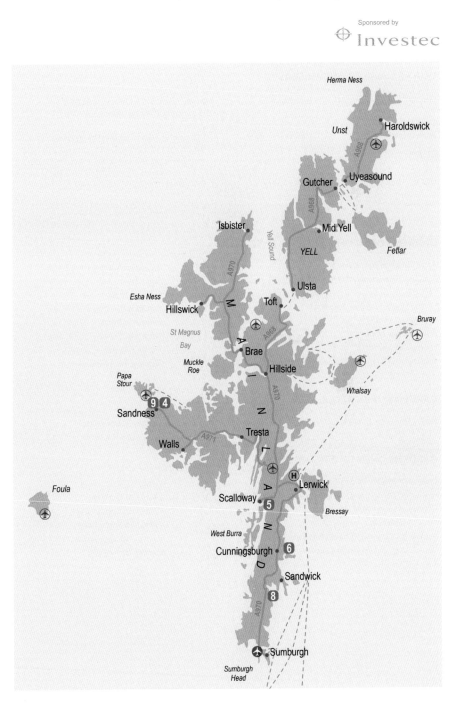

Caithness, Sutherland, Orkney & Shetland

OUR VOLUNTEER ORGANISERS

District Organiser:	Sara Shaw	Amat, Ardgay, Sutherland IV24 3BS E: info@scotlandsgardens.org
Area Organisers:	Caroline Critchlow	Old Granary Quoy, Orphir, Orkney KW17 2RD
	Mary Leask	VisitScotland, Market Cross, Lerwick ZE1 0LU
	Steve Mathieson	VisitScotland, Market Cross, Lerwick ZE1 0LU
District Photographer:	Colin Gregory	Iona, Reay, Caithness, KW14 7RG
Treasurer:	Nicola Vestey	

GARDENS OPEN ON A SPECIFIC DATE

Amat, Amat Lodge, Ardgay	Saturday/Sunday, 28/29 May
Auchlea, Balnapolaig Muir, Dornoch	Saturday, 16 July
Old Granary Quoy and The Quoy of Houton, Orphir, Orkney	Sunday, 17 July
Skelbo House, Skelbo, Dornoch	Saturday/Sunday, 23/24 July
42 Astle, Dornoch	Saturday/Sunday, 23/24 July
Amat, Amat Lodge	Saturday/Sunday, 30/31 July
Langwell, Berriedale	Sunday, 31 July
Old Granary Quoy and The Quoy of Houton, Orphir, Orkney	Sunday, 4 September

GARDENS OPEN REGULARLY

Norby, Burnside, Sandness, Shetland	1 April - 31 December

GARDENS OPEN BY ARRANGEMENT

Cruisdale, Sandness, Shetland	1 April - 31 December
Highlands Garden, East Voe, Scalloway, Shetland	1 May - 31 October
Nonavaar, Levenwick, Shetland	1 May - 30 September
Amat, Amat Lodge, Ardgay	1 May - 15 September
Keldaberg, Cunningsburgh, Shetland	1 June - 30 September
Oape, Strath Oykel, Ardgay, Sutherland	1 June - 31 July

Caithness, Sutherland, Orkney & Shetland

1

42 ASTLE
Dornoch IV25 3NH
Fay Wilkinson

Organic wildlife garden at the edge of boggy moorland. Mixed planting of trees, shrubs, herbaceous perennials and fruit and vegetables, many on raised beds for improved drainage. There is a natural pond.

Open: Saturday/Sunday, 23/24 July, 11am - 4pm, admission £4.00, children free.

Directions: A9 from the south: pass the turn off to Dornoch, take the first left after the *Tall Pines Restaurant*, signposted *Astle*. After one and a half miles take the left fork, cross the river and no. 42 is the second house on the left. A9 from the north: turn right 100 yards before the *Tall Pines Restaurant*. As above.

Opening for: Bumblebee Conservation Trust

42 Astle © Colin Gregory

2

AMAT
Amat Lodge, Ardgay IV24 3BS
Jonny and Sara Shaw
T: 07712266500 E: sara.amat@aol.co.uk

Over the last two years there have been big changes in the garden and thanks to two very talented friends, and the arrival this summer of a wonderful new part time-gardener, it has changed the feel of the garden and we now have interest into late summer. Half the lawn has been given over to wild flowers and there is a new mini stumpery along with some more unusual plants. The river Carron flows around the edge of the garden and the old Amat Caledonian Forest is close by. Large specimen trees surround the house, plus many new ones planted in the policies in the last few years. There are several herbaceous borders, rhododendrons, trees and shrubs all set in a large lawn. It is possible to go on a short woodland and river walk and you may see red squirrels which were reintroduced some years ago and are often in and around the garden.
Champion Trees: Abies Procera, Noble Fir.

Open: Saturday/Sunday, 28/29 May, 2pm - 5pm. Also open Saturday/Sunday, 30/31 July, 2pm - 5pm. And open by arrangement 1 May - 15 September. Admission £5.00, children free.

Directions: Take the road from Ardgay to Croick, nine miles. Turn left at the red phone box and the garden is 500 yards on the left.

Opening for: Horatio's Garden & International Dendrology Society

Caithness, Sutherland, Orkney & Shetland

3 AUCHLEA

Balnapolaig Muir, Dornoch IV25 3HY
John and Fiona Garvie

The creation of Auchlea garden from its natural state as a wetland of rushes and whins began in 1998 with the drainage and sowing of a lawn on introduced topsoil. The planting of trees, mostly around its periphery was also begun then. Extensive herbaceous borders with a wide variety of colour and species have been gradually developed. There is also a sheltered vegetable garden, made more productive using raised beds, alongside a recently replanted bog garden. The habitual, accumulated use of garden and household compost has progressively improved stony ground around the boundary, where a mixed hedge has made good progress.

Open: Saturday 16 July, 10am - 4pm, admission £5.00, children free. Cream teas by donation.

Directions: Situated on the B9168. This B road is on the right driving up the A9. Take the B road and Auchlea is the first house on the right.

Opening for: Blythswood Care

4 CRUISDALE
Sandness, Shetland ZE2 9PL
Alfred Kern
T: 01595 870739

The garden is in a natural state with many willows, several ponds and a variety of colourful hardy plants that grow well in the Shetland climate. Work started in 2003 and the garden has continued to expand over the years, with more work planned.

Open: by arrangement 1 April - 31 December, admission £3.00, children free.

Directions: From Lerwick head north on the A970, then at Tingwall take the A971 to Sandness, on the west side of Shetland. Cruisdale is opposite the school, on the right-hand side with a wind generator in the field.

Opening for: Royal Voluntary Service

5 HIGHLANDS GARDEN
East Voe, Scalloway, Shetland ZE1 0UR
Sarah Kay
T: 01595 880526 / 07818 845385 E: info@easterhoull.co.uk
W: www.selfcatering-shetland.co.uk/the-garden and www.sarahkayarts.com

The garden is in two parts. The upper garden is mostly a rockery, with a large selection of plants, shallow pond, seating area, polycrub and greenhouse with fruit and vegetables. The lower garden is on a steep slope with a spectacular sea view over the village of Scalloway. There is a path to lead visitors around and the garden features a large collection of plants, vegetable patch, deep pond and pergola. It was awarded a *Shetland Environmental Award* in 2014 for its strong theme of recycling. The owner also has an art studio which you are most welcome to visit when you view the garden.

Open: by arrangement 1 May - 31 October, admission £3.50, children free. Dogs are not allowed.

Directions: Follow the A970 main road towards the village of Scalloway. Near the top of the hill heading towards Scalloway take a sharp turn to the left, signposted *Easterhoull Chalets*. Follow the road to chalets (painted blue with red roofs) and you will see the yellow *SGS* sign for the garden. Bus 4 from Lerwick/Scalloway.

Opening for: Macmillan Cancer Support

Caithness, Sutherland, Orkney & Shetland

6 **KELDABERG**
Cunningsburgh, Shetland ZE2 9HG
Mrs L Johnston
T: 01950 477331 E: linda.keldaberg@btinternet.com

A 'secret garden' divided into four areas. A beach garden of grasses, flowers and driftwood. The main area is a sloping perennial border leading down to a greenhouse, vegetable plot, up to a decked area with containers and exotic plants including agaves, pineapple lilies, cannas and gunneras. The new area has trees, raised vegetable beds, a rockery, retaining walls and an arbour in which to rest. There is a pond with goldfish and aquatic plants and now a polycrub to grow vegetables, fruit trees and a grapevine.

Open: by arrangement 1 June - 30 September, admission £3.50, children free.

Directions: On the A970 south of Lerwick is Cunningsburgh, take the Gord junction on the left after passing the village hall. Continue along the road to the second house past the *Kenwood* sign.

Opening for: Chest Heart & Stroke Scotland

7 **LANGWELL**
Berriedale KW7 6HD
Welbeck Estates
T: 01593 751278 / 751237 E: caithness@welbeck.co.uk

A beautiful and spectacular old walled garden with outstanding borders situated in the secluded Langwell Strath. Charming wooded access drive with a chance to see deer.

Open: Sunday 31 July, noon - 4pm, admission £4.00, children free.

Directions: Turn off the A9 at Berriedale Braes, up the private (tarred) drive signposted *Private – Langwell House*. It is about one-and-a-quarter miles from the A9.

Opening for: RNLI

8 **NONAVAAR**
Levenwick, Shetland ZE2 9HX
James B Thomason
T: 01950 422447

This is a delightful country garden, sloping within drystone walls and overlooking magnificent coastal views. It contains ponds, terraces, trees, bushes, varied perennials, annuals, vegetable garden and greenhouse.

Open: by arrangement 1 May - 30 September, admission £4.00, children free.

Directions: Head south from Lerwick. Turn left at the *Levenwick* sign soon after Bigton turnoff. Follow the road to the third house on the left after the Midway stores. Park where there is a *Garden Open* sign. Bus 6 from Lerwick – Sumburgh.

Opening for: Cancer Research UK

Caithness, Sutherland, Orkney & Shetland

9 NORBY
Burnside, Sandness, Shetland ZE2 9PL
Mrs Gundel Grolimund
T: 01595 870246 E: gundel.g5@btinternet.com

A small but perfectly formed garden and a prime example of what can be achieved in a very exposed situation. Blue painted wooden pallets provide internal wind breaks and form a background for shrubs, climbers and herbaceous plants, while willows provide a perfect wildlife habitat. There are treasured plants such as *Chionochloa rubra*, pieris, Chinese tree peonies, a selection of old-fashioned shrub roses, lilies, hellebores and grasses from New Zealand. There is also a lovely selection of interesting art and textiles in the house.

Open: 1 April - 31 December, dawn – dusk, admission £3.00, children free.

Directions: Head north on the A970 from Lerwick then west on the A971 at Tingwall. At Sandness, follow the road to Norby, turn right at the Methodist Church, Burnside is at the end of the road. Bus 10 Sandness – Walls.

Opening for: Survival International

10 OAPE
Strath Oykel, Ardgay, Sutherland IV24 3DP
Michele Buss and John Raworth
T: 07999 817715 E: scrumpyjack9@yahoo.co.uk

Abundant, exuberant planting and refurbishment of a small cottage garden with generous usage of recycled materials, on a fairly difficult, windy site, against a backdrop of mature Aspen trees in a quiet corner of the Strath.

Open: by arrangement 1 June - 31 July, admission £4.00. Children not admitted. No dogs. We offer homemade teas on request at an extra cost. A wee plant stall. On 25/26th June we offer a Propagation Course, which is hands on, in small groups, from approx 10am-2pm. Light lunch and beverages included, please email for further information and to book.

Directions: Take the A837 west, through Rosehall, a quarter of a mile further on, take the left turning signposted *Culrain*, go over *Bailey Bridge*, take the next right near the top of the hill, quarter of a mile, Oape is the first cottage on the left.

Opening for: Maggie's

11 OLD GRANARY QUOY AND THE QUOY OF HOUTON
The Quoy of Houton, Orphir, Orkney KW17 2RD
Caroline Critchlow and Colleen Batey
T: 01856 811355

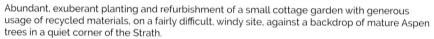

Old Granary Quoy (NEW) KW17 2RD (Caroline Critchlow): A newly planted and designed garden, adjacent to The Quoy of Houton. Fabulous views over Scapa Flow, ponds and a water garden. The home of Orkney perennial geraniums and an extensive range of plants suitable for this exposed coastal location. The lantern greenhouse is a new acquisition featuring an indoor peach tree. Caroline Critchlow has designed award winning gardens and is the resident gardening guru on *BBC Radio Orkney*.
The Quoy of Houton KW17 2RD (Colleen Batey): An unusual historic walled panoramic garden with 60-foot rill which leads the eye to the spectacular coastal views of Scapa Flow. Carefully planted to withstand winds in excess of 60 mph, with floral interest from March to September. Winner of *Gardeners' World* Britain's best challenging garden 2017 and listed in the top ten *UK coastal gardens*. Featured on *BBC Beechgrove* and in the book *Island Gardens*.

Caithness, Sutherland, Orkney & Shetland

Open: Sunday 17 July, 10am - 4pm. Also open Sunday 4 September, 10am - 4pm. Admission £4.00 per garden, children free. Teas in the lantern greenhouse, bookable in advance, £10.00 per person.

Directions: From Orphir take the turning to Houton Ferry at the first junction signed *Quoy of Houton*, turn right by the car park. Park here and walk 10 minutes along coastal road around bay to the gardens. Disabled access please ring to arrange as parking is very limited. The gardens are a ten minute walk from the bus stop.

Opening for: Friends of the Neuro Ward

The Quoy of Houton

12 SKELBO HOUSE

Skelbo, Dornoch IV25 3QG
Alison Bartlett
E: SkelboHouseGarden@gmail.com

Extensive woodland garden with spectacular views over Loch Fleet. Mixed herbaceous borders, rose garden and shrubberies surround the house. Lawns slope down to a small lochan and river walkway. Mature trees throughout. Large kitchen garden.

Open: Saturday/Sunday, 23/24 July, 11am - 4pm, admission £5.00, children free.

Directions: from the south: on the A9 take the small turning opposite *Trentham Hotel* (just past the Dornoch turn offs). At the side of Loch Fleet turn left, at the ruined castle take the second farm road which is fairly rough, and follow round to your right. If coming from the north take the Loch Fleet road signposted to *Embo* from the A9.

Opening for: Mary's Meals International or MMI

Dumfriesshire

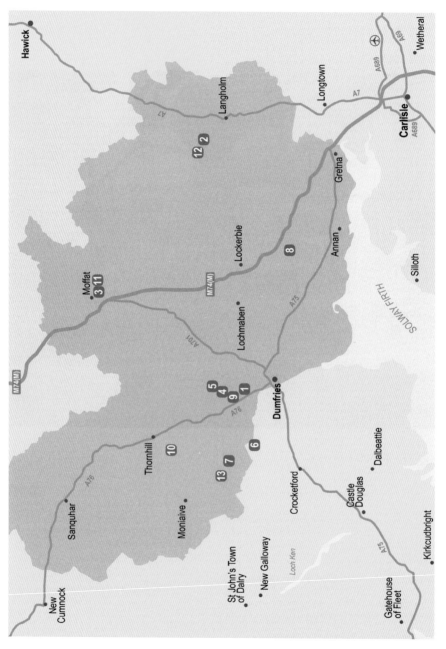

Dumfriesshire

OUR VOLUNTEER ORGANISERS

District Organiser:	Sarah Landale	Dalswinton House, Dalswinton, Auldgirth DG2 0XZ E: info@scotlandsgardens.org
Area Organisers:	Fiona Bell-Irving	Bankside, Kettleholm, Lockerbie DG11 1BY
	Guy Galbraith	Stanemuir Parkgate, Dumfries DG1 3NE
	Liz Mitchell	Drumpark, Irongray DG2 9TX
District Photographer:	Stuart Littlewood	E: stu@f8.eclipse.co.uk
Treasurer:	Leslie Jack	Gledenholm House, Ae, Dumfries DG1 1RF

GARDENS OPEN ON A SPECIFIC DATE

Portrack, The Garden of Cosmic Speculation, Holywood	Date to be confirmed
Craig, Langholm	Sunday, 20 February
The Old Mill, Keir Mill, Thornhill	Sunday, 24 April
Dalswinton House, Dalswinton	Sunday, 15 May
Drumpark, Irongray	Sunday, 22 May
Westerhall, Bentpath, Langholm	Sunday, 5 June
Cowhill Tower, Holywood	Sunday, 12 June
Craigieburn House, by Moffat	Sunday, 12 June
Garden Cottage, Knockhill, Lockerbie, Dumfries	Sunday, 19 June
Dunesslin, Dunscore	Sunday, 3 July
Whiteside, Dunscore	Sunday, 17 July
Dalswinton Mill, Dalswinton, Dumfries	Sunday, 7 August
Drumpark, Irongray	Sunday, 25 September

GARDENS OPEN BY ARRANGEMENT

Waterside Garden, Waterside, Moffat, Dumfriesshire	1 May - 30 September

Dumfriesshire

1 COWHILL TOWER
Holywood DG2 0RL
Mr and Mrs P Weatherall
T: 01387 720304 E: clara@cowhill.co.uk

This is an interesting walled garden. There are topiary animals, birds and figures and beautiful woodland and river walks. Splendid views can be seen from the lawn right down the Nith Valley. There is also a variety of statues, including several from the Far East.

Open: Sunday 12 June, 2pm - 5pm, admission by donation.

Directions: Holywood is one-and-a-half miles off the A76, five miles north of Dumfries.

Opening for: Maggie's

2 CRAIG
Langholm DG13 0NZ
Mr and Mrs Neil Ewart
T: 013873 70230 E: nmlewart@googlemail.com

Craig snowdrops have evolved over the last 30 or so years. Round the house and policies, a large variety has been planted with a varied flowering season stretching from the start of January until April and peaking mid-February. Large drifts of *Leucojum vernum* (winter snowflake) have started to naturalise here, and along the riverbank a variety of snowdrops swept down by the river have naturalised in the adjacent woodland, known as the Snowdrop Walk.

Open: Sunday 20 February, noon - 4pm, admission £5.00, children free. Teas will be available at Bentpath Village Hall. Bentpath is one mile further on towards Eskdalemuir.

Directions: Craig is three miles from Langholm on the B709 towards Eskdalemuir.

Opening for: Kirkandrews Kirk Trust

3 CRAIGIEBURN HOUSE
by Moffat DG10 9LF
Janet and Peter McGowan
T: 07557 928648 E: bideshi@aol.com

A beautiful and varied five-acre plant lovers' garden in a natural location in scenic Moffat Dale. Meconopsis, trilliums, rhododendrons, magnolias, arisaemas, bamboos, hoherias and many more types of plants flourish in the shelter of mature woodland. Garden Manager, Datenji Sherpa has recreated a Himalayan gorge with native plants where the Craigie Burn tumbles down through a series of waterfalls. Candelabra primulas, rodgersias, cardiocrinum, ferns and other rare plants thrive in the bog garden and woodland glades. Double herbaceous borders come into their own later in the summer and keep the display going throughout the season. Other garden areas include a Rose Garden, formal pond and Autumn Garden. A nursery sells hardy plants propagated on site, many of them rare or unusual. The garden has been created over the past 25 to 30 years, building on its old setting. Its links to Robert Burns – including his song 'Craigieburn Wood' – provide another layer of history.

Open: Sunday 12 June, 2pm - 5pm, admission £5.00, children free. Parking for the garden is limited. Please check the website before you visit for any parking updates or options.

Directions: Three miles from the motorway (junction 15), two miles east of Moffat on the A708 Selkirk Road. Coming from Moffat, there are traffic lights straight ahead at the end of the bend. You can't miss the lodge and prayer flags.

Opening for: Practical Action

Dumfriesshire

4 DALSWINTON HOUSE

Dalswinton DG2 0XZ
Mr and Mrs Peter Landale
T: 01387 740220 E: sarahlandale@gmail.com

Late 18th-century house sits on top of a hill surrounded by herbaceous beds and well established shrubs, including rhododendrons and azaleas, overlooking the loch. Attractive walks through woods and around the loch. It was here that the first steamboat in Britain made its maiden voyage in 1788 and there is a life-size model beside the water to commemorate this. Over the past years, there has been much clearing and development work around the loch, which has opened up the views considerably.

Open: Sunday 15 May, noon - 5pm, admission £5.00, children free. Homemade teas will be available from 2pm-5pm. Picnics are allowed in the Walled Garden and around the loch during the day.

Directions: Take the A76 north from Dumfries to Thornhill. After seven miles, turn right to Dalswinton. Drive through Dalswinton village, past the orange church on the right and follow the estate wall on the right. Entrance is by either the single lodge or double lodge entrance set in the wall.

Opening for: Kirkmahoe Parish Church of Scotland

Dalswinton House © Stuart Littlewood

Dumfriesshire

5 DALSWINTON MILL
Dalswinton, Dumfries DG2 0XY
Colin and Pamela Crosbie
T: 01387 740070 E: colincrosbiehort@btinternet.com

A newly created plantsman's garden set around an 18th-century watermill with the Pennyland Burn running through it. The garden contains a wide range of perennials, trees and shrubs that favour the local climate and have been planted during the last few years. A variety of statuary can be found throughout the garden which sits in a hollow and can be only accessed by steps and there are slopes throughout the garden. Unfortunately, this makes the garden unsuitable for anyone with mobility requirements.

Open: Sunday 7 August, 2pm - 6pm, admission £5.00, children free.

Directions: Garden lies in Dalswinton, halfway between the A76 and the A701 on the Auldgirth to Kirkton Road. From Auldgirth take the first left after the Dalswinton Village Hall. The Mill is on the corner before the bridge. We are unable to offer disabled parking.

Opening for: IFDAS

Dalswinton Mill © Stuart Littlewood

Dumfriesshire

6 **DRUMPARK**
Irongray DG2 9TX
Mr and Mrs Iain Mitchell
T: 01387 820323 E: iain.liz.mitchell@gmail.com

Well contoured woodland garden and extensive policies nurture mature azaleas, rhododendrons and rare shrubs among impressive specimen trees. Water garden with primulas and meconopsis. Victorian walled garden with fruit trees and garden produce. There is also a beautiful herbaceous border. All planting is set in a natural bowl providing attractive vistas.

Open: Sundays 22 May and 25 September, 2pm - 5pm. Admission £5.00, children free. There will be Teas and a Plant Stall for the May opening but not for the September opening.

Directions: Dumfries bypass, head north on the A76 for a half mile, turn left at the signpost to *Lochside Industrial Estates* and immediately right onto Irongray Road; continue for five miles; gates in sandstone wall on left (half mile after Routin' Brig).

Opening for: *Loch Arthur*

Drumpark © Stuart Littlewood

7 **DUNESSLIN**
Dunscore DG2 0UR
Iain and Zara Milligan
E: zaramilligan@gmail.com

Set in the hills with wonderful views and borrowed landscapes, the principal garden consists of a series of connecting rooms filled with a great and interesting variety of herbaceous plants, beautifully designed and maintained. There is a substantial rock garden with alpines and unusual plants and a very pretty pond. There is a short walk to three cairns by Andy Goldsworthy, through an evolving woodland garden.

Open: Sunday 3 July, 2pm - 5pm, admission £5.00, children free.

Directions: From Dunscore, follow the road to Corsock. About one-and-a-half miles further on, turn right at the post box, still on the road to Corsock and at small crossroads half a mile on, turn left.

Opening for: *Alzheimer Scotland*

Dumfriesshire

8 GARDEN COTTAGE, KNOCKHILL
Lockerbie, Dumfries DG11 1AW
Mrs Yda Morgan
T: 01576 300232 E: yda@morganbellows.co.uk

Part of the old Walled Garden of Knockhill, recently redesigned as a garden for the renovated garden bothy. A wildflower meadow is an interesting aspect, ever changing and Yda loves sharing her observations of the last five years. Two borders of shrubs and herbaceous plants, fruit trees and other nooks and crannies of interest. Lovely parkland with magnificent trees adjoins the garden and you are welcome to roam there.

Open: Sunday 19 June, 2pm - 5pm, admission £5.00, children free.

Directions: Five miles from Annan and Lockerbie just off the B723. From Lockerbie fork left at the sharp right-handed bend one mile before Hoddom Bridge. Knockhill is 300 yards on your left.

Opening for: Marie Curie

9 PORTRACK, THE GARDEN OF COSMIC SPECULATION
Holywood DG2 0RW
John Jencks
W: www.gardenofcosmicspeculation.com

Forty major areas, gardens, bridges, landforms, sculpture, terraces, fences and architectural works. Covering 30 acres, The Garden of Cosmic Speculation, designed by the late Charles Jencks, uses nature to celebrate nature, both intellectually and through the senses, including the sense of humour.

Open: We hope the garden will open in early June with tickets available online in March. Details will be available nearer the date via our e-newsletter, website and social media channels. Entrance will be by pre-paid ticket only, bookable online.

Directions: Portrack is one-and-a-half miles off the A76, five miles north of Dumfries.

Opening for: Maggie's

10 THE OLD MILL
Keir Mill, Thornhill DG3 4DF
Mr Robin and Mrs Margaret Thomson

This is a maturing garden of shrubs and azaleas with beautiful herbaceous borders. There is also a naturalised pond and riverside boundary.

Open: Sunday 24 April, 2pm - 5pm, admission £5.00, children free.

Directions: Situated in the village of Keir Mill on C125, one mile from Penpont on the Auldgirth road. There is car parking at the Village Hall.

Opening for: Penpont Keir & Tynron Church of Scotland

Dumfriesshire

11 WATERSIDE GARDEN
Waterside, Moffat, Dumfriesshire DG10 9LF
Ronnie Cann
T: 01683 221583 E: waterside-garden@holestone.net
W: www.holestone.net

Set in beautiful Moffat Dale and bounded on one side by the Moffat Water, Waterside Garden is home to woods, riverside walks and three acres of cultivated garden. There are many mature trees including oak, birch, beech and much more. Collections of species and hybrid rhododendrons and azaleas, bamboos, and other flowering shrubs give year-round interest. There are herbaceous beds, giving colour in spring and summer, alpines, mixed plantings, spring bulbs, especially daffodils, and wildflower meadows.

Open: by arrangement 1 May - 30 September, admission £5.00, children free.

Directions: Three miles north of Moffat on the A708 opposite Craigieburn Forest Car Park. From Selkirk the garden is about 14.5 miles south of St Mary's Loch.

Opening for: Moffat Water Hall & Moffat & District Men's Shed

12 WESTERHALL
Bentpath, Langholm DG13 0NQ
Mrs Peter Buckley
E: mary.buckley@hotmail.co.uk

An extensive collection of azaleas, rhododendrons, rare shrubs and mature trees set in a landscape of follies, sculpture and stunning vistas. The redesigned walled garden contains a glasshouse with some exotic plants collected from around the world.

Open: Sunday 5 June, 2pm - 5pm, admission £5.00, children free. Cream teas will be served in the village hall,

Directions: From Langholm take the B709 towards Eskdalemuir. After approximately five miles in the village of Bentpath, turn right by white house. Go down through the village, over a bridge and turn right by the church. Continue on this road for approximately one mile. Parking at farm which will be signed.

Opening for: Westerkirk Parish Trust

13 WHITESIDE
Dunscore DG2 0UU
John and Hilary Craig
T: 01387 820501 E: hjcraig19@gmail.com

The garden, which extends to several acres, is 600 feet above sea level on a north-facing slope with views across to Queensberry and the Lowther Hills. There are some mature trees around the house but the rest of the garden is relatively new, having been created from a bare hillside over the last 20 years. There are shrubs, young trees, a rowan avenue, a walled vegetable garden, orchard and courtyard garden. Several burns run through the property and there is a pond and an enclosure for runner ducks.

Open: Sunday 17 July, noon - 5pm, admission £5.00, children free.

Directions: From Dunscore, take the Corsock road. Continue two miles on, turn right opposite the post box. Continue for one and three quarters miles, over the humpback bridge and past the white farmhouse on the left. *Whiteside* is signed on the left.

Opening for: Music in Dumfries

Dunbartonshire

Sponsored by

⊕ Investec

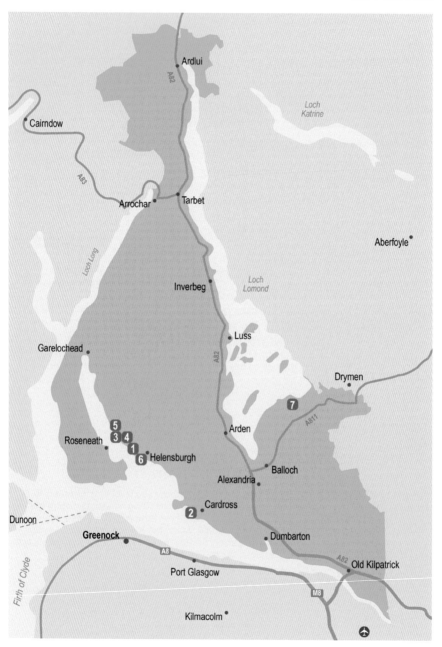

Dunbartonshire

OUR VOLUNTEER ORGANISERS

District Organiser:	Tricia Stewart	High Glenan, 24a Queen Street, Helensburgh G84 9LG E: info@scotlandsgardens.org
Area Organisers:	Kathleen Murray	4 Cairndhu Gardens, Helensburgh G84 8PG
	Lesley and Norman Quirk	Glenard, Upper Torwoodhill Road, Rhu G84 8LE
Treasurer:	Claire Travis	54 Union Street, Alexandria G83 9AH

GARDENS OPEN ON A SPECIFIC DATE

Hillcroft with Stonecroft, Helensburgh	Sunday, 15 May
Ross Priory, Gartocharn	Sunday, 22 May
Geilston Garden, Main Road, Cardross	Sunday, 5 June
4 Cairndhu Gardens Plant Sale, Helensburgh	Sunday, 19 June
Glenarn Plant Sale, Glenarn Road, Rhu, Helensburgh	Sunday, 21 August
James Street Community Garden Plant Sale, Helensburgh	Sunday, 4 September

GARDENS OPEN REGULARLY

Glenarn, Glenarn Road, Rhu, Helensburgh	21 March - 21 September

Dunbartonshire

1 | **4 CAIRNDHU GARDENS PLANT SALE**
Helensburgh G84 8PG
Mrs Kathleen Murray

This large Plant Sale offers an opportunity to obtain locally grown perennials, shrubs and alpines, some rare and unusual as well as border favourites. Kathleen's redesigned garden is now well stocked with trees, shrubs, herbaceous perennials, grasses and alpines. Visitors are welcome to view the work in progress.

Open: Sunday 19 June, 2pm - 5pm, admission by donation.

Directions: 4 Cairndhu Gardens is one-third of a mile west from the Commodore Hotel on the A814. Please follow signs. Park in Cairndhu Avenue.

Opening for: Macular Society

2 | **GEILSTON GARDEN**
Main Road, Cardross G82 5HD
The National Trust for Scotland
T: 01389 849187 E: geilstongarden@nts.org.uk
W: www.nts.org.uk/visit/places/Geilston-Garden

Geilston Garden has many attractive features including the walled garden with herbaceous border providing summer colour, tranquil woodland walks and a large working kitchen garden. This is the ideal season for viewing the Siberian iris in flower along the Geilston Burn and the Japanese azaleas.

Open: Sunday 5 June, 1pm - 5pm, admission details can be found on the garden's website. Plant Sale and Homemade Teas will be served.

Directions: On the A814, one mile from Cardross towards Helensburgh.

Opening for: Donation to SGS

3 | **GLENARN**
Glenarn Road, Rhu, Helensburgh G84 8LL
Michael and Sue Thornley
T: 01436 820493 E: masthome@btinternet.com
W: www.gardens-of-argyll.co.uk

Glenarn survives as a complete example of a ten-acre garden which spans from 1850 to the present day. There are winding paths through miniature glens under a canopy of oaks and limes, sunlit open spaces, a vegetable garden with beehives, and a rock garden full of surprise and season-long colour, with views over the Gareloch. The famous collections of rare and tender rhododendrons and magnolias give way in midsummer to roses rambling through the trees and climbing hydrangeas, followed by the starry white flowers of hoherias and eucryphias to the end of the season. A new feature is our Silent Space at the top of the garden.

Open: 21 March - 21 September, dawn – dusk, admission £5.00, children free.

Directions: On the A814, two miles north of Helensburgh, up Pier Road. Cars to be left at the gate unless passengers are infirm.

Opening for: Donation to SGS

Dunbartonshire

Glenarn

4 GLENARN PLANT SALE

Glenarn Road, Rhu, Helensburgh G84 8LL
Michael and Sue Thornley
T: 01436 820493 E: masthome@btinternet.com
W: www.gardens-of-argyll.co.uk

Magnolias, rhododendrons, maples, meconopsis and other ericaceous plants raised by cuttings from Glenarn plants or from specialist seed exchanges plus lots of other interesting plants.

Open: Sunday 21 August, 2pm - 5pm, admission £5.00, children free.

Directions: On the A814, two miles north of Helensburgh, up Pier Road. Cars to be left at the gate unless passengers are infirm.

Opening for: Rhu and Shandon Parish Church of Scotland & Helensburgh & Lomond Carers (SCIO)

Dunbartonshire

5 HILLCROFT WITH STONECROFT
Rhu, Helensburgh G84 8LW
Fiona Baker and Jim and Adrienne Kerr

Hillcroft (NEW) Station Road, Rhu, Helensburgh G84 8LW (Fiona Baker): Hillcroft is a medium-sized mature, semi-woodland garden with terraces, shrubs and borders, ponds, an alpine bed and a kitchen garden. The owner describes it as 'abundant and a little on the wild side'.
Stonecroft (NEW) Ardenconnel Way, Rhu, Helensburgh G84 8RZ (Jim and Adrienne Kerr) Stonecroft sits on a hill overlooking the Gareloch, with lovely views. The mature azaleas make a dazzling display in May, and the current owners have used flotsam, jetsam and sometimes just plain rubbish to create quirky landscaping and features. The love of plants and wildlife, however, is the driving force in this garden and it has a plethora of lovingly chosen and raised plants.

Open: Sunday 15 May, 2pm - 5pm, admission £5.00, children free.

Directions: A814 at Rhu Marina, turn up Pier Road and continue up the hill and turn left into Lineside Walk, Hillcroft is on the right hand side of the road.

Heading west along the A814, turn into Hall Road in Rhu, continue across Cumberland Road into Upper Hall Road. Turn Left into Ardenconnel Way and Stonecroft is on the right hand side at the end of the road.

Opening for: Helensburgh & Lomond Carers (SCIO) & St Michael & All Angels Church

6 JAMES STREET COMMUNITY GARDEN PLANT SALE
Helensburgh G84 8EY
The Gardeners of James Street

Developed from a children's derelict playground, the Community Garden is a relaxed area for contemplation with mixed herbaceous beds, maze and young trees. The plant sale will include a wide selection of nursery-grown perennials and locally grown trees, shrubs, herbaceous, alpine and house plants.

Open: Sunday 4 September, noon - 4pm, admission by donation.

Directions: Travel west along Princes Street from Sinclair Street through Colquhoun Square, turn right up James Street and the Community Garden is on the left. Park on the street.

Opening for: James Street Community Garden

Dunbartonshire

James Street Community Plant Sale © Stephen Skivington

7

ROSS PRIORY
Gartocharn G83 8NL
University of Strathclyde

Mansion house with glorious views over Loch Lomond with adjoining garden. Wonderful rhododendrons and azaleas are the principal plants in the garden, with a varied selection of trees and shrubs throughout. Spectacular spring bulbs, border plantings of herbaceous perennials, shrubs and trees. Extensive walled garden with glasshouses, pergola and ornamental plantings. Children's play area and putting green beside the house.

Open: Sunday 22 May, 2pm - 5pm, admission £5.00, children free.

Directions: Gartocharn one-and-a-half miles off the A811. Bus from Balloch to Gartocharn.

Opening for: *Friends Of Loch Lomond & The Trossachs & CHAS*

East Lothian

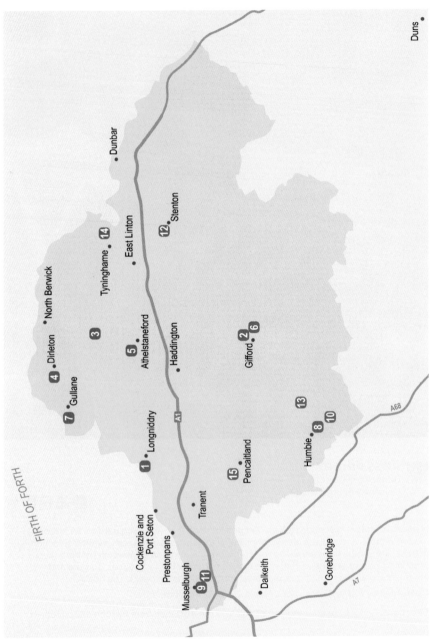

Duns

Dunbar

Stenton

12

East Linton

14 Tyninghame

North Berwick

Dirleton

3

Athelstaneford 5

Haddington

Gifford 2 6

A68

Gullane

7

13

4

8 Humbie 10

1 Longniddry

A1

15 Pencaitland

Tranent

FIRTH OF FORTH

Cockenzie and Port Seton

Prestonpans

Gorebridge

Musselburgh 9 11

Dalkeith

A7

East Lothian

OUR VOLUNTEER ORGANISERS

District Organisers:	Joan Johnson	The Round House, Woodbush, Dunbar EH42 1HB E: info@scotlandsgardens.org
Area Organisers:	Frank Kirwan Ian Orr Judy Riley	Humbie E: frank.kirwan@gmail.com Inveresk E: ianorrgardens@gmail.com Dunbar
Treasurer:	Colin Wilson	

GARDENS OPEN ON A SPECIFIC DATE

Shepherd House, Inveresk, Musselburgh	Tues and Thurs 10 - 24 February
Shepherd House, Inveresk, Musselburgh	Saturdays/Sundays, 19/20 February
Winton Castle, Pencaitland	Sunday, 3 April
Humbie Dean, Humbie	Thursdays, 14 April, 12 May, 9 June, 14 July, 11 August & 8 September
A Blackbird Sings, 20 Kings Park, Longniddry	Saturdays, 16 April, 14 May, 18 June, 16 July, 13 August & 17 September
Shepherd House, Inveresk, Musselburgh	Tues and Thurs 21 April - 21 July
Shepherd House, Inveresk, Musselburgh	Saturday/Sunday, 23/24 April
Tyninghame House and The Walled Garden, Dunbar	Sunday, 8 May
Stobshiel House, Humbie	Thurs, 12 May, 9 June, 14 July & 11 Aug.
Longwood, Humbie	Thurs, 12 May, 9 June, 14 July & 11 Aug.
Fairnielaw, Athelstaneford, North Berwick	Sunday, 29 May
Congalton House, North Berwick	Sunday, 29 May
Dirleton Village, Dirleton	Saturday/Sunday, 11/12 June
Inveresk Village, Inveresk, Musselburgh	Saturday/Sunday, 18/19 June
Gullane House, Sandy Loan, Gullane	Saturday/Sunday, 25/26 June
Tyninghame House and The Walled Garden, Dunbar	Sunday, 26 June
Stenton Village, Stenton, Dunbar	Sunday, 3 July
Broadwoodside, Gifford	Friday/Saturday, 8/9 July
Gifford Bank, Gifford	Friday/Saturday, 8/9 July
Fairnielaw, Athelstaneford, North Berwick	Sunday, 18 September

GARDENS OPEN BY ARRANGEMENT

A Blackbird Sings, 20 Kings Park, Longniddry	1 January - 1 December (for groups)
Shepherd House	1 January - 1 December (for groups)
Stobshiel House, Humbie	6 April - 29 September (Weds only)

East Lothian

1 A BLACKBIRD SINGS
20 Kings Park, Longniddry EH32 0QL
Graham and Maxine Pettigrew
T: 01875 853003

A long garden (35m) in a corner site of Glassel Park Estate. Planting is mostly by plant type – heathers, hosta, grasses, ferns, paeony, iris, alpine, rose – in 'gardens within the garden'. Water features abound and an unheated conservatory contains cacti and insectivorous plants. Liquidambar, 'kousa' cornuses, contorted robinia, cherries, magnolia and rowan hupehensis provide vertical structure within the limited space. A flowering presence throughout the year complements our interest in bees and butterflies.

Open: Saturdays 16 April, 14 May, 18 June, 16 July, 13 August & 17 September, 10am - 5pm, admission by donation. Please telephone us on 01875 853003 if you intend to come so that we can manage numbers. Also open by arrangement for groups.

Directions: By car: enter Dean Road from A198, right at Kings Avenue, right at Kings Park. By bus (124): Old Dean Road stop, down Old Dean Road, right at Kings Avenue, right at Kings Park.

Opening for: St Columba's Hospice Care & Leuchie

A Blackbird Sings

2 BROADWOODSIDE
Gifford EH41 4JQ
Anna and Robert Dalrymple
W: www.broadwoodside.co.uk

'Tucked into a fold in the landscape near Gifford in East Lothian sits a collection of traditional farm buildings that were imaginatively restored to form an elegant family home. Broadwoodside steading is an exercise in polished vernacular, from the yellow limewash of its low, ogee-roofed tower to the oxblood paintwork around its many windows. This is a house that seems to grow out of its environment, the hue of its stone walls and pantiled roof echoed in the colours of the fertile soil of the surrounding farmland, and around the steading

East Lothian

has grown up. It has been described as one of the finest contemporary gardens in Scotland, a garden that employs all the classical devices of symmetry, perspective and precise alignment but does so in such a witty fashion that here, in this agricultural setting, the familiar becomes fresh and exciting.' *Garden Design Journal.*

Open: Friday/Saturday, 8/9 July, 11am - 5pm, admission £6.00, children free. Gifford Bank will also be open this weekend (see number 6)

Directions: On the B6355 going out of Gifford towards Pencaitland, at the Golf Course junction.

Opening for: Leuchie

---

 3 ### CONGALTON HOUSE
North Berwick EH39 5JL
Clare and John Carson

The garden, which surrounds a stone built Victorian house, is an attractive family garden with a wide variety of plants and good colour throughout the summer months. It has a number of mature trees and herbaceous borders, most of which have been planted over the last 20 years (this is since we have had a full time, trained gardener, Bruce Rankine). Other attractions include rose beds, usually at their best in June, a sunken garden and a rockery. The woodland garden, which was planted about 15 years ago, is now beginning to mature.

Open: Sunday 29 May, 11am - 5pm, admission £5.00, children free.

Directions: On the B1347 between Haddington and North Berwick.

Opening for: Camphill Senior Cohousing Aberdeen

---

4 ### DIRLETON VILLAGE
Dirleton EH39 5EH
The Gardeners Of Dirleton and Historic Scotland

Dirleton is widely recognised as one of Scotland's prettiest conservation villages. Its traditional houses are clustered around the extensive village green, medieval castle dating from the 13th century, and a 400-year-old parish church. Expect the village to be a blaze of colour on the opening weekend, when up to 18 of its gardens will be open to the public for charity. These are scattered throughout the village, each within a short walking distance of the village green, where ample free parking is available. The gardens can all be visited on a single ticket. They are very different in size and style and you will find that their owners love to share their knowledge and answer questions. Compact gardens around the village centre contrast with larger ones on Chapelhill, which provide extensive views south over the surrounding countryside. Your ticket will also admit you to the castle gardens. These contain an impressive formal parterre and a herbaceous border extending to over 200 yards in length, claimed to be one of the longest such borders in the world.

Open: Saturday/Sunday, 11/12 June, 2pm - 5:30pm, admission £7.00, children free. Parking, tickets and village map are available at the Green. Delicious teas will be served in the church hall by RNLI supporters and church helpers.

Directions: By car – two miles west of North Berwick off the A198. By public transport – East Coast buses X5 and 124 from Edinburgh.

Opening for: Dirleton Village Association & RNLI

East Lothian

5 FAIRNIELAW
Athelstaneford, North Berwick EH39 5BE
Alison Johnston
T: 07747862841 E: alison@fairnielawhouse.co.uk

Fairnielaw is a two-and-a-half-acre garden set on a rocky ridge where the wind blows frequently through the Garleton Hills and hits us side on. To provide shelter we planted a mixed-tree, mini forest and created a series of 'rooms' enclosed by beech hedges and dry-stone walls. The garden is on several levels and is a mixture of both formal and wild areas with beautiful views towards Traprain Law and the Garleton Hills at the highest point.

Open: Sunday 29 May, 11am - 5pm. Also open Sunday 18 September, 11am - 5pm. Admission £5.00, children free.

Directions: Fairnielaw House is in the village of Athelstaneford set back from the road behind tall trees opposite the church. It is served by a bus service that runs between Haddington and North Berwick several times a day.

Opening for: Trellis

6 GIFFORD BANK
Gifford EH41 4JE
Mr and Mrs Austin

Gifford Bank is a Georgian house set in four acres on the edge of the village. Lawns to the front and side of the house are edged by woodland whilst a walled garden provides a more formal area. The four quadrants of the walled garden include a circular lawn area, raised beds for soft fruit, a herb and rose garden and an orchard. There are large herbaceous borders on all four sides. Beautiful scented roses grow over six arches that connect the gravel path. The garden to the rear of the house includes water features and a large fire bowl planter.

Open: Friday/Saturday, 8/9 July, 11am - 5pm, admission £6.00, children free. Broadwoodside will also be open this weekend (see number 3).

Directions: When leaving Gifford on the B6355 Edinburgh Road, Gifford Bank is the last property on the right before the de-restriction signs. Regular Gifford Circle bus service from Haddington

Opening for: British Heart Foundation

7 GULLANE HOUSE
Sandy Loan, Gullane EH31 2BH
William and Judy Thomson

A traditional walled garden of three acres. The front of the house looks onto rose-hedged twin herbaceous borders of delphinium, peonies and lupins followed by dahlias, phlox and salvias and preceded by tulips and alliums. A small lily pond leads through to the rose and lavender garden planted in 2018. The next 'room' is reached through a beech hedge and houses soft fruits and vegetables and an informal barbecue area. The orchard boasts a selection of fruit trees and there are magnificent mature trees throughout the garden.
Champion Trees: Elm, Oak.

Open: Saturday/Sunday, 25/26 June, 2pm - 5pm, admission £5.00, children free.

East Lothian

Directions: Gullane House is situated on Sandy Loan about 30 yards from the main street in Gullane. Public transport: regular buses from Edinburgh stop in Gullane.

Opening for: The Salvesen Mindroom Centre

Gifford Bank © Richard Austin

8 HUMBIE DEAN
Humbie EH36 5PW
Frank Kirwan
E: frank.kirwan@gmail.com

A two-acre ornamental and woodland garden sandwiched between two burns at 600 feet with interest throughout a long season. A limited palette of plants with hosta, hellebores, perennial geranium, primula, meconopsis, martagon lilies, clematis, spring bulbs, ground cover, herbaceous and shrub planting, bluebell meadow, mature and recent azalea and rhododendron planting. A short woodland walk has been created, only accessible by a series of steps.

Open: Thursdays 14 April, 12 May, 9 June, 14 July, 11 August and 8 September, 10am - 4pm. Admission £5.00, children free.

Directions: Enter Humbie from the A68, pass the school and the village hall on the left then immediately turn right just before the Humbie Hub. Take the second left and Humbie Dean is on the left between two small bridges. Limited parking.

Opening for: Mamie Martin Fund

East Lothian

9 INVERESK VILLAGE
Inveresk, Musselburgh EH21 7TT
The Gardeners of Inveresk
E: ianorrgardens@gmail.com

Inveresk has said goodbye to two very loyal garden openers, but is presenting new gardens – one a moderate-sized garden attached to a Victorian villa, the other a well-developed garden attached to a gatehouse cottage. These are in addition to previously opened gardens – one a television star, one complementing an eco house, one large tiered garden and one garden surrounding the house of the previous area coal mine manager. The National Trust Scotland property, Inveresk Lodge Garden, has great potential for children with pond dipping an ever-popular pursuit at this venue. Musselburgh's highly-rated allotments will also be open within the circular trail which passes a very interesting topiary hedge outside a cottage in Double Dykes. The mix of large and small gardens, some of which are wrapped around by high stone walls and others more exposed to the wind and relatively dry climate, will offer visitors many ideas to think over when they return home. The Romans recognised the quality of the soil in this area when they settled here during the Antonine era between 140 and 165 AD and some of the land may well have been in continuous cultivation since then. The village gardens are open over two days for the first time; the owner of the Japanese garden hopes to open on one of these days. Enthusiasts can visit on both days if they retain their village map and a sticky badge.

Open: Saturday/Sunday, 18/19 June, 2pm - 5pm, admission £7.00, children free. Catering may be available on one of the days and ONLY on a bring your own cup or mug basis. Full details can be found by checking updated information available on the SGS website just prior to the event.

Directions: Southside of Musselburgh on the A6124- Please follow all parking advice. Parking on both sides of the village road is FORBIDDEN as it would impede emergency vehicles. The 140 bus stops in the village.

Opening for: Live Music Now Scotland

10 LONGWOOD
Humbie EH36 5PN
Linda Flockhart and Sandra Gentle

An extensive, long-established country garden at 800 feet, undergoing renewal. There are ducks and hens, stream and ponds as well as areas of wild garden and borders including roses, vegetables, lawns and woodlands. Stunning views over the Forth.

Open: Thursday 12 May, Thursday 9 June, Thursday 14 July & Thursday 11 August, 10am - 4pm, admission £5.00, children free.

Directions: From the B6368 (Humbie to Haddington road) about one mile east of Humbie take the direction south to *Blegbie Farm* (signposted). Follow the road for circa two miles, passing Humbie Mains Farm as you go. You will find Blegbie Farm at a hard right-hand bend. The drive for Longwood will be straight in front of you, right beside Blegbie. Go straight up the drive and park at the bottom of the cottages. Do not turn right or left.

Opening for: Médecins Sans Frontières

East Lothian

11 SHEPHERD HOUSE

Inveresk, Musselburgh EH21 7TH
Sir Charles and Lady Fraser
T: 0131 665 2570 E: ann.shepherdhouse@gmail.com
W: www.shepherdhousegarden.co.uk

A constantly evolving artist's garden that never stands still, with lots of surprises including a shell house built in 2014, lavender parterres, a rill and fountains. At its heart are the plants filling every border, spilling over arches and lining paths, which are the inspiration for Ann's paintings. The season starts with the snowdrop collection of over 70 cultivars, moves on through hellebores, tulips, irises and roses. One of the garden's features is a mirror steel diamond sculpture to commemorate the Frasers' diamond wedding anniversary and 60 years in this garden.

Open: Saturday/Sunday, 19/20 February, 11am - 4pm and Tuesdays & Thursdays 10 - 24 February 2 - 4pm for Snowdrops. Also open Saturday/Sunday, 23/24 April, 11am - 4pm. And open Tuesdays and Thursdays 21 April - 21 July, 2 - 4pm. Also open by arrangement all year for groups email: ann@shepherdhousegarden.co.uk. Admission £5.00, children free. The garden will also be open as part of the Inveresk Village opening on 18/19 June from 2 - 5pm.

Directions: The garden is near Musselburgh. From the A1 take the A6094 exit signposted Wallyford and Dalkeith and follow signs to Inveresk.

Opening for: *Live Music Now Scotland*

Longwood © Delia Ridley-Thomas

East Lothian

12 STENTON VILLAGE
Stenton, Dunbar EH42 1TE
Gardeners of Stenton Village

Stenton (Stane Toon), with its ancient cottages of pink-purple hued sandstone and orange pantile roofs set around three village greens, has been awarded Outstanding Conservation status. The Neo-Gothic parish church designed by William Burn presides over the ruins of a 16th century tower and 17th and 18th century monuments in the kirkyard. There is a thriving horticultural society which holds a biennial horticultural show. The Open Gardens include a mix of walled cottage gardens of various sizes. Many are divided into garden-rooms with lush planting, garden ornaments, wild flower areas, ponds, seating areas, vegetable and fruit cultivation and much more. The gardens are managed intensively to provide year-round colour, interest and produce.

Open: Sunday 3 July, 1pm - 5pm, admission £7.00, children free. Stenton Village Hall will be open for its renowned teas.

Directions: Follow signs from the A199/A1. There is a local bus run twice daily from Dunbar, information on www.eveinfo.co.uk. Parking, teas and toilet facilities are available at the Village Hall.

Opening for: St Columba's Hospice Care

13 STOBSHIEL HOUSE
Humbie EH36 5PD
Mr Maxwell and Lady Sarah Ward
T: 01875 833646 E: stobshiel@gmail.com

The walled garden at Stobshiel has recently lost all the box hedging due to blight. The garden has been redesigned with stone and gravel paths and soft edging. A large, formal lily pond now forms the focal point in front of the house. Through the walled garden, the paths lead you towards the greenhouse, potting shed and down to the cut-flower and vegetable garden. Outside the wall the garden is full of shrubs, roses, bulbs, trees, clematis and more. There are paths to wander around with plenty of seating. There is a large pond, another lily pond and a woodland garden with a burn running through. In May and June it is full of rhododendrons and azaleas.

Open: Thursday 12 May, Thursday 9 June, Thursday 14 July & Thursday 11 August, 10am - 4pm. Admission £5.00, children free. Also open by arrangement 6 April - 29 September, Wednesdays only 10am - 3pm. Please call the owners to book a visit.

Directions: On the B6368 Haddington/Humbie road; sign to *Stobshiel* one mile.

Opening for: Fostering Compassion, SCIO

East Lothian

14 TYNINGHAME HOUSE AND THE WALLED GARDEN

Tyninghame House, Dunbar EH42 1XW
Mrs C Gwyn, Tyninghame Gardens Ltd

The formal walled garden combines the lawn, sculpture and yew hedges, an Apple Walk, extensive herbaceous planting including roses and peonies with an informal arboretum. Splendid 17th century sandstone Scottish baronial house, remodelled in 1829 by William Burn. The gardens include herbaceous border, formal rose garden, Lady Haddington's Secret Garden with old fashioned roses and an extensive Wilderness spring garden with rhododendrons, azaleas, flowering trees and bulbs. Grounds include a one-mile beech avenue to the sea. The Romanesque ruin of St Baldred's Church commands views across the Tyne Estuary and Lammermuir Hills. Tyninghame has been awarded 'Outstanding' for every category in the Inventory of Gardens and Designed Landscapes of Scotland. Champion Trees: Two British and seven Scottish.

Open: Sunday 8 May, 1pm - 5pm. Also open Sunday 26 June, 1pm - 5pm. Admission £6.00, children free.

Directions: Gates on the A198 at Tyninghame Village. Bus 120.

Opening for: Lynton Day Centre (Sunday 8 May) & Tyninghame Village Hall (Sunday 26 June)

Tyninghame House and The Walled Garden © Jannie Bos

15 WINTON CASTLE

Pencaitland EH34 5AT
Sir Francis Ogilvy, Winton Trust
T: 01875 340222
W: www.wintoncastle.co.uk

The gardens continue to mature and evolve. In addition to the natural areas around Sir David's Loch and the Dell, extensive mixed borders provide interest along the terraces and in the walled garden. In spring, a glorious covering of daffodils makes way for cherry and apple blossoms. Enjoy informative garden tours and walk off delicious lunches and home baking around the estate. Castle tours may be available if restrictions allow. A visit to Winton Castle is a wonderful family day out.

Open: Sunday 3 April, noon - 4:30pm, admission £5.00, children free.

Directions: Entrance off the B6355 Tranent/Pencaitland Road.

Opening for: Marie Curie

Edinburgh, Midlothian & West Lothian

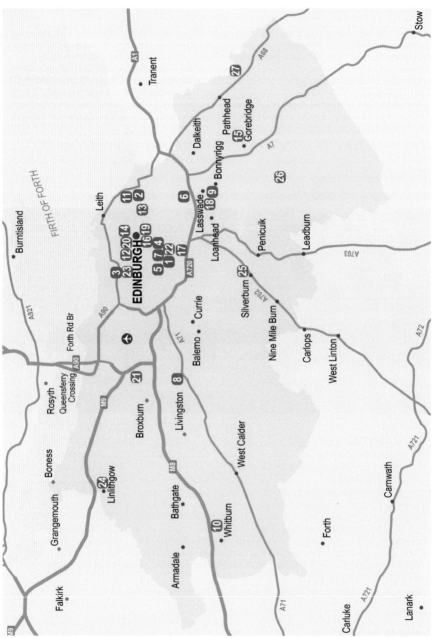

Edinburgh, Midlothian & West Lothian

OUR VOLUNTEER ORGANISERS

District Organiser:	Victoria Reid Thomas	Riccarton Mains Farmhouse, Currie EH14 4AR
		E: info@scotlandsgardens.org
Area Organisers:	Kate Fearnley	23 Lasswade Road, Eskbank EH22 3EE
	Jerry & Christine Gregson	101 Greenbank Crescent, Edinburgh EH10 5TA
	Caroline Pearson	42 Pentland Avenue, Edinburgh EH13 0HY
	Gillian Polley	3 Swanston Road, Edinburgh EH10 7BB
Treasurer:	Michael Pearson	42 Pentland Avenue, Edinburgh EH13 0HY

GARDENS OPEN ON A SPECIFIC DATE

Bonnington House by Jupiter Artland, Wilkieston	Date to be confirmed
Kevock Garden, 16 Kevock Road, Lasswade	Sunday, 10 April
101 Greenbank Crescent, Edinburgh	Saturday/Sunday, 23/24 April
Spring Temple Gardens, The Mill House, Temple	Saturday, 23 April
Moray Place and Bank Gardens, Edinburgh	Sunday, 24 April
41 Hermitage Gardens, Edinburgh	Saturday, 30 April
Newliston, Kirkliston	Wednesdays - Sundays, 1 May - 4 June
Greentree, 18 Green Hill Park, Edinburgh	Saturday, 7 May
Dr Neil's Garden, Duddingston Village	Saturday/Sunday, 7/8 May
Redcroft, 23 Murrayfield Road, Edinburgh	Saturday/Sunday, 14/15 May
Dean Gardens, Edinburgh	Sunday, 5 June
Broomieknowe Gardens, 2 Lower Broomieknowe, Lasswade	Saturday/Sunday, 11/12 June
Rivaldsgreen House, 48 Friars Brae, Linlithgow	Sunday, 12 June
Meadow Place, 19 Meadow Place	Sunday, 19 June
89 Ravenscroft Street, Edinburgh	Sunday, 19 June
Moray Place and Bank Gardens, Edinburgh	Sunday, 19 June
19 Gardiner Road, Edinburgh	Saturday, 25 June
Even More Gardens of the Lower New Town, Edinburgh	Sunday, 26 June
5 Greenbank Crescent, Edinburgh	Sunday, 26 June
Claremont, Redmill	Sundays, 26 June & 17 July
9 Braid Farm Road, Edinburgh	Sunday, 24 July
Craigentinny Telferton Allotments, Edinburgh	Sunday, 24 July
Pentland Crescent Gardens, 2 Pentland Crescent, Edinburgh	Sunday, 24 July
Hunter's Tryst, 95 Oxgangs Road, Edinburgh	Sunday, 7 August
Claremont, Redmill	Sunday, 7 August
Whitburgh House Walled Garden, Pathhead, Midlothian	Tuesday/Wednesday, 30/31 August
Silverburn Village, 23 Biggar Road, Silverburn	Friday, 30 September
Moray Place and Bank Gardens, Edinburgh	Sunday, 11 December

Edinburgh, Midlothian & West Lothian

GARDENS OPEN BY ARRANGEMENT

Hunter's Tryst, 95 Oxgangs Road, Edinburgh	1 April - 30 September
Finlay's Wee Garden, 8 Newlandrig, Gorebridge, Midlothian	15 May - 28 August
14 East Brighton Crescent, Portobello, Edinburgh	1 June - 31 August

Claremont © Yerbury Studio

Edinburgh, Midlothian & West Lothian

1 101 GREENBANK CRESCENT
Edinburgh EH10 5TA
Jerry and Christine Gregson
T: 0131 447 6492 E: jerry_gregson@yahoo.co.uk

The house is on a busy bus route but hides a fascinating garden on a steeply sloped site. There are views over Braidburn Valley Park to the Pentland hills. Paths wind down from the oval lawn, past a handsome magnolia tree, to a terrace which overlooks a water feature and established flowering shrubs. Less common species include *Neillia thibetica* and dierama. Further steps lead past a scree bed of azalea and rhododendron to a productive area of vegetable beds and fruit trees. A neatly concealed composting area includes wood and earth piles as a home for wildlife. We aim to have colour, contrast, and interest all year round. This past year more terracing has been created to make the garden easier to maintain but unfortunately it is still unsuitable for those of limited mobility.

Open: Saturday/Sunday, 23/24 April, 2pm - 5pm, admission £5.00, children free.

Directions: From the city centre take the A702 through Morningside. Continue uphill and turn right at Greenbank Church on to Greenbank Crescent. Buses 5 and 16; the stop is for Greenbank Row.

Opening for: Shelter Scotland

2 14 EAST BRIGHTON CRESCENT
Portobello, Edinburgh EH15 1LR
Jim and Sue Hurford
E: suehurford@gmail.com

Roughly two-thirds of an acre suburban garden, developed over 40 years. People have said the following about it: 'A little bit of countryside in the town', 'Booming with green', 'A bosky bower' and 'There is such a wide range of plant material and every little corner holds a new gem'.

Open: by arrangement 1 June - 31 August, admission £4.00, children free. Please book garden visit by email.

Directions: Buses 21, 42 and 49 to Brighton Place, and 15, 26, 40 and 45 to Portobello High Street. Brighton Place intersects Portobello High Street just east of the bus stops.

Opening for: The Trussell Trust

3 19 GARDINER ROAD
Edinburgh EH4 3RP
Ms Rae Renwick
E: rae_renwick@yahoo.com

This is a newly designed (and surprisingly large) south-facing garden which had been neglected for some years. While the design retains much of the original structure, a circular theme was introduced to help define grass, pond and seating areas. The hard landscaping is specifically designed to give a feeling of space and openness and effectively joins the living quarters of the house to the garden itself. Some established trees, hedges and shrubs were retained and some much loved trees and shrubs from a previous garden were incorporated. Mixed planting of evergreens and herbaceous plants help to ensure year-round interest. There are also raised beds, vegetable and fruit plots as well as a greenhouse. The front area is minimalist and deliberately low maintenance.

Open: Saturday 25 June, 2pm - 5pm, admission £5.00, children free.

Directions: Buses 43 from St Andrew Square or 41 from Kings Buildings. Get off at Blackhall Post Office.

Opening for: Alzheimer Scotland

Edinburgh, Midlothian & West Lothian

4 41 HERMITAGE GARDENS
Edinburgh EH10 6AZ
Dr and Mrs Tony Toft
E: toft41@hotmail.com

This relatively large city garden on the corner of Hermitage Gardens and Hermitage Drive is at its best in spring with its rock garden, rhododendrons, camellias, acers, tulips and mature trees.

Open: Saturday 30 April, 2pm - 5pm, admission £5.00, children free.

Directions: Buses 5, 11, 15, 16, 23.

Opening for: St Giles' Neighbourhood Group

5 5 GREENBANK CRESCENT
Edinburgh EH10 5TE
Sandy Corlett
T: 0131 447 1119 E: sandycorlett@hotmail.co.uk

South-facing, newly designed, sloping terraced garden with views over Braidburn Valley Park to the Pentlands. Colourful chaos of herbaceous plants, shrubs, roses and small trees. Hard features include a gazebo, pergola, greenhouse and water feature.

Open: Sunday 26 June, 2pm - 5pm, admission £5.00, children free.

Directions: From the city centre take the A702 through Morningside, continue uphill on Comiston Road, turn right at Greenbank Church on to Greenbank Crescent. Buses 5, 16, 11.

Opening for: Parkinsons UK

5 Greenbank Crescent

Edinburgh, Midlothian & West Lothian

6 **89 RAVENSCROFT STREET**
Edinburgh EH17 8QS
Andrew and Alex Gray Muir

A large walled garden, full of surprises, in the old mining village of Gilmerton. Planting includes mature trees, roses and herbaceous borders. There is also a potager. Andrew and Alex Gray Muir have been there for over 50 years but say the garden is still a work in progress. There are plenty of seats so bring a thermos and sit and enjoy the garden.

Open: Sunday 19 June, 2pm - 5pm, admission £5.00, children free.

Directions: Buses 29 and 3 come to the end of the street – look out for *Tanz* on the left and get off at the next stop. It is a nine-minute walk up Ravenscroft Street. Buses 7 and 11 come to Hyvots Bank. A short walk up Ravenscroft Place will bring you to Ravenscroft Street, where you turn right up a short stretch of unmetalled road. If you come by car, park on the public road and walk up the last 50 yards. If necessary, passengers can be dropped off in the yard in front of the house.

Opening for: Bethany Christian Trust

7 **9 BRAID FARM ROAD**
Edinburgh EH10 6LG
Mrs G Paul
T: 0131 447 3482

An interesting and quirky organic garden of different styles and areas. There is a cottage garden with pond, a Mediterranean courtyard, and colourful exotic-decked areas with mosaics and a wildlife pond. A recent addition is a playhouse with a sedum roof.

Open: Sunday 24 July, 2pm - 5pm, admission £5.00, children free.

Directions: Near Braid Hills Hotel, on the 11 and 15 bus routes.

Opening for: Marie Curie

8 **BONNINGTON HOUSE BY JUPITER ARTLAND**
Bonnington House Steadings, Wilkieston EH27 8BY
Robert and Nicky Wilson
T: 01506 889900
W: jupiterartland.org

The gardens at Bonnington House were designed by Nicky Wilson and Arabella Lennox-Boyd, comprising a parterre, laburnum arch, labyrinth, terrace gardens and a lawn tennis court. A swimming pool designed by Joana Vasconcelos and the surrounding garden designed by Nicky Wilson and Thomas Unterdorfer were opened in 2019 and featured in many publications, both national and international. Bonnington House is surrounded by Jupiter Artland, an award-winning contemporary sculpture park founded in 2009 by Robert and Nicky Wilson. Please note that entry to Jupiter Artland can be booked separately.

Open: date is still to be confirmed, check Scotland's Gardens website.

Directions: Follow the postcode EH27 8BY and access via the main entrance to Jupiter Artland on the B7015, just off the A71. There is no access via Bonnington village. Jupiter Artland is well signposted and there is ample parking within the grounds. Frequent bus services from Edinburgh. Buses X27 and X28. For further details please visit the garden's website.

Opening for: to be confirmed

Edinburgh, Midlothian & West Lothian

9 BROOMIEKNOWE GARDENS
2 Lower Broomieknowe, Lasswade EH18 1LN
Ruth Mehlsen

Several charming and individual gardens are to be found in the Broomieknowe Conservation Area of Lasswade. They all differ in size and design, yet are complementary in style, witness to the skill and imagination of their owners. Many interesting trees and shrubs, with a variety of unusual herbaceous and bedding plants, brilliant colour, foliage and form. Lots of ideas and unusual garden features to interest the keen gardener.

Open: Saturday/Sunday, 11/12 June, 2pm - 6pm, admission £4.00, children free. Dogs on leads.

Directions: Broomieknowe is signposted off the B704 between Lasswade and Bonnyrigg. Lothian Bus 31. Get off at Nazareth House Nursing Home at Hillhead.

Opening for: Lothian Cat Rescue

10 CLAREMONT
Redmill EH47 0JY
Trevor & Faye Yerbury
E: info@yerburystudio.com

Claremont is an eclectic garden created over the past 18 years. Before the owners moved in it was just grass with a few rhododendrons. The garden has three areas, with various herbaceous borders to the front, some hostas from the owners' collection to the side – in all the garden contains over 150 hostas and more herbaceous borders, plus a newly created stumpery to the rear. There are three ponds (one very large), a rockery, a dovecot, rose patio and a few interesting trees including a grand monkey puzzle. Even though the garden is situated only two minutes from Junction 4 of the M8, it is yet an idyllic peaceful oasis.

Open: Sundays 26 June, 17 July & 7 August, 2pm - 5pm, admission £5.00, children free.

Directions: Take the M8 and leave at Junction 4 heading for Whitburn. At the first set of traffic lights turn right for Whitburn. After only 100 metres turn first right at a slightly hidden turning with bollards, come straight down, without turning, to the bottom of the hill to Claremont. The house name is on the small pillar to the right.

Opening for: Alzheimer Scotland & Breast Cancer Campaign Scotland

11 CRAIGENTINNY TELFERTON ALLOTMENTS
Telferton Road, off Portobello Road, Edinburgh EH7 6XG
The Gardeners of Craigentinny and Telferton
W: ctallotments@gmail.com

Established in 1923, this independent allotment site is a tranquil and charming space, hidden away in a built-up area, where the local community benefit from growing their own vegetables and fruit. Yarn bombing of allotments, and display of scarecrows. Come and enjoy tea, home baking and a chat with our friendly plot-holders.

Open: Sunday 24 July, 2pm - 5pm, admission £4.00, children free.

Directions: Park on Telferton Road. Buses 15, 26, 45.

Opening for: Craigentinny Telferton Allotments

Edinburgh, Midlothian & West Lothian

12 **DEAN GARDENS**
Edinburgh EH4 1QE
Dean Gardens Management Committee
E: fimason@hotmail.com
W: www.deangardens.org

Nine acres of semi-woodland garden with spring bulbs on the steep banks of the Water of Leith in central Edinburgh. Founded in the 1860s by local residents, the Dean Gardens contain part of the great structure of the Dean Bridge, a Thomas Telford masterpiece of 1835. Lawns, paths, trees, and shrubs with lovely views to the weir in the Dean Village and to the St Bernard's Well. There is also a children's play area.

Open: Sunday 5 June, 2pm - 5pm, admission £4.00, children free.

Directions: Entrance at Ann Street or Eton Terrace.

Opening for: Macmillan Cancer Support

Claremont © Yerbury Studio

13 **DR NEIL'S GARDEN**
Duddingston Village EH15 3PX
Dr Neil's Garden Trust
E: info@drneilsgarden.co.uk
W: www.drneilsgarden.co.uk

A wonderful, secluded, landscaped garden on the lower slopes of Arthur's Seat including conifers, heathers, alpines, a physic garden, herbaceous borders and ponds.

Open: Saturday/Sunday, 7/8 May, 2pm - 5pm, admission £3.00, children free.

Directions: Park at the kirk car park on Duddingston Road West and then follow signposts through the manse garden.

Opening for: Dr Neil's Garden Trust

Edinburgh, Midlothian & West Lothian

14 EVEN MORE GARDENS OF THE LOWER NEW TOWN

St Stephen's Church, Edinburgh   EH3 5AB
Gardeners of Lower New Town
E: jw.homeoffice@gmail.com

A fascinating variety of horticultural creations bringing fresh air and wildlife into the heart of the city. From a steeply terraced Georgian town garden to newly landscaped front and back in a cul-de-sac; from densely-planted courtyards behind traditional tenements to the inspiring 2021 winner of Channel 4's *My Chelsea Garden* competition. Lots of creative solutions to gardening in the city with year-round interest through a mix of seasonal planting and structural evergreens, which gardeners will be on hand to talk about.

Open: Sunday 26 June, noon - 4:30pm, admission £8.00, children free. Information about tickets and trail maps will be available at Scotland's Gardens Scheme website closer to the date.

Directions: Buses 23, 27 to Dundas Street and Canonmills, 8 to Rodney Street and Canonmills, 36 to Hamilton Place and Broughton Road.

Opening for: Shelter Scotland & Médecins Sans Frontières

Even More Gardens of the Lower New Town

15 FINLAY'S WEE GARDEN

8 Newlandrig, Gorebridge, Midlothian   EH23 4NS
Laurie Barbour
T: 0756 83357766 E: laurie@madflap.co.uk
W: www.madflap.net

Finlay's Wee Garden is a small, sort of wild round the edges, work in progress, growing and sprouting with ideas and experiments. Enthusiastically branching out with family-friendly activities. 2022 has been designated 'Scotland's Year of Stories' so we are going to have our themes linked to tales about land, gardens, plants, manure and muck.

Open: by arrangement 15 May - 28 August, admission £5.00, children free. Walkers and cyclists are welcome – please call when you are in the area.

Directions: Take the A68 if coming from Edinburgh or the Borders, take B6367 at the turning for Oxenford Equestrian Centre. Newlandrig is 600 yards further on from the front gate of Vogrie Country Park. No direct transport to village. The closest bus is 51 to Edgehead village.

Opening for: Edinburgh Children's Hospital Charity

Edinburgh, Midlothian & West Lothian

16 GREENTREE
18 Green Hill Park, Edinburgh EH10 4DW
Alison Glen
T: 0131 447 4151 E: ahmglen@gmail.com

A rare opportunity to appreciate a mature garden which, with the exception of one magnificent old copper beech tree, is completely planted and created by its owner Alison Glen. Designed with an artist's appreciation of form, this woodland garden shelters a large collection of rhododendrons. There are many beautiful specimen trees and shrubs including *Hoheria glabrata*, *Helesia carolina* and several Magnolia species. The garden is fully wheelchair accessible and there are several ways to move through it; from the Japanese inspired stream garden presided over by a mature *Pinus wallichiana* at one end, to the newly developed borders at the other.

Open: Saturday 7 May, 10am - 5pm, admission £5.00, children free.

Directions: Buses 11, 16, 15, 23, 5. By car: from the east – Chamberlain Road, Strathearn Road, from the north – Morningside Road, from the west – Colinton Road.

Opening for: Alzheimer Scotland

17 HUNTER'S TRYST
95 Oxgangs Road, Edinburgh EH10 7BA
Jean Knox
T: 0131 477 2919 E: jean.knox@blueyonder.co.uk

Well stocked and beautifully designed, mature, medium-sized town garden comprising herbaceous and shrub beds, lawn, fruit and some vegetables, water features, seating areas, trees and an example of cloud pruning. This is a wildlife-friendly garden that has been transformed from a wilderness 38 years ago and continues to evolve. In 2017 two raised beds were added to the front garden. This hidden treasure of a garden was featured on *The Beechgrove Garden* in June 2015 and on *The Instant Gardener* in June 2016. As we were unable to open in 2021 due to serious house damage, it is particularly exciting to be able to welcome everybody back in 2022.

Open: Sunday 7 August, 2pm - 5pm. Also open by arrangement 1 April - 30 September. Admission £5.00, children free.

Directions: From Fairmilehead crossroads head down Oxgangs Road to Hunter's Tryst roundabout and it's the last house on the left. Buses 4, 5, 27, 400. The bus stop is at Hunter's Tryst and the garden is opposite.

Opening for: St Columba's Hospice Care & Lothian Cat Rescue

Edinburgh, Midlothian & West Lothian

18 KEVOCK GARDEN
16 Kevock Road, Lasswade EH18 1HT
David and Stella Rankin
T: 07811 321585 E: stella@kevockgarden.co.uk
W: www.kevockgarden.co.uk

This wonderful hillside garden has magnificent views over the North Esk Valley and the steep slope creates a range of different habitats with a wide diversity of plants, ranging from those that love hot, sunny conditions to those that prefer the cool, damp places near the pond and woodland glades. Mature specimen trees, rhododendrons, azaleas and unusual shrubs are underplanted with many rare woodland plants. Lawns have been relaid, surrounding borders have been planted, and there is a new rock garden. Kevock Garden has featured in many magazine articles and gardening programmes.

Open: Sunday 10 April, 11am - 5pm, admission £5.00, children free.

Directions: Kevock Road lies to the south of the A678 Loanhead/Lasswade Road. Five minutes from the city bypass Lasswade Junction and on the 31 Lothian Bus route to Polton/Bonnyrigg Rd.

Opening for: Fischy Music

19 MEADOW PLACE
19 Meadow Place EH9 1JR
Jan Wilson
T: 0131 229 8316 E: janwilson1920@gmail.com

The secret garden of Meadow Place is the walled garden of a Georgian house that was built in 1816. The owner has been tending the garden for 46 years and the garden is now patios, pots and flower beds rather than the lawn and roses of yesteryear. The planting is a mixture of trees, shrubs and herbaceous flowers.

Open: Sunday 19 June, 1:30pm - 4:30pm, admission £4.00, children free.

Directions: The garden is down the lane off Roseneath Terrace. Look for the brown garage door. Buses 24, 41.

Opening for: Maggie's

20 MORAY PLACE AND BANK GARDENS
Edinburgh EH3 6BX
Residents of the Moray Feu

Join us in our bicentenary year to enjoy spring, summer and winter flowers and foliage.
Bank Gardens Edinburgh EH3 6BX : Nearly six acres of secluded wild gardens with lawns, trees and shrubs, banks of bulbs down to the Water of Leith and stunning views towards Dean Bridge.
Moray Place Edinburgh EH3 6BX : Private garden of three-and-a-half acres in the Georgian New Town is framed by the polygon of Moray Place, and is laid out with shrubs, trees and flower beds offering an atmosphere of tranquility in the city centre.

Open: Sundays 24 April, and 19 June, 2pm - 5pm. Also open Sunday 11 December, 11am - 2pm. Admission £5.00, children free. There will be tea, coffee and home baking.

Directions: Bank Gardens Enter by the gate at the top of Doune Terrace.

Moray Place Enter by the north gate in Moray Place.

Opening for: Euan Macdonald Centre for Motor Neurone Disease Research

Edinburgh, Midlothian & West Lothian

21 NEWLISTON
Kirkliston EH29 9EB
Mr and Mrs R C Maclachlan
T: 0131 333 3231 E: newliston@gmail.com

A well preserved 18th-century parkland/designed landscape rather than a garden as such. Full of mature rhododendrons and azaleas, fine vistas and allées of trees. The walk around the woods and lake is a carpet of wild garlic and bluebells in the spring. The wood to the east of the house is in the pattern of the Union Jack, best appreciated by standing in the centre where all the radiating paths meet. The house, designed by Robert Adam, is also open.

Open: 1 May - 4 June (not Mondays & Tuesdays), 2pm - 6pm. Admission £5.00, children free.

Directions: Four miles south of the Forth Road Bridge, entrance off the B800.

Opening for: CHAS

22 PENTLAND CRESCENT GARDENS
2 Pentland Crescent, Edinburgh EH10 6NP
Jan Polley
T: 07801 439299 E: jpolley@blueyonder.co.uk

Three neighbouring gardens (two of which are new for 2022). They are all laid out very differently, offering a wide range of ideas for visitors. The gardens include colourful herbaceous borders, a range of fruit and vegetables and a woodland garden which shows what can be done with a sloping site. There are ideas for planting in the sun and shade, rockeries and various patios and seating areas.

Open: Sunday 24 July, 2pm - 5pm, admission £6.00, children free.

Directions: From the city centre take the A702 through Morningside, continue uphill and turn right at Comiston Springs Avenue. Pentland Crescent is first left. Bus 11 – get off at the Comiston Springs Avenue stop.

Opening for: Marie Curie

Edinburgh, Midlothian & West Lothian

23 REDCROFT
23 Murrayfield Road, Edinburgh EH12 6EP
James and Anna Buxton
T: 0131 337 1747 E: annabuxtonb@aol.com

Redcroft is a mature walled garden surrounding an attractive Arts and Crafts house. It is a hidden haven off a busy road with a variety of different features and habitats: old shrubberies, an orchard, a rockery, a pond, and a large lawn with contrasting longer grass. It is well maintained with many clipped shrubs and some cloud pruning. Early May is very colourful with rhododendrons and many other flowering shrubs and wall plants, and the greenhouse is full of tender plants. There will be tulips in pots and many other spring bulbs. Children and buggies are very welcome and there will be plenty of activities. We hope older children will enjoy our treehouse.

Open: Saturday/Sunday, 14/15 May, 2pm - 5pm. Admission £5.00, children free. A bumper SGS PLANT SALE.

Directions: Murrayfield Road runs north from Corstorphine Road to Ravelston Dykes. There is easy free parking available. Buses 12, 26, 31, get off at Murrayfield Stadium. Bus 38 goes up Murrayfield Road.

Opening for: Canine Partners

24 RIVALDSGREEN HOUSE
48 Friars Brae, Linlithgow EH49 6BG
Dr Ian Wallace
T: 01506 845700 E: Ianwjw1940@gmail.com

Mature two-acre garden with lovely mixed herbaceous, rose, and tree planting.

Open: Sunday 12 June, 2pm - 5pm, admission £5.00, children free.

Directions: From the west end of the High Street turn into Preston Road, after crossing the canal turn left into Priory Road and at the T junction turn left down Friars Brae. There is car parking available.

Opening for: St John Scotland

Rivaldsgreen House

Edinburgh, Midlothian & West Lothian

25 SILVERBURN VILLAGE
23 Biggar Road, Silverburn EH26 9LJ
Mrs K M Hill

Come and celebrate over 30 years of SGS openings at the heart of the Pentland Hills with our Harvest Festival. Share the experience of surviving above 900 feet, enjoy the beautiful *Beechgrove* garden – now 12 years old, explore the arboretum, a woodland walk and a wild garden.

Open: Friday 30 September, 2pm - 5:30pm, admission £5.00, children free. Teas and delicious home baking in the village hall. Specialist plant, local craft and harvest stalls. Children's nature trail, messy cakes and an 'eco' treasure hunt.

Directions: Parking available. Disabled access. Buses 101/102 Edinburgh-Dumfries bus route. On the A702 10 miles from Edinburgh city centre, six miles from city bypass.

Opening for: Mary's Meals

26 SPRING TEMPLE GARDENS
The Mill House, Temple EH23 4SH
Sandy Delap
T: 0187 583 0253 E: delapsandy@gmail.com

42 Glebe Cottage Temple EH23 4SQ (Jan Paterson): Glebe cottage at the top of the village, stands at 700ft (height of Arthur's Seat), has a charming appeal and wonderful views of the fields and woodlands behind, with a range of flowers, shrubs and young trees. This house is the last of the original settlement built in 1890 next to land owned by the church, hence the name.
The Mill House Temple EH23 4SH (Sandy Delap): The Mill House is a listed building renovated in 1710 and has the remains of the old grain mill in the garden and a river. In April, this garden is full of spring bulbs and oriental hellebores. This is our first opening in spring and the garden has many levels and each part has its own personality.

Open: Saturday 23 April, 2pm - 5pm, admission £5.00, children free. Dogs on leads. Tea and home baking will be available in both gardens.

Directions: On the B6352, three miles off the A7 from Gorebridge. Parking is in the village only, please park carefully and walk if possible. There will be disabled parking at the bottom of the village for access to the Mill House.

Opening for: Temple Village Halls Association & Marie Curie

27 WHITBURGH HOUSE WALLED GARDEN
Pathhead, Midlothian EH37 5SR
Mrs Elizabeth Salvesen
E: eesal39@gmail.com

This contemporary, stylish one-acre walled garden, 700 feet above sea level, is a lively forward-looking and an unexpected gem. The solidity and graphic quality of clipped foliage act as a foil for the many perennials, grasses, annuals, fruit and vegetables. A spiral path leads through an acre of white birches. There is also a variety of ponds and fine sculptures spread around 14 acres of policies. Whitburgh garden has featured recently in *Gardens Illustrated* and other publications.

Open: Tuesday/Wednesday, 30/31 August, 2:30pm - 5:30pm, admission £7.00, children free.

Directions: From north – a half mile south of Pathhead on the A68 turn left and follow the *SGS* signs. From south – one mile north of Blackshiels on the A68 turn right at the sign to *Fala Dam* and follow *SGS* signs. Whitburgh House is about two miles from either turn off and south east of Pathhead.

Opening for: Horatio's Garden

Fife

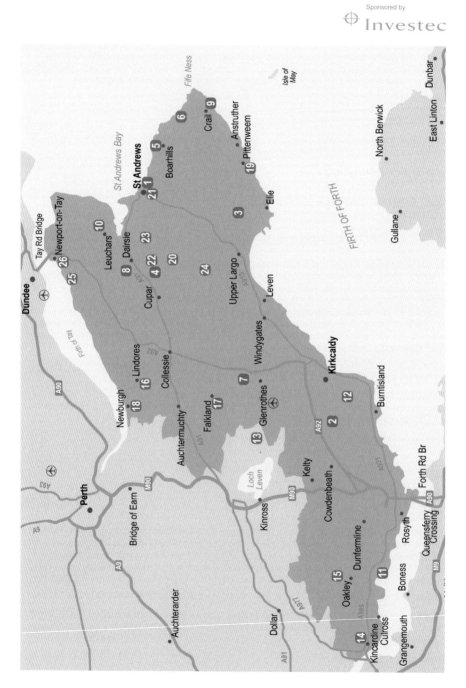

Fife

OUR VOLUNTEER ORGANISERS

District Organisers:	David Buchanan-Cook	Helensbank, 56 Toll Road, Kincardine FK10 4QZ
	Julia Young	South Flisk, Blebo Craigs, Cupar KY15 5UQ
		E: info@scotlandsgardens.org
Area Organisers:	Alison Aiton	Craigview Cottage, Blebo Craigs KY15 5UQ
	Jeni Auchinleck	2 Castle Street, Crail KY10 3SQ
	Pauline Borthwick	96 Hepburn Gardens, St Andrews KY16 9LP
	Lorna Duckworth	The Old Coach House, Dunbog KY14 6JF
	Anne Lumgair	Falside Cottage, Kingsbarns KY16 8PT
	Barbara Pickard	Straiton Farmhouse, Balmullo KY16 0BN
	Fay Smith	37 Ninian Fields, Pittenweem KY10 2QU
District Photographers:	Mike Bell	6 Strathearn Terrace, Perth PH2 0LS
	Carolyn Bell	6 Strathearn Terrace, Perth PH2 0LS
Treasurer:	David Buchanan-Cook	Helensbank, 56 Toll Road, Kincardine FK10 4QZ

GARDENS OPEN ON A SPECIFIC DATE

Auchtertool House, Auchtertool, Fife	Sunday, 6 March
Willowhill, Forgan, Newport-on-Tay	Sats & Mons, 26/28 March, 23/25 April, 28/30 May, 25/27 June, 23/25 July & 6 - 29 August
Teasses Gardens, near Ceres	Sunday, 3 April
Cambo Spring Plant & Garden Market, Kingsbarns	Sunday, 10 April
South Flisk, Blebo Craigs, Cupar	Sunday, 24 April
Lindores House, by Newburgh	Sunday, 15 May
South Flisk, Blebo Craigs, Cupar	Sunday, 22 May
Blebo Craigs Village Gardens, Blebo Craigs, Cupar	Sunday, 22 May
Kirklands, Saline	Sunday, 22 May
Strathkinness Community Garden and Orchard, Bonfield Road	Sunday, 22 May
Auchtertool House, Auchtertool, Fife	Sunday, 29 May
Earlshall Castle, Leuchars	Sunday, 29 May
Pittenweem: Gardens in the Burgh, Pittenweem	Sunday, 12 June
The Tower, 1 Northview Terrace, Wormit	Saturday/Sunday, 25/26 June
Newburgh – Hidden Gardens, Newburgh	Sunday, 26 June
Boarhills Village Gardens, Boarhills, St Andrews	Sunday, 26 June
Balcarres, Colinsburgh	Sunday, 26 June
Earlshall Castle, Leuchars	Sunday, 3 July
Craigfoodie, Dairsie	Sunday, 3 July
Crail: Gardens in the Burgh, Crail	Saturday/Sunday, 9/10 July
Coul House, Coul House, Maree Way, Glenrothes	Suns 17 July, 21 Aug & Sat 24 Sept.
Greenhead Farmhouse, Greenhead of Arnot, Leslie	Sunday 18 September
SGS Plant Sale at St Andrews Botanic Garden, St Andrews	Sunday, 2 October

Fife

GARDENS OPEN REGULARLY

Millfield Garden, Millfield House, Falkland	6 - 27 February (Suns only)
Gardener's Cottage, Crombie Point, Shore Road, Crombie	Weds & Thurs, 1 June - 31 July

GARDENS OPEN BY ARRANGEMENT

46 South Street, St Andrews	1 April - 31 July
South Flisk, Blebo Craigs, Cupar	1 April - 30 June
Glassmount House, by Kirkcaldy	1 April - 30 September
Kirklands, Saline	1 April - 30 September
The Tower, 1 Northview Terrace, Wormit	1 April - 30 September
Rosewells, Pitscottie	1 April - 30 September
Helensbank, Kincardine	1 June - 30 September

Gardener's Cottage © Fay Johnstone

Fife

1 46 SOUTH STREET

St Andrews KY16 9JT
Mrs June Baxter
T: 01334 474995

Renowned town garden in medieval long rigg, with orchard underplanted with wildflowers and bulbs. Many unusual flowering shrubs will be looking their best. Roses and other climbers clothe the surrounding high walls. Shrub roses planted in a delightful central parterre fill the air with scent. An historic and unique feature in St Andrews, but also a wonderfully planted space where different styles of planting complement the range of plants used. Historic doocot.

Open: by arrangement 1 April - 31 July, admission £5.00, children free.

Directions: Access and parking information on request.

Opening for: Friends of Craigtoun

2 AUCHTERTOOL HOUSE

Auchtertool, Fife KY2 5XW
Jonathan Leitch
T: 07990551180 E: info@auchtertoolhouse.com
W: www.auchtertoolhouse.com

The gardens cover three acres and comprise mature woodland, lawns, productive flower beds and mature shrubbery. The south-facing lawn ends in a ha-ha and gives views towards the Firth of Forth and East Lothian. The garden includes over 50 varieties of rhododendron which flower in stages during May and June. The top wood is covered in snowdrops in the early spring, giving way to an assortment of bulbs, native bluebells and narcissi. There is approximately an acre of mature trees, including beech, acer, walnut, and two very large Western Red Cedars.

Open: Sunday 6 March, 10am - 3pm for Snowdrops and Winter Walks. Also open Sunday 29 May, 10am - 6pm. Admission £5.00, children free.

Directions: Located on the B925 to the west of Auchtertool, before the Auchtertool sign and 30 mph zone. Auchtertool is accessible by bus from Cowdenbeath and Kirkcaldy. Visitors are advised to park in the village and walk to the garden.

Opening for: Maggie's

Fife

3 BALCARRES

Colinsburgh KY9 1HN
Lord and Lady Balniel
T: 01333 340205 (Estate Office)

Balcarres House has been owned by the Lindsay family since the late 16th century and each generation has made their mark on the house and gardens. The formal gardens with their magnificent yew hedges and terraces were laid out by Sir Coutts Lindsay in the 1870s. Since then other changes have been made but the largest impact has come from the late Lady Crawford. She has been the inspiration for the garden and the driving force of much of what has been created in the past fifty years. The gardens come into their own in early summer with the Rose Garden in full bloom with a variety of Hybrid Teas and climbing roses such a Blairi II, Shropshire Lad & Lady Hillingdon. Herbaceous borders are bursting into life with a variety of Geranium, Astrantia, Viola, oriental poppies and Aquilegia. The Woodland & Chapel Walks will also be at their best with many different Hostas, Smilacina, and other diverse plants, shrubs and trees. Enjoy the walks to the Sawmill Pond planting, the Den and the Balcarres Craig.

Open: Sunday 26 June, 2pm - 5pm, admission £6.00, children free.

Directions: Half-a-mile north of Colinsburgh off A942. Bus to Colinsburgh.

Opening for: Colinsburgh Community Trust Ltd

Balcarres © Angus Blackburn

Fife

4 **BLEBO CRAIGS VILLAGE GARDENS**
Blebo Craigs, Cupar KY15 5UG
Gardeners of Blebo Craigs

A selection of cottage gardens in this charming, rural village, situated between Cupar and St Andrews; most gardens have stunning views over the surrounding countryside. The gardens range from well-established cottage gardens to some which are being redesigned, and one or two which have risen like a phoenix from the ashes! They will be joining South Flisk, the large quarry garden at the top of the village – see separate entry for South Flisk's other openings. Part of the enjoyment of visiting these gardens is walking round the narrow lanes and paths, encountering the village's historic cottages – one of which has a 'green' roof – and larger houses, many of which are over 200 years old.

Open: Sunday 22 May, 11am - 5pm, admission £5.00, children free. Teas available at South Flisk.

Directions: From St Andrews: B939 for five miles, village sign on your left at the bus stop pointing right, taking you directly into the village. From Cupar: B940 to Pitscottie, turn left onto the B939 and, after a couple of miles, turn left into the village.

Opening for: Médecins Sans Frontières

5 **BOARHILLS VILLAGE GARDENS**
Boarhills, St Andrews KY16 8PP
Gardeners of Boarhills
E: bd.com.trust@btinternet.com
W: www.boarhillsanddunincommunitytrust.org

A varied group of village gardens, including some new gardens for 2022. An opportunity to stroll around this delightful village. Do not miss the community-owned Boarhills Doocot which is undergoing major restoration following a three-year fundraising campaign. The doocot is in the Boarhills Green Space – which also contains a small community orchard.

Open: Sunday 26 June, 1pm - 5pm, admission £5.00, children free. Plants for sale, teas available.

Directions: Enter the village off the A917 and follow the *yellow* signs.

Opening for: Boarhills and Dunino Community Trust

6 **CAMBO SPRING PLANT & GARDEN MARKET**
Kingsbarns KY16 8QD
Trustees of Cambo Heritage Trust
T: 01333 451040 E: hello@camboestate.com
W: www.cambogardens.com

Pop in to Cambo to freshen up your garden for spring. We will have a unique selection of plants and bulbs from visiting nurseries, garden goods and local crafts to browse. Outdoor cafe open all day. Gardens, woodlands and play area to visit.
National Plant Collection: Galanthus.

Open: Sunday 10 April, 11am - 3pm, admission £3.00, children free.

Directions: A917 between Crail and St Andrews.

Opening for: Cambo Heritage Trust

Fife

7 COUL HOUSE

Coul House, Maree Way, Glenrothes KY7 6NW
Dean & Clare Ansell
T: 07525791277 E: Clareansell5@gmail.com

A hidden gem, Coul garden lies within the grounds of Coul House, an imposing B-listed Victorian farmhouse which dates back to circa 1875. A mix of hydrangeas, roses, rhododendron and wisteria are contained in this ever-evolving amateur garden. The garden has more recently been redesigned with hard landscaping and includes a small pond. Come and take a walk around and enjoy a cup of tea and home baking.

Open: Sunday 17 July, Sunday 21 August and Saturday 24 September, 11am - 3pm. Admission £5.00, children free.

Directions: From the A92, follow signs for Pitcairn

Opening for: Juvenile Diabetes Research Foundation Limited & Glenrothes & District Foodbank

8 CRAIGFOODIE

Dairsie KY15 4RU
Mr and Mrs James Murray
T: 01334 870291

Unusually, Craigfoodie House sits in its walled garden and the garden itself is on a sloping site, with the view from the upper terraces stretching beyond the garden into the valley below. The walled garden is quartered: the clock lawn is an original feature, as is a plump topiary bird. The parterre with its weeping silver pear trees, the malus lawn, pump garden, fountain garden and herbaceous border are traditional but recent features. An under-planted, pleached lime hedge, shrub rose border and a corridor of espalier fruit trees divide the various sections of the walled garden. Enjoy the Mediterranean-style terraces, informal woodland garden, the grass tennis court and planting of young trees and shrubs (a current development area) and a stroll round the Knoll to its magnificent viewpoint. Craigfoodie has featured on *The Beechgrove Garden* and in articles in several national magazines.

Open: Sunday 3 July, 2pm - 5pm, admission £5.00, children free.

Directions: On A91 from Cupar to St Andrews turn left at Dairsie School then follow signs.

Opening for: The Pitcairn Trust

Craigfoodie © David Nunn

Fife

9 CRAIL: GARDENS IN THE BURGH
Crail KY10 3TT
Gardeners of Crail
T: 01333 450797 E: sueellen.jerdan@gmail.com

Take an enjoyable stroll around this quintessential East Neuk village and explore its many beautiful gardens. A number of gardens in varied styles and planting schemes: cottage, historic, plantsman's and bedding. The stunning coastal location of the gardens presents some challenges for planting but also allows for a great range of more tender species to flourish.

Open: Saturday/Sunday, 9/10 July, 2pm - 5pm, admission £6.00, children free. Tickets and maps are available on the day from Mrs Jeni Auchinleck, 2 Castle Street, where there will also be a plant stall, or from Mrs Sue Jerdan, 74 Bow Butts.

Directions: Approach Crail from either St Andrews or Anstruther on the A917. Parking available in Marketgate.

Opening for: Crail Preservation Society

10 EARLSHALL CASTLE
Leuchars KY16 0DP
Paul and Josine Veenhuijzen
T: 01334 839205

Extensive, exquisitely designed garden, which perfectly complements the Castle also restored by Sir Robert Lorimer in the 1890s. Fascinating topiary lawn, the finest in Scotland and for which Earlshall is renowned, rose terrace, croquet lawn with herbaceous borders, shrub border, box garden, orchard, kitchen and herb garden. Spectacular spring bulbs.

Open: Sunday 29 May, 2pm - 5pm. Also open Sunday 3 July, 2pm - 5pm. Admission £5.00, children free. Due to grass areas and steps, the garden is not fully wheelchair accessible. Dogs only on leads please!

Directions: On Earlshall Road, three-quarters of a mile east of Leuchars Village (off A919). Bus/train to Leuchars.

Opening for: Royal Scots Dragoon Guards Regimental Trust (Sunday 29 May) & Leuchars St Athernase Parish Church (Sunday 3 July)

11 GARDENER'S COTTAGE
Crombie Point, Shore Road, Crombie, Dunfermline KY12 8LQ
Fay Johnstone and Jamie Andrews
T: 07921174212 E: fay.johnstone@gmail.com

Originally part of the Craigflower Estate, the garden was transformed by the late Scottish-German botanist Ursula McHardy to demonstrate models of natural vegetation patterns of the Southern Hemisphere. Within the walled garden you will find an Australian eucalyptus forest and a South American forest with southern beeches and monkey-puzzles. There is also a South African area and a New Zealand section with five pools as well as traditional mixed borders. What remains of the original botanical collection is maintained by the current owners in an informal manner in line with Fay's work with plants supporting holistic health and wellbeing.

Open: 1 June - 31 July (Wednesdays & Thursdays), 2pm - 5pm, admission £5.00, children free.

Directions: Park at, or get the bus to, the Ness in Torryburn then walk 15 minutes along Shore Rd.

Opening for: Sea Shepherd UK

Fife

12 GLASSMOUNT HOUSE

by Kirkcaldy KY2 5UT
Peter, James and Irene Thomson
T: 01592 890214 E: mcmoonter@yahoo.co.uk

Densely planted walled garden with surrounding woodland. An A-listed sun dial, Mackenzie & Moncur greenhouse and historical doocot are complemented by a number of newer structures. Daffodils are followed by a mass of candelabra and cowslip primula, meconopsis and *Cardiocrinum giganteum*. Hedges and topiary form backdrops for an abundance of bulbs, clematis, rambling roses and perennials, creating interest through the summer into September. The garden is now extending beyond the walls, with new areas of naturalistic planting blending the boundary between the surrounding fields and the woodland.

Open: by arrangement 1 April - 30 September, admission £5.00, children free.

Directions: From Kirkcaldy, head west on the B9157. Turn left immediately after the railway bridge on the edge of town. Follow the single track road for one-and-a-half miles and cross the crossroads. Glassmount House is the first turning on your right.

Opening for: Parkinsons UK

13 GREENHEAD FARMHOUSE

Greenhead of Arnot, Leslie KY6 3JQ
Mr and Mrs Malcolm Strang Steel
T: 01592 840459
W: www.fife-bed-breakfast-glenrothes.co.uk

The south-facing garden combines a sense of formality in its symmetrical layout, with an informal look of mixed herbaceous and shrub borders. The garden is constantly evolving with new themes and combinations of plants, all unified by a fantastic use of colour. There is also a well-stocked polytunnel which is used to augment the highly productive fruit and vegetable garden.

Open: Sunday 18 September, 2pm - 5pm, admission £5.00, children free.

Directions: A911 between Auchmuir Bridge and Scotlandwell.

Opening for: SSAFA Forces Help

Greenhead Farmhouse

Fife

14 HELENSBANK

Kincardine FK10 4QZ
David Buchanan-Cook and Adrian Miles
T: 07739 312912 E: Helensbank@aol.com
W: www.helensbank.com

Hidden away from public view, this is an 18th-century walled garden, with main feature a Cedar of Lebanon, reputedly planted in 1750 by the sea captain who built the house. The tree is registered as a 'Notable Tree' and while it provides challenges for planting, in terms of shade and needle fall, the microclimate it provides has encouraged the owners' passion for pushing boundaries and growing unusual and exotic plants. Distinctive garden 'rooms' in part of the garden comprise a perennial blue and white cottage garden, a formal rose garden and an Italian double courtyard with citrus trees in pots. A 'hot' courtyard contains exotics including varieties of banana, acacia, iochroma, impatiens, melianthus and brugmansia. A shaded walk along the bottom of the garden leads to a Japanese themed area including a pagoda. A large glasshouse hosts various exotic and climbing plants. The garden has well over a hundred roses, including the National Collection of Portland roses. These are best viewed from mid June to early July.
National Plant Collection: Portland Roses.
Champion Trees: The garden has a 'notable' Cedar of Lebanon, the second largest in Fife.

Open: by arrangement 1 June - 30 September, admission £5.00, children free. There is an annual garden concert late July/early August – for details and to book tickets contact the owners.

Directions: The garden is down a lane off the main Toll Road. *SGS* signs.

Opening for: Scottish Veterans Residences

15 KIRKLANDS

Saline KY12 9TS
Peter and Gill Hart
T: 07787 115477 E: gill@i-comment360.com
W: www.kirklandshouseandgarden.co.uk

Kirklands, built in 1832, has been the Hart family home for 41 years. Over the years we have re-instated the walled garden from a paddock and constructed terraces with raised beds. There are 18 espalier apple trees against the walls and box hedging with a display of tulips. The woodland garden starts with snowdrops and bluebells, then rhododendrons, trilliums, fritillaries, meconopsis, erythroniums and candelabra primulas follow. The rockery displays dwarf rhododendrons and azaleas. The herbaceous borders reach their peak in the summer. The bog garden by the Saline Burn is home to giant *Gunnera manicata*. Over the bridge we have 20 acres of woodland with a pathway by the burn. To keep the grandchildren occupied, Peter built a tree house, climbing frame and rope swing, though we hope they will take an interest in gardening too!

Open: Sunday 22 May, 2pm - 5pm. Also open by arrangement 1 April - 30 September. Admission £5.00, children free.

Directions: Junction 4, M90, then B914. Parking in the centre of the village, then a short walk to the garden. Limited disabled parking at Kirklands.

Opening for: Saline Environmental Group

Fife

16 LINDORES HOUSE
by Newburgh KY14 6JD
Robert and Elizabeth Turcan & John and Eugenia Turcan
T: 01337 840369

Lindores House overlooks the loch. Woodland walks beside the loch and stunning views from the garden. Herbaceous borders, wonderful snowdrops, leucojums, trilliums, primulae, rhododendrons and species trees including *Nothofagus* and *Davidia involucrata*, the handkerchief tree. Don't miss the 17th-century yew, believed to be the largest in Fife, which you can walk inside!

Open: Sunday 15 May, 10am - 5pm, admission £5.00, children free.

Directions: Off A913 two miles east of Newburgh. Bus from Cupar.

Opening for: RC Diocese Of Dunkeld: St Columba's, Cupar

17 MILLFIELD GARDEN
Millfield House, Falkland, Fife KY15 7BN
Sarah & Aaron Marshall
T: 07584620534

Millfield is set on the edge of the beautiful and historic village of Falkland. Falkland Gardening Group is developing a snowdrop trail in the village. Millfield has a walled garden, bulb meadows, woodland paths, all with snowdrops. There are also over 100 different snowdrop varieties set around the driveway area at waist height, for ease of viewing! The garden also houses a selection of hellebores and winter flowering shrubs.

Open: 6 February - 27 February (Sundays only), 11am - 3pm for Snowdrops and Winter Walks, admission £5.00, children free.

Directions: From the A912 turn into the village, travel straight past the central fountain. Follow the road until it makes a sharp left – Millfield is straight ahead.

Opening for: Chest Heart & Stroke Scotland

Millfield Garden

Fife

18 NEWBURGH – HIDDEN GARDENS
Newburgh KY14 6AH
Gardeners of Newburgh

Hidden behind the 18th-century facades of Newburgh High Street lie a jumble of wonderful old gardens, some of them dating back centuries. Many have spectacular views of the Tay Estuary. We are opening for the third time, having had to cancel last year's planned openings. The gardens will include some previously opened, as well as some opening in 2022 for the first time. Those previously opened will have been developed considerably, and, as before, there will be a wide mix of flowers, vegetables, herbaceous borders, orchards and a fair few hens and ducks.

Open: Sunday 26 June, noon - 5pm, admission £5.00, children free. Newburgh sits on a hill. In addition, access to some gardens is via narrow closes and vennels. As such, disabled access to some gardens may be restricted.

Directions: On the A913 between Perth and Cupar. There is a car park at each end of the town, with tickets and teas available nearby.

Opening for: Newburgh Community Trust

19 PITTENWEEM: GARDENS IN THE BURGH
Pittenweem KY10 2PQ
Gardeners of Pittenweem
T: 07718 000802

An inspiring variety of gardens, many tucked away behind houses and garden walls. These gardens display a wide range of styles: from traditional to landscaped, and to include those which are richly productive and others incorporating many interesting and unusual plants. This is a chance to re-visit old favourites and also discover new projects.

Open: Sunday 12 June, 11am - 5pm, admission £5.00, children free.

Directions: On the A917 coast road, enter Pittenweem following the signs to the West Braes car park, next to the Crazy Golf and newly refurbished swimming pool. For traffic from east, stop and park at Milton Road, or, from Ovenstone, there is a car park at the cemetery/football park off Charles Street.

Opening for: Parkinsons UK & PSPA

Fife

20 ROSEWELLS

Pitscottie KY15 5LE
Birgitta and Gordon MacDonald
E: g.macdonald54@hotmail.co.uk

Rosewells, designed by the garden owners, has developed over the last 25 years with an underlying theme that each part of the garden should work in relation to the rest, to create one overall effect. The design centres on texture and foliage to provide a lively effect with structure and shape all year. The winter 'bones' are provided by trees and shrubs with features such as contorted stems and peeling or coloured bark. In spring and summer, texture and coloured foliage of shrubs and perennials add to the overall design. Birgitta sees flowers as an added bonus with scent and colour being important and combinations of yellow, blue and white colour schemes are preferred. The garden has many varieties of cornus, magnolias, trilliums, meconopsis, agapanthus, rhododendrons, primulas, auriculas, fritillaries, erythroniums, peonies and acers, which are favourites.

Open: by arrangement 1 April - 30 September, admission £5.00, children free.

Directions: B940 between Pitscottie and Peat Inn, one mile from Pitscottie. Rosewells is the ochre-coloured house.

Opening for: Save the Children UK

St Andrews Botanic Garden

21 SGS PLANT SALE AT ST ANDREWS BOTANIC GARDEN

St Andrews KY16 8RT
St Andrews Botanic Garden

The famous annual SGS Fife Autumn Plant Sale returns for a second year to the Botanic Garden in St Andrews. In addition to a fabulous selection of bare root and potted plants, all grown locally, watch the SGS website for updates on an exciting selection of stall holders and other activities being planned for the day. Plant donations – large and small – will be extremely welcome on the day preceding the sale.

Open: Sunday 2 October, 11am - 3pm, admission £3.00, children free.

Directions: The garden is located on Canongate and is a 10/15 minute walk from the centre of St Andrews. Follow the signs from the town down Viaduct walk, which is a shared path for bikes and walkers. The 99C bus route goes past the garden and takes five minutes from the

Fife

bus stop in St Andrews. The nearest train station is Leuchars on the 99 bus route. There is a free car park at the garden.

Opening for: St Andrews Botanic Garden Trust

22 SOUTH FLISK
Blebo Craigs, Cupar KY15 5UQ
Mr and Mrs George Young
T: 01334 850859 E: southfliskgarden@gmail.com
W: www.standrewspottery.co.uk

The spectacular views over Fife to Perthshire and Angus, and the large flooded quarry full of fish (and the occasional otter) and planted with impressive marginals, make this garden very special. Flights of old stone steps, cliffs, huge boulders, exotic ferns and mature trees form a backdrop for carpets of primroses, bluebells, spring bulbs and woodland plants like trilliums, camassia, meconopsis and colourful primulas. There are different rhododendrons in flower in the garden from March until July. In front of the house is a charming, mature walled garden with traditional cottage-garden planting. Next to the house is the St Andrews Pottery where George will be demonstrating his pottery skills for those who need a break from the garden!

Open: Sunday 24 April & Sunday 22 May, 11am - 5pm. Also open by arrangement 1 April - 30 June. Admission £5.00, children free.

Directions: Six miles west of St Andrews off the B939 between Strathkinness and Pitscottie. There is a small stone bus shelter opposite the road into the village and a small sign saying *Blebo Craigs*. Or check out the map on our website. Bus to Blebo Craigs.

Opening for: Médecins Sans Frontières

South Flisk © Carolyn Bell

Fife

23 STRATHKINNESS COMMUNITY GARDEN AND ORCHARD

Bonfield Road KY16 9RR
Strathkinness Community Trust
T: 01334 850 649

This two-acre garden was established in 2011 and consists of the Primary School garden, small allotment plots, a polytunnel producing fruit and vegetables throughout the year, habitat planting, herbaceous beds, shrub beds, herb garden, soft fruit cage, and a 50 tree orchard of apples, pears, plums and quince, some of which should be in blossom. Whilst in the village, you may wish to look at the new village green with an interesting named tree collection and Bishop's Wood just outside the village, now owned and being developed by the Strathkinness Community Trust.

Open: Sunday 22 May, 2pm - 5pm, admission £5.00, children free.

Directions: The Community Garden and Orchard is on Bonfield Road, which is accessed off Main Street, Strathkinness.

Opening for: Strathkinness Community Trust

24 TEASSES GARDENS

near Ceres KY8 5PG
E: events@teasses.com
W: www.teasses.com

The season at Teasses erupts in colour in April with vibrant tulip blooms punctuating the verdant green of fresh perennials in the walled garden. Meander through our 'Millennium Wood' to witness a mass of Spanish Bluebells and early flowering rhododendrons. In the open spaces enjoy the lingering blooms of 'Pheasant Eye' *Narcissus*, *Narcissus* , 'Thalia' and fragrant *Narcissus* ,'Bridal Crown'.

Open: Sunday 3 April, 10am - 4pm. Also open through the year. Admission details can be found on the garden's website.

Directions: Between Ceres and Largo. Enter by Teasses Estate farm road, half-a-mile West of Woodside Village.

Opening for: Donation to SGS

25 THE TOWER

1 Northview Terrace, Wormit DD6 8PP
Peter and Angela Davey
T: 01382 541635 M: 07768 406946 E: adavey541@btinternet.com

Situated four miles south of Dundee, this one-acre Edwardian landscaped garden has panoramic views over the River Tay. Set on a hill, a series of paths meander around ponds and a small stream, rockeries featuring hellebores and low-level planting, a curved lawn and larger borders. Original woodland paths lead to a granite grotto with a waterfall pool. At the rear of the house the vegetable garden features raised beds made from granite sets. The garden is colourful throughout the summer, with many architectural plants accentuating the clever hard landscape design.

Open: Saturday/Sunday, 25/26 June, 1pm - 5pm. Also open by arrangement 1 April - 30 September. Admission £5.00, children free.

Directions: From B946, park on Naughton Road outside Spar shop and walk up path on left. Follow signs.

Opening for: Dundee Chamber Music Club

Fife

26 **WILLOWHILL**
Forgan, Newport-on-Tay DD6 8RA
Eric Wright and Sally Lorimore
T: 01382 542890 E: e.g.wright@dundee.ac.uk
W: www.willowhillgarden.weebly.com

An evolving three-acre garden. The house is surrounded by a series of mixed borders designed with different vibrant colour combinations for effect all season. Spectacular mix of roses, herbaceous perennials and annuals planted through the wide borders are a highlight in mid to late summer. A new 'no dig' 160-foot border in shades of white, blue, purple and pale yellow created in 2019/2020. Come and see! April and May for late spring bulbs and flowers; June and July for roses and high summer colour; August for late summer colour.

Open: Saturday & Monday 26 & 28 March, 11:30am - 3pm. Also open Saturdays & Mondays 23 & 25 April, 28 & 30 May, 25 & 27 June, 23 & 25 July, 6 & 8 August, 13 & 15 August, 20 & 22 August, 27 & 29 August, 2pm - 5pm. Admission £5.00, children free. A **season ticket** for all these dates is £20 plus p&p and will admit the ticket holder plus a guest. It comes with a limited-edition copy of the Willowhill Garden Guide; 35 pages of beautiful photographs with descriptions of key garden features and planting. A season ticket with garden guide would make a perfect gift and do treat yourself as well! Tickets are available online: www.bit.ly/38xbjcQ or by post (send a cheque for £23 payable to Scotland's Gardens Scheme) to S Lorimore, Willowhill, Forgan, Newport on Tay, Fife DD6 8RA. The plant stall includes a lovely selection from the garden. Visitors are welcome to bring their own refreshments and picnic in the garden.

Directions: One-and-a-half miles south of Tay Road Bridge. Take the B995 to Newport off the Forgan roundabout. Willowhill is the first house on the left-hand side next to West Friarton Farm Strawberry Shed.

Opening for: Rio Community Centre

Willowhill

Glasgow & District

Sponsored by
Investec

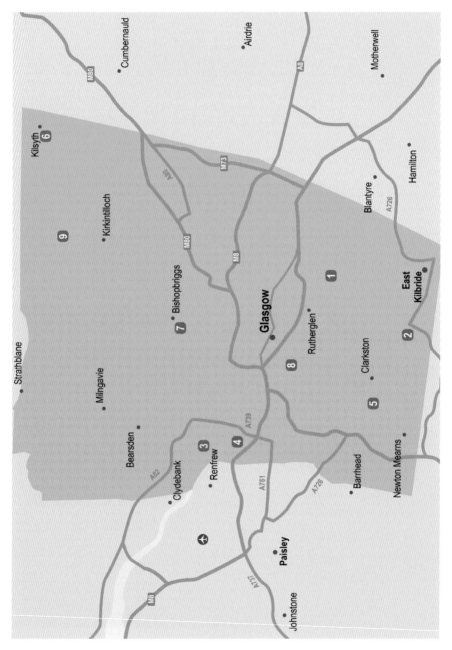

Glasgow & District

OUR VOLUNTEER ORGANISERS

District Organisers:	Heidi Stone	E: info@scotlandsgardens.org
Area Organisers:	Caroline Anderson	
	Ian Angus	
	Hilda Kelly	
	Anne Murray	
	Jim Murray	
Treasurer:	James Shearer	

GARDENS OPEN ON A SPECIFIC DATE

Heart of Scotstoun Community Garden, 64 Balmoral Street, Glasgow	Sunday, 22 May
Kilsyth Gardens, Allanfauld Road, Kilsyth	Sunday, 29 May
12 Chatelherault Avenue (The Good Life Garden), Cambuslang	Sunday, 12 June
The Gardens of Milton of Campsie, Milton of Campsie	Sunday, 19 June
Strathbungo Garden, March Street, Glasgow	Sunday, 26 June
Horatio's Garden, National Spinal Unit, Govan Road, Glasgow	Sunday, 3 July
Milton Community Garden, Liddesdale Square, Milton, Glasgow	Sunday, 10 July
Kamares, 18 Broom Road, Newton Mearns, Glasgow	Sunday, 17 July
Braehead House, 20 Braehead Road, Thorntonhall	Sunday, 24 July

GARDENS OPEN BY ARRANGEMENT

Kilsyth Gardens, Allanfauld Road, Kilsyth	1 April - 31 August

Glasgow & District

12 CHATELHERAULT AVENUE (THE GOOD LIFE GARDEN)
Cambuslang, Glasgow G72 8BJ
Paul and Sheona Brightey

The front is split into a gravel garden and a white scented woodland garden. Go through the gate to the back and you will find a garden where the aim of the owners is to grow as many different edibles as possible: herbs, soft fruit, vegetable beds, fruit arches, and edible hedging. Lots of research has revealed more unusual edibles, such as fuschia berries, cannas and hosta. There is also a greenhouse which, in addition to a very productive grapevine, helps Paul indulge his passion for growing chillies. Seven fluffy hens live here too, as well as the new addition for 2022, bees indulging in 'penthouse living' on an eye-level wild flower roof. There are two ponds, one of which has a healthy population of frogs, and the other little pond in a Victorian sink (for closer wildlife inspections). There are herbaceous perennials and a cut flower bed, a pizza oven and BBQ and around the corner is a food smoker. Lots of lovely places to sit, in the sun or the shade, in a garden that aims to be as much a living and socialising space as a productive garden.

Open: Sunday 12 June, 2pm - 5pm, admission £6.00, children free.

Directions: M74 Glasgow to Cambuslang at junction two exit onto Cambuslang Road/A724 towards Rutherglen, stay on Cambuslang Road/A724. Turn right onto Buchanan Drive, right onto Richmond Drive which become Chatelherault Avenue. Follow yellow *SGS* signs.

Opening for: MAF UK

12 Chatelherault Avenue (The Good Life Garden)

Glasgow & District

2 BRAEHEAD HOUSE
20 Braehead Road, Thorntonhall G74 5AQ
Karin and Walter Hecht

The original part of the house was built in 1775 with the main Georgian part completed in 1830. We have nurtured and developed the garden for 40 years, which has resulted in the well stocked, largely woodland garden of today, shielded by a dense circle of trees. The large rockeries and woodland beds ranging in colours of white through to blues, lavenders and pinks, to burgundies and gold, are rich in varieties of hostas, meconopses, peonies and various shrubs. They all grow under a canopy of walnut, copper beach and acers. By midsummer the garden is ablaze with agapanthus, pelargoniums and fuchsias of every shape, hue and form, with many more to see in the greenhouse.

Open: Sunday 24 July, 2pm - 5pm, admission £6.00, children free. Teas will be served and there will be a good selection of plants for sale.

Directions: Thorntonhall is signposted off the A727 between Busby, Carmunnock and East Kilbride orbital, take the A726, and then follow directions from SatNav. Locally, follow Peel Road then turn onto Braehead Road we are the second last house on Braehead Road.

Opening for: Macmillan Cancer Support

Braehead House

Glasgow & District

3 **HEART OF SCOTSTOUN COMMUNITY GARDEN**
64 Balmoral Street, Glasgow G14 0BL
June Mitchell
T: 07958 7660169

Heart of Scotstoun Community Garden has been developed into an outdoor space open to the Scotstoun community to enjoy tranquil and beautiful surroundings. The gardens feature planted flower beds, wildflower areas, orchard borders, raised beds, an activity lawn, a biodiversity garden, a Wellbeing Trail and secluded seating areas in which to sit and contemplate, surrounded by aromatic plants. Native species, ornamental trees and colourful shrubs have been planted throughout and the various areas are linked by paths with wooden arch and pergola and willow tunnel gateways inviting visitors to explore at leisure. The aspiration of the volunteer gardeners is to create interesting, often quirky, art installations using natural garden materials. To date, these include the blue painted tree, the cuckoo clock, the alcove of contemplation, four seasons gargoyles, with much more planned in the future.

Open: Sunday 22 May, 2pm - 5pm, donation £5.00, children free. Home baked teas served in The Cherry Tree Café.

Directions: A814 Dumbarton Road to junction with Queen Victoria Drive/Balmoral Street. Bus Routes 1/2/3/400.

Opening for: Heart of Scotstoun Limited

Heart of Scotstoun Community Garden

Glasgow & District

4 HORATIO'S GARDEN

National Spinal Unit, Queen Elizabeth University Hospital, Govan Road, Glasgow G51 4TF
Horatio's Garden
E: sallie@horatiosgarden.org.uk
W: Horatiosgarden.org.uk

Carefully created by acclaimed garden designer and RHS Judge, James Alexander-Sinclair, Horatio's Garden Scotland opened in 2016 and supports patients, their loved ones and NHS staff affected by spinal cord injury from across the whole of Scotland. The gardens provide peaceful, yet vibrant horticultural havens. Horatio's Garden Scotland features a woodland garden awash with striking seasonal blooms and framed by a beautiful collection of Betula pendula trees, as well as artfully planted borders, courtyard garden, gorgeous garden room, fruitful glasshouse and much more, there's plenty to explore in this thoughtful, therapeutic garden; one which rarely opens to the public and is unusually nestled right in the heart of a Greater Glasgow & Clyde NHS hospital.

Open: Sunday 3 July, 2pm - 5pm, admission £7.00, children free.

Directions: From the east or west of the city: On the M8 motorway to Junction 25, follow signs for the *Clyde Tunnel* (A739) for three-quarters of a mile, then follow signs for the *Queen Elizabeth Hospital*. Turn left into Govan Road and the hospital is on the left. From north of the River Clyde: go through the Clyde Tunnel (A739) and follow signs for the hospital. Please look at our website for the hospital estate map for directions to the garden and available parking.

Opening for: Horatio's Garden

5 KAMARES

18 Broom Road, Newton Mearns, Glasgow G77 5DN
Derek and Laura Harrison
E: laurah6367@gmail.com

Sitting in two-thirds of an acre, Kamares is a hacienda-style house surrounded by mature trees and a beautiful beech hedge. The garden has much of interest including a well-established pond, acers, Japanese grasses, colourful mixed shrubs, herbaceous borders and rare US sequoias. There are several patio gardens and a delightful courtyard with a rockery and miniature waterfall. Sculptures and topiary can be found around the garden where you are also welcome to visit the garden shed known as 'Owl Cottage'. The artist owner and her husband have had fun playing with spaces, colour and contrasting textures as an alternative canvas.

Open: Sunday 17 July, 2pm - 5pm, admission £7.00, children free. Bring your own picnic.

Directions: From the A77 heading south, turn left into Broom Estate and sharp left again into Broom Road. Kamares is the last house on the left near the top of the hill. On road parking is available beyond the house on Broom Road, Broomcroft Road, Sandringham Road and Dunvegan Avenue.

Opening for: Jewish Care Scotland

Glasgow & District

6 **KILSYTH GARDENS**
Allanfauld Road, Kilsyth G65 9DE
Mr George Murdoch, Mr and Mrs A Patrick
T: 07743 110908 E: alan.patrick3@googlemail.com

Aeolia Allanfauld Road, Kilsyth G65 9DE (Mr George Murdoch): A third-of-an-acre woodland garden developed since 1960 and designed to have something in flower every month of the year. The garden contains a large variety of mature specimen trees and shrubs, maples, primulas, hardy geraniums and herbaceous plants. Spring bulbs provide early colour and lilies and dahlias provide late season interest. There are a couple of small ponds for wildlife, two greenhouses and a fruit production area. The owners are members of the Scottish Rhododendron Society and have a collection of over 100 specimens, some grown from seed. Areas of the garden are often under development to provide something new to see and provide material for the extensive plant sale, which is all home grown.

Blackmill Allanfauld Road, Kilsyth G65 9DE (Mr and Mrs A Patrick): Across the road from Aeolia is Blackmill through which the Garrel Burn flows. The garden includes the magnificent seven-metre waterfall with its ever-changing moods throughout the year. On one side of the property, on the site of an old water-powered sickle mill, is an acre of mature specimen trees, rhododendrons and shrubs with an ornamental pond and a rock pool built into the remains of the mill building. Across the burn there is a further two acres of woodland glen with paths along the waterside offering glimpses of the many cascading waterfalls. A large area of wildflowers has been newly introduced alongside the burn. A micro-hydro scheme is on view, along with many different examples of dry stone walls. Visitors remark on the sense of tranquility and peace they experience in the garden and appreciate the works of art created from repurposed stone and salvaged material.

Open: Sunday 29 May, 2pm - 5pm. Also open by arrangement 1 April - 31 August. Admission £7.00, children free. By arrangement openings for parties of six or more. WC available but not for disabled.

Directions: Turn off the A803 into Parkburn Road up to the crossroads (parking attendant will advise on parking). The 89 bus Glasgow – Kilsyth has a stop at the crossroads a couple of minutes walk to the gardens. The nearest station is Croy, then take the bus 147 or 344 to Kilsyth. Follow *Scotland's Gardens Scheme yellow road signs.*

Opening for: Strathcarron Hospice

Kilsyth Gardens, Blackmill

Glasgow & District

7 MILTON COMMUNITY GARDEN

Liddesdale Square, Milton, Glasgow G22 7BT
North Glasgow Community Food Initiative
T: 07422 375524 E: gardens@ngcfi.org.uk
W: www.ngcfi.org.uk

This community garden is a wildlife and visitor friendly organic growing space in the heart of Milton. It offers a peaceful environment for the local community to walk through or sit in, to volunteer to help develop the space or to spend time with our gardener and landscaper to learn how to 'grow your own' or build things from recycled wood. It features a pond, a green roof, a Ridan composter, a children's garden complete with mud kitchen and willow sculptures as well as lots of raised beds bursting with fruit, vegetables and flowers.

Open: Sunday 10 July, 2pm - 5pm, admission by donation.

Directions: From the M8 leave at Junction 15 onto Springburn Road (A803). After two miles turn left into Colston Road then at the T junction turn right onto Ashgill Road. At the roundabout take the first left into Shillay Street then left into Liddesdale Place. Turn left into Liddesdale Square, garden is at the opposite corner. Parking in the square or there is on street parking. By bus take the 75 bus to Ashgill Road, get off at the back of St Augustine's Church and the square is a short walk through an alley-way.

Opening for: Milton Community Garden and Food Hub

8 STRATHBUNGO GARDEN

March Street, Glasgow G41 2PX
Frank Burns
W: facebook.com/strathbungogarden

Nestled behind Glasgow's busy main road artery to the Southside, you will happen upon a hidden walled terrace garden which marks the historical boundary to Strathbungo. It's an unexpected cottage-style city garden, showing how a piece of ground can be turned into a lovely colourful space for all the occupants of the terrace to enjoy. Inventive container planting is a key feature of this distinct urban retreat, which holds year-round interest. There are a range of fruit trees, some of which are trained as minarettes and stepovers. Why not visit Strathbungo Garden on Facebook and see what's been happening in the garden over the past months?

Open: Sunday 26 June, 2pm - 5pm, admission £4.00, children free.

Directions: From the south take the M74 to Junction 1A Polmadie. Turn left onto Polmadie Road, then turn right at the next traffic lights onto Calder Street. Proceed to Nithsdale Drive, then turn left into March Street where ample parking can be found. From the north take the M8 and join the M74, turn right into Polmadie Road at Junction 1A.

Opening for: ALVO Rural South Lanarkshire

Glasgow & District

9 THE GARDENS OF MILTON OF CAMPSIE

Milton of Campsie G66 8EA
The Gardeners of Milton of Campsie
T: 07958 760169

18 James Boyle Square (NEW) G66 8JN (Hugh and Vivian Prichard) Developed from scratch a few years ago, this peaceful, colourful garden holds a wide variety of perennial plants as well as hanging baskets, a well-stocked greenhouse and summer bedding plants which can be grown by anyone who loves gardening.

19 Maple Avenue (NEW) G66 8BB (Dr John Wallace Hinton) This south facing and sloping garden has a central wild 'meadow' with wild orchids and other wildflowers. Surrounded by trees and creepers, it gives a feeling of being in the countryside. This is a garden where grass cutting and weeding is avoided! There are seats and benches on the terraces for visitors to relax.

2 Kirton Crescent (NEW) G66 8DP (Mr and Mrs McFarlane) This very pretty cottage style garden is a great example of what can be achieved. It has lots of traditional cottage plants, and a greenhouse. The Garden Owner shows an ability to make the most of an error of measurement, in his words 'On purchasing a new garden table, our crazy paved patio was too small, we had to re-lay the area and used the pavers to build three small retaining walls.'

Attadale, 31 Birdston Road (NEW) G66 8BX (Ian and Helen McCulloch): A Victorian garden with lovely rockeries to the front. At the rear, there are borders with flowers and ferns, a raised pond and seating areas with an impressive and beautiful bank of rhododendrons in the main garden.

56 Lochiel Drive (NEW) G66 8EU (Ann Pert) A small garden with a variety of plants, including Himalayan poppies, Virginia creeper, wood anemones, mature jasmine, philadelphus, flowering currant, forsythia, herbs and many more. The balcony is made from recycled scaffold boards.

Marengo Cottage, 8 Campsie Road (NEW) G66 8EA (Angela Welsh): This garden emphasises wildlife and has many quirky features. It contains fruit trees, a vegetable patch, a small pond and if you can spot him, a topiary rabbit. The garden is surrounded by various mature trees where birds can nest and insects can hide. There are lots of nooks and crannies which will delight children.

Milton of Campsie Community Garden (NEW) Campsie Road G66 8EU: The community garden is the creation of one man covering roughly an acre of hillside beside the Glazert Water. Memorial gardens, various bespoke and unusual seating, a barbecue and pond areas, borders with local brick and willow woven fencing. It is a work in progress, the latest addition being a 'ruin' with a usable chimney. There is a steep slope down to the garden which requires caution.

Willow Cottage, 11 Lochiel Drive (NEW) G66 8EU (Glynis and Sarah Ainsworth) Our Mother and Daughter Garden has evolved over many years. This garden shows our eclectic taste which is reflected in the planting, themed garden rooms, planters, and pots. Colour, scent and texture are important aspects with several varieties of David Austin roses. The 'Indian Cottage' affords a superb view of our much-loved pond. We encourage a variety of wildlife to our garden. The honeysuckle pergola is brimming with flora and fauna. It is our hope that we have created a welcoming space that intrigues, delights and inspires all who visit.

Open: Sunday 19 June, 1am - 5pm, admission £7.00, children free. Dogs on a lead welcome in some gardens. Plant sales at 18 James Boyle Square, Marengo Cottage and Willow Cottage.

Directions: From Glasgow, Kirkintilloch, Bishopbriggs Bus numbers X85, 89, 88. By road B757 SatNav using postcode G66 8EU. There will be various parking signs posted around the village.

Opening for: Royal Free Charity: Amyloidosis Research Fund

Glasgow & District

The Gardens of Milton of Campsie, Willow Cottage

The Gardens of Milton of Campsie, Attadale

The Gardens of Milton of Campsie, 2 Kirkton Crescent

Inverness, Ross, Cromarty & Skye

Sponsored by

Investec

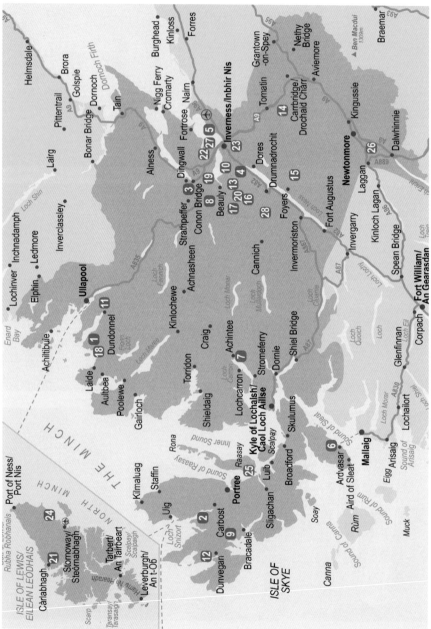

Inverness, Ross, Cromarty & Skye

OUR VOLUNTEER ORGANISERS

District Organisers:	Lucy Lister-Kaye	House of Aigas, Aigas, Beauly IV4 7AD
	Sheila Kerr	Lilac Cottage, Struy, By Beauly IV4 7JU
Area Organiser:	Emma MacKenzie	Glenkyllachy, Tomatin IV13 7YA
Treasurer:	Sheila Kerr	Lilac Cottage, Struy, By Beauly IV4 7JU

GARDENS OPEN ON A SPECIFIC DATE

Dundonnell House, Little Loch Broom, Wester Ross	Thursday, 21 April
House of Gruinard, Laide, by Achnasheen	Wednesday, 25 May
Gorthleck House Garden, Stratherrick	Daily 27 May - 5 June
Dundonnell House, Little Loch Broom, Wester Ross	Thursday, 2 June
Field House, Belladrum, Beauly	Sunday, 12 June
Old Allangrange, Munlochy	Sunday, 19 June
House of Aigas and Field Centre, by Beauly	Sunday, 26 June
Torcroft, Balnain, Glenurquhart	Mondays, 4 - 25 July
2 Durnamuck, Little Loch Broom, Wester Ross	Saturday, 9 July
7 Braes of Conon, Conon Bridge	Saturday/Sunday 9/10 July
Kiltarlity Gardens, Kiltarlity	Sunday, 17 July
Ar Dachaigh, Redhill Farm, Allanfearn, Inverness	Sunday, 24 July
House of Aigas and Field Centre, by Beauly	Sunday, 31 July
2 Durnamuck, Little Loch Broom, Wester Ross	Saturday, 20 August
Dundonnell House, Little Loch Broom, Wester Ross	Thursday, 1 September
Old Allangrange, Munlochy	Sunday, 11 September

GARDENS OPEN REGULARLY

Oldtown of Leys Garden, Inverness	1 January - 31 December (not open Thurs & Fris 1 April - 31 October)
Highland Liliums, 10 Loaneckheim, Kiltarlity	1 January - 31 December
Raasay Walled Garden, Isle of Raasay	1 January - 31 December
Abriachan Garden Nursery, Loch Ness Side	1 February - 30 November
Armadale Castle, Gardens & Museum, Armadale, Sleat, Isle of Skye	1 March - 31 October
Attadale, Strathcarron	1 April - 30 October
Dunvegan Castle and Gardens, Isle of Skye	1 April - 15 October
Glenkyllachy, Tomatin	1 April - 31 October (Mons & Tues)
Balmeanach House, Balmeanach, nr Struan, Isle of Skye	1 May - 1 October
Leathad Ard, Upper Carloway, Isle of Lewis	2 May - 30 September (not Sundays)
Pabbay House Woodland Garden, 23 Back, Isle of Lewis	2 May - 31 August (not Saturdays & Sundays)
5 Knott, Clachamish, Portree, Isle of Skye	26 June - 18 September (Mons, Fris & Suns)

Inverness, Ross, Cromarty & Skye

GARDENS OPEN BY ARRANGEMENT

Old Allangrange, Munlochy	1 January - 31 December
Glenkyllachy, Tomatin	1 April - 31 October
Berryfield House, Lentran, Inverness	1 April - 1 August
House of Aigas and Field Centre, by Beauly	1 April - 31 October
Torcroft, Balnain, Glenurquhart	1 April - 31 October
Dundonnell House, Little Loch Broom, Wester Ross	1 April - 30 September
Aultgowrie Mill, Aultgowrie, Urray, Muir of Ord	1 April - 30 September
Leathad Ard, Upper Carloway, Isle of Lewis	1 April - 30 April
5 Knott, Clachamish, Portree, Isle of Skye	1 June - 30 September
The Lookout, Kilmuir, North Kessock	1 June - 30 September (Wednesdays & Thursdays)
2 Durnamuck, Little Loch Broom, Wester Ross	1 July - 30 September
Shanvall, Glentruim, Newtonmore	1 July - 15 August
Kilcoy Castle, Redcastle, by Muir of Ord	15 August - 22 August

Field House

Inverness, Ross, Cromarty & Skye

1 2 DURNAMUCK
Little Loch Broom, Wester Ross IV23 2QZ
Will Soos and Susan Pomeroy
T: 01854 633761 E: sueandwill@icloud.com Also find us on Facebook

Our garden is south-east facing on the edge of Little Loch Broom. It is a coastal plantsman's garden with a rich mix of herbaceous borders, trees and shrubs, vegetables, drystone wall planting, South African/Mediterranean plants, a wild meadow and stunning views. Many of the plants have been collected from all over the world, and growing them has provided obvious challenges but with a pleasing outcome. Featured in 2019 entries in *Gardens Illustrated, Homes & Gardens* and the *Beechgrove Garden.* Entry in the *English Garden* magazine in September 2020. A wood and stone Wee Garden Hut accommodation soon to be available for garden passionate people. Enquiries to sueandwill@icloud.com. Small and compact but very beautiful in its own garden.

Open: Saturday 9 July, 11am - 5pm. Also open Saturday 20 August, 11am - 5pm. And open by arrangement 1 July - 30 September. Admission £5.00, children free. Teas by donation.

Directions: On the A832, between Dundonnell and Ullapool, take the turning along the single-track road signed *Badcaul*, continue to the yellow salt bin, turn right, go to the bottom of the hill and 2 Durnamuck is the house with the red roof. There is parking down by the house if needed.

Opening for: Butterfly Conservation & An Talla Solais Ullapool Visual Arts: Dolphin Arts Project

2 5 KNOTT
Clachamish, Portree, Isle of Skye IV51 9NZ
Brian and Joyce Heggie
T: 01470 582213 E: jbheggie@hotmail.co.uk
W: knottcottageselfcatering.co.uk

An informal, organic garden on a gently sloping half-acre site. Perimeter hedging has enabled a sheltered and tranquil oasis to be created. Winding paths meander through the densely planted borders filled with a diverse range of perennials, annuals and shrubs. There is also a vegetable area with raised beds and a large polytunnel. A developing wild flower meadow with sea loch views leads onto a sheltered bay and a shoreside walk to the headland. There are regular sightings of seals, otters, sea eagles and harbour porpoises. Garden seating in several locations. The garden is situated in an easily reached, particularly quiet and scenic area of Skye.

Open: 26 June - 18 September (Mondays, Fridays & Sundays), 2pm - 5pm. Also open by arrangement 1 June - 30 September. Admission £4.00, children free.

Directions: From Portree, take the A87 to Uig/Dunvegan. After approximately three miles, take the A850 towards Dunvegan. Six miles on, pass the *Treaslane* sign. Turn right on the bend at the signpost for *Knott.*

Opening for: Crossroads Care Skye & Lochalsh

Inverness, Ross, Cromarty & Skye

3 7 BRAES OF CONON
Conon Bridge IV7 8AX
Mr Nigel Stanton

This small cottage garden is a specialist's treat by a professional. After growing flowers commercially for 27 years in England, Nigel Stanton moved to the Highlands in 2014. The garden needed imported local topsoil and lots of manure. Now, seven years later, with the help of raised beds and paved paths, the fruits of his endeavours are a delight. Specialities include magnificent delphiniums, rampant sweet peas and subtly blended roses.

Open: Saturday/Sunday, 9/10 July, 2pm - 5pm, admission £4.00, children free. Teas £4.00.

Directions: Coming into Conon Bridge on the A862 from Muir of Ord, turn right into the Braes of Conon, and follow road signs to No 7. From Dingwall, take the A835 towards Tore at the Maryburgh roundabout, then turn first right towards Conon Bridge, and follow the signs.

Opening for: British Red Cross (Saturday 9 July) & Highland Hospice: Aird Branch (Sunday 10 July)

4 ABRIACHAN GARDEN NURSERY
Loch Ness Side IV3 8LA
Mr and Mrs Davidson
T: 01463 861232 E: info@lochnessgarden.com
W: www.lochnessgarden.com

This is an outstanding garden with over four acres of exciting plantings with winding paths through native woodlands. Seasonal highlights include snowdrops, hellebores, primulas, meconopsis, hardy geraniums and colour-themed summer beds. Views over Loch Ness.

Open: 1 February - 30 November, 9am - 7pm, admission £3.00, children free.

Directions: On the A82 Inverness/Drumnadrochit road, about eight miles south of Inverness.

Opening for: Highland Hospice

5 AR DACHAIGH
Redhill Farm, Allanfearn, Inverness IV2 7JA
Mrs Tina Ross
T: 07920 803410 E: tinaross463@hotmail.co.uk

This sloping garden has stunning views towards Kessock Bridge, the Black Isle, and the Great Glen. The site is very exposed and over the last three years, a lot of time and effort has been spent erecting hedging and fences to create shelter for numerous well stocked flower beds in various planting styles. There are two ponds, five decking areas and a secret nook, a large greenhouse and a large display of plants in pots.

Open: Sunday 24 July, 2pm - 5pm, admission £4.00, children free. Homemade teas £4.00

Directions: Ar Dachaigh is to be found on a farm directly off the A96, four-and-a-half miles east of Inverness. From Inverness head east along the A96. Shortly after the turn off for Alturlie, there is a turn off on the left with an old phonebox – this is the drive for Ar Dachaigh.
From the East: Once you have passed the Balloch junction, the turn off for the garden will be on your right hand side at the old telephone box. PLEASE TAKE CARE as this is a busy stretch of the A96, and there are no filter lanes. There is a railway crossing on the drive, but this will be staffed on the day.

Opening for: Teenage Cancer Trust

Inverness, Ross, Cromarty & Skye

6 ARMADALE CASTLE, GARDENS & MUSEUM
Armadale, Sleat, Isle of Skye IV45 8RS
T: 01471 844305 E: office@armadalecastle.com
W: www.armadalecastle.com

Armadale Castle Gardens sit in a magnificent setting on the southern tip of the Isle of Skye, with sweeping views over the Sound of Sleat to the mountains of Knoydart. The estate was once the seat of the Macdonalds of Sleat and is now run by a charitable trust. Visitors can enjoy 40 acres of historic woodland gardens featuring 19th century specimen trees and exotic shrubs. Formal lawns, tranquil ponds and colourful herbaceous borders are set around the romantic ruins of Armadale Castle. There's also an adventure playground, café and fascinating museum telling the story of the Highlands & Islands through the eyes of Clan Donald.

Open: 1 March - 31 October, 9:30am - 5:30pm, these dates may be subject to change. Dates and admission details can be found on the garden's website.

Directions: On the A851, close to the Armadale Ferry terminal and approx 30 minutes drive from the Skye Bridge. Public transport: Local buses from Broadford; or train to Mallaig then 25 minutes ferry to Armadale (CalMac ferries) and then a 10 minutes walk.

Opening for: Donation to SGS

Armadale Castle, Gardens & Museum

7 ATTADALE
Strathcarron IV54 8YX
Mr Ewen Macpherson
T: 01520 722603 E: info@attadalegardens.com
W: www.attadalegardens.com

The Gulf Stream, surrounding hills and rocky cliffs create a microclimate for 20 acres of outstanding water gardens, old rhododendrons, unusual trees and a fern collection in a geodesic dome. There is also a sunken fern garden developed on the site of an early 19th-century drain, a waterfall into a pool with dwarf rhododendrons, sunken garden, peace garden and kitchen garden. Other features include a conservatory, Japanese garden, sculpture collection and giant sundial.

Open: 1 April - 30 October, 10am - 5:30pm, admission £10.00, children £1.00. Seniors £8.00

Directions: On the A890 between Strathcarron and South Strome.

Opening for: The Howard Doris Centre

Inverness, Ross, Cromarty & Skye

8 AULTGOWRIE MILL
Aultgowrie, Urray, Muir of Ord IV6 7XA
Mr and Mrs John Clegg
T: 01997 433699 E: john@johnclegg.com

Aultgowrie Mill is an 18th century converted water mill set in gardens, river and woodlands of 13 acres. Features include a wooded island, a half-acre wildflower meadow and a large wildlife pond, all with views of the surrounding hills. The maturing gardens have terraces, lawns, two mixed orchards and raised vegetable beds with glasshouse and a third-of-a-mile river walk. *The Beechgrove Garden* featured this garden in July 2014. Well behaved dogs on leads welcome.

Open: by arrangement 1 April - 30 September, admission £4.50, children free.

Directions: From the south, turn left at Muir of Ord Distillery, Aultgowrie Mill is then about three miles. From the north and west, after Marybank Primary School, Aultgowrie Mill is about one-and-a-half miles up the hill.

Opening for: RNLI

9 BALMEANACH HOUSE
Balmeanach, nr Struan, Isle of Skye IV56 8FH
Mrs Arlene Macphie
T: 01470 572320 E: info@skye-holiday.com
W: www.skye-holiday.com

Very much a plantsman's garden, begun in the early 1990s after a third-of-an-acre of croft land was fenced. A shelter belt now permits a plethora of diverse plants in exuberant herbaceous borders, which give nectar and pollen to keep the buzzing and fluttering going until autumn, plus rockeries and raised beds. Native trees rub shoulders with more exotic ornamental varieties, providing a canopy for shade-loving plants and nesting sites for the many birds who make the garden their home. A small pond in a sunken garden, a large pond divided in two by a path over a culvert and a bog garden, give scope for marginal and moisture-loving plants. Meandering pathways lead through a small bluebell wood, an arbour garden, shrubbery and a small birch wood, full of azaleas and rhododendrons. Plenty of seating throughout provides an invitation to sit, relax and enjoy the garden and stunning scenery beyond.

Open: 1 May - 1 October, 10am - 3:30pm, admission £3.00, children free.

Directions: A87 to Sligachan, turn left, Balmeanach is five miles north of Struan and five miles south of Dunvegan.

Opening for: Scottish SPCA

10 BERRYFIELD HOUSE
Lentran, Inverness IV3 8RJ
Lynda Perch-Nielsen
T: 01463 831346 M: 07547 960341 E: lyndazpn@gmail.com

An open garden of trees and bushes with views across the Beauly Firth to Ben Wyvis. There are large swathes of bulbs: crocus, dogtooth violets and heritage daffodils. A three-acre wildflower meadow with meandering paths adjoins the garden giving interest until the start of autumn foliage and crocus.

Open: by arrangement 1 April - 1 August, admission by donation.

Inverness, Ross, Cromarty & Skye

Directions: Halfway between Inverness and Beauly on the A862. From Inverness, four-and-a-quarter miles on the left from crossing over the Clachnaharry railway bridge. From Beauly, one-and-a-quarter miles on the right from The Old North Inn.

Opening for: Action Medical Research

11 DUNDONNELL HOUSE

Little Loch Broom, Wester Ross IV23 2QW
Dundonnell Estates
T: 07789 390028 E: sueandwill@icloud.com

Camellias, magnolias and bulbs in spring, rhododendrons and laburnum walk in this ancient walled garden. Exciting planting in new borders gives all year colour, centred around one of the oldest yew trees in Scotland. A new water sculpture, midsummer roses, recently restored unique Victorian glass house, riverside walk, arboretum – all in the valley below the peaks of An Teallach. Champion Trees: Yew and Holly.

Open: Thursday 21 April, 2pm - 5pm. Also open Thursday 2 June, 2pm - 5pm. And open Thursday 1 September, 2pm - 5pm. And open by arrangement 1 April - 30 September. Admission £5.00, children free. Teas only available on 2 June.

Directions: Turn off the A835 at Braemore on to the A832. After 11 miles take the Badralloch turn for a half mile.

Opening for: Sylva Foundation & Euan Macdonald Centre for Motor Neurone Disease Research

12 DUNVEGAN CASTLE AND GARDENS

Isle of Skye IV55 8WF
Hugh Macleod of Macleod
T: 01470 521206 E: info@dunvegancastle.com
W: www.dunvegancastle.com

Any visit to the Isle of Skye is incomplete without enjoying the wealth of history and horticultural delights at award-winning 5* Dunvegan Castle & Gardens. The five acres of formal gardens began life in the 18th century. In stark contrast to the barren moorland and mountains which dominate Skye's landscape, the Castle's Water Garden, Round Garden, Walled Garden and woodland walks provide an oasis for an eclectic mix of flowers, exotic plants, shrubs and specimen trees, framed by shimmering pools fed from waterfalls. After visiting the Water Garden with its ornate bridges and islands replete with colourful plants along the riverbanks, wander through the elegant formal Round Garden. The Walled Garden, formerly the Castle's vegetable garden, now has a diverse range of plants and flowers completing the attractive features, including a water lily pond, garden museum, 17th century lectern sundial, glass house and the 'Dunvegan Pebble', a rotating 2.7 ton Carrara marble sculpture. The informal areas of the garden are kept wild to encourage wildlife, creating a more natural aesthetic framed by the coastal scenery. The present Chief, Hugh MacLeod, and his dedicated team of gardeners continue to build on this unique legacy for future generations to enjoy.

Open: 1 April - 15 October, 10am - 5:30pm, admission details can be found on the garden's website. Please be sure to check Dunvegan's website for up-to-date opening details before starting out because of COVID-19 restrictions.

Directions: One mile from Dunvegan village, 23 miles west of Portree. Follow the signs for *Dunvegan Castle.*

Opening for: Donation to SGS

Inverness, Ross, Cromarty & Skye

13 FIELD HOUSE
Belladrum, Beauly IV4 7BA
Mr and Mrs D Paterson
W: www.dougthegarden.co.uk

Informal country garden developed over 30 years. Set in one acre with woodland area, ponds, terraces, attractive features and hidden corners. Large variety of interesting trees, shrubs and perennials. Raised decking area with fabulous views over farmland and surrounding countryside.

Open: Sunday 12 June, 2pm - 4:30pm, admission £4.00, children free.

Directions: Four miles from Beauly on the A833 Beauly to Drumnadrochit road, then follow the signs to *Belladrum*.

Opening for: Highland Disability Sport: Swim Team

14 GLENKYLLACHY
Tomatin IV13 7YA
Mr and Mrs Philip Mackenzie
E: emmaglenkyllachy@gmail.com

In a magnificent Highland glen, at 1200 feet above sea level, Glenkyllachy offers a glorious garden of shrubs, herbaceous plants, rhododendrons, trees and spectacular views down the Findhorn River. There are some rare specimens and a recently planted arboretum. Rhododendrons and bulbs flower in May/June, herbaceous plants bloom through July/August with glorious autumn colours in September and October. Original sculptures and a Highgrove-inspired wall provide year-round interest. Featured on the *Beechgrove Garden* in 2018. We took advantage of Lockdown in 2020 to re-assess existing plant schemes and create new borders and paths. We have also extended the garden with a 'wild area' blending the garden into the beautiful birch and juniper natural hillside.

Open: 1 April - 31 October (Mondays & Tuesdays), 11am - 5pm. Also open by arrangement any time from 1 April - 31 October. Admission £5.00, children free.

Directions: Turn off the A9 at Tomatin and take the Coignafearn/Garbole single-track road down the north-side of the River Findhorn, there is a cattle grid and gate on the right 500 yards AFTER the humpback bridge and the sign to *Farr*.

Opening for: Marie Curie

15 GORTHLECK HOUSE GARDEN
Stratherrick IV2 6UJ
Steve and Katie Smith
T: 07710 325903 E: gorthleckgarden@gmail.com

Gorthleck is an unusual 20-acre woodland garden built in an unlikely place, on and around an exposed rocky ridge which offers long views of the surrounding countryside in the 'borrowed landscape' tradition of Japanese gardens. The layout of the garden works with the natural features of the landscape with numerous paths, hedges and shelter belts creating clearly defined areas where a large collection of trees and shrubs are thriving. The garden includes over 400 different varieties of rhododendrons, half of which are species, and a large variety of bamboos. It is a large garden so allow sufficient time to see it properly.

Open: Daily 27 May - 5 June, 10am - 6pm, admission £5.00, children free.

Directions: From the A9, take the B851 towards Fort Augustus to join the B862. Go through the village of Errogie where there is a sharp left-hand bend on the road. After approximately one

Inverness, Ross, Cromarty & Skye

mile, there is a small church on the left. The Gorthleck drive is directly opposite the church and the house can be seen on the hill to the left as you follow the drive to the left of the new house. Visitors can park on the verges at the top of the drive.

Opening for: Maggie's

---

16 HIGHLAND LILIUMS

10 Loaneckheim, Kiltarlity IV4 7JQ
Neil and Frances Macritchie
T: 01463 741365 E: accounts@highlandliliums.co.uk
W: www.highlandliliums.co.uk

Highland Liliums is a working retail nursery with spectacular views over the Beauly valley and Strathfarrar hills. A wide selection of home-grown plants available including alpines, ferns, grasses, herbaceous, herbs, liliums, primulas and shrubs.

Open: 1 January - 31 December, 9am - 5pm, admission free. Also open as part of Kiltarlity Gardens, on Sunday 17th July.

Directions: Signposted from Kiltarlity village, which is just off the Beauly to Drumnadrochit road (A833), approximately 12 miles from Inverness.

Opening for: Donation to SGS

---

17 HOUSE OF AIGAS AND FIELD CENTRE

by Beauly IV4 7AD
Sir John and Lady Lister-Kaye
T: 01463 782443 E: info@aigas.co.uk
W: www.aigas.co.uk

The House of Aigas has a small arboretum of named Victorian specimen trees and modern additions. The garden consists of extensive rockeries, herbaceous borders, ponds and shrubs. Aigas Field Centre rangers lead regular guided walks on nature trails through woodland, moorland and around a loch.
Champion Trees: Douglas fir, Atlas cedar and *Sequoiadendron giganteum*.

Open: Sunday 26 June, 2pm - 5pm. Also open Sunday 31 July, 2pm - 5pm. And open by arrangement 1 April - 31 October. Admission £4.00, children free. Teas by donation.

Directions: Four-and-a-half miles from Beauly on the A831 Cannich/Glen Affric road.

Opening for: Highland Hospice: Aird branch

---

18 HOUSE OF GRUINARD

Laide, by Achnasheen IV22 2NQ
The Hon Mrs A G Maclay
T: 01445 731235 E: office@houseofgruinard.com

Superb hidden and unexpected garden developed in sympathy with stunning west coast estuary location. Wide variety of interesting herbaceous and shrub borders with water garden and extended wild planting.

Open: Wednesday 25 May, 2pm - 5pm, admission £4.50, children free. Donations for teas.

Directions: On the A832, 12 miles north of Inverewe and nine miles south of Dundonnell.

Opening for: Highland Hospice

Inverness, Ross, Cromarty & Skye

19 KILCOY CASTLE
Redcastle, by Muir of Ord IV6 7RX
Kilcoy Castle Estate
T: 07766 445511

To the front of the castle are steps which lead on to grass terraces surrounded by shrubs and trees: the walled garden leads off to the east. The area farthest from the castle has been restyled based on the poem *Solitude* by Thomas Merton. The shape is rhomboid with a central point from which the design radiates, planted with pleached hornbeam, underplanted with willow. Box, holly and yew hedges are still to grow to fruition. Work is ongoing with new herbaceous border and different planting using annuals and herbaceous plants; the garden will host a further vibrant display of colourful plants within the walled garden along with a greenhouse in full production.

Open: by arrangement 15 August - 22 August, admission £6.50, children free.

Directions: From the Tore roundabout, take the A832, go past Fettes Sawmill on the left. Turn right at Kilcoy Kindergarten (an old church) heading towards Kilcoy. Go along the single track road for about a quarter of a mile and you will see the Kilcoy Castle entrance on the left.

Opening for: Nansen Highland

20 KILTARLITY GARDENS
Kiltarlity IV4 7JH
Sheila Ross, Neil and Frances Macritchie
T: 01463 741365 E: accounts@highlandliliums.co.uk
W: www.highlandliliums.co.uk

Aird View 30a Camault Muir, Kiltarlity IV4 7JH (Sheila Ross): The garden at Aird View offers a mix of borders, a water feature, an arbour and a newly added herbaceous border. There are also fruit trees and vegetable beds.
Highland Liliums 10 Loaneckheim, Kiltarlity IV4 7JQ (Neil and Frances Macritchie): Highland Liliums is a working retail nursery with spectacular views over the Beauly valley and Strathfarrar hills. A wide selection of home-grown plants are available including alpines, ferns, grasses, herbaceous, herbs, liliums, primulas and shrubs.

Open: Sunday 17 July, noon - 5pm, admission £3.00, children free. Admission tickets available at either garden. Homemade teas and discounted plants for sale at Highland Liliums

Directions: For Aird View, take the A833 Beauly to Drumnadrochit road, pass Brockies Lodge. Turn right at the bus shelter and follow the single track road to junction at school. Turn left up the hill to the top at junction. Aird View is on the right. For Highland Liliums, turn up Post Office Brae in Kiltarlity then turn right after the Free Church. Follow the road signposted to Highland Liliums.

Opening for: Highland Hospice: Aird branch

21 LEATHAD ARD
Upper Carloway, Isle of Lewis HS2 9AQ
Rowena and Stuart Oakley
T: 01851 643204 E: stuart.oakley1a@gmail.com
W: www.leathadard.org.uk

A one-acre sloping garden with stunning views over East Loch Roag. It has evolved along with the shelter hedges that divide the garden into a number of areas giving a new view at every corner. With shelter and raised beds, the different conditions created permit a wide variety of

Inverness, Ross, Cromarty & Skye

plants to be grown. Features include herbaceous borders, cutting borders, bog gardens, grass garden, exposed beds, patios, a pond and vegetables and fruit grown both in the open ground and the Keder greenhouse. Some of the vegetables are grown to show standards.

Open: 2 May - 30 September (not Sundays), 10am - 6pm. Also open by arrangement 1 April - 30 April. Admission £4.00, children free.

Directions: On the A858 Shawbost-Carloway, first right after the Carloway football pitch, and the first house on the right. By bus take the Westside circular bus, exit Stornoway, head for Carloway football pitch.

Opening for: British Red Cross

---

22 OLD ALLANGRANGE
Munlochy IV8 8NZ
J J Gladwin
T: 01463 811304 E: office@blackislegardendesign.com

The original garden surrounds an 18th-century orange lime-washed house. There is a formalish parterre in front of the house with loose planting in the individual beds, a terrace garden, lime pom pom bed planted with roses, herb garden, mound, orchard, all linked with various styles of hedges – pleached lime, yew, beech, box, holly, mixed. Recently we have started to remove perimeter wire fences and replace them with log walls and brash hedges. The hedges are treated with different degrees of formality. There is a five-acre organic vegetable garden laid out in a Triskele form, with two polytunnels. We use a no-dig system of cultivation within a permaculture design. We will also run workshops on all matters horticultural starting from 22 January.
Champion Trees: Yew and sweet chestnut.

Open: Sunday 19 June, 2pm - 5pm. Also open Sunday 11 September, 2pm - 5pm. And open by arrangement 1 January - 31 December. Admission £4.00, children free. Homemade teas by donation. Groups by arrangement, minimum of 10 people.

Directions: From Inverness head four miles north on the A9, and follow the directions for *Black Isle Brewery*. Park up at the Brewery and walk down to the garden. Directions will be given in the shop.

Opening for: Black Isle Bee Gardens

---

23 OLDTOWN OF LEYS GARDEN
Inverness IV2 6AE
David and Anne Sutherland
T: 01463 238238 E: ams@oldtownofleys.com

Established in 2003, on the outskirts of Inverness, with views over the town, this large garden of three acres has year-round interest. Spring rhododendrons and azaleas, summer herbaceous plantings, autumn trees and shrubs and winter appeal from the conifers, evergreens and structures. Features include a rockery, ponds, musical instruments, a new stumpery and, in construction for 2022, an area of prairie planting.

Open: 1 January - 31 December, dawn – dusk. Not open Thursdays & Fridays from 1st April to 31st October. Admission by donation.

Directions: Turn off southern distributor road (B8082) at Leys roundabout towards Inverarnie (B861). At the T junction turn right. After 50 meters turn right into Oldtown of Leys.

Opening for: Scotland's Gardens Scheme, Highland Hospice and Alzheimer's Scotland.

Inverness, Ross, Cromarty & Skye

24 PABBAY HOUSE WOODLAND GARDEN

Pabbay House, 23 Back, Isle of Lewis HS2 0LQ
Barbara & Boyd Mackenzie
T: 01851 820443 E: info@pabbayhouse.com
W: www.pabbayhouse.com

Pabbay House Woodland is a two-acre site on the east coast of Lewis, comprising mostly native trees and wildflowers. It incorporates all the trees associated with the mediaeval Celtic ogham. The Back burn meanders through the woods along a short walk. Visitors will find tranquility and are encouraged to bring a picnic and stay as long as they wish. Suggestions on improving the woodland are always welcome.

Open: 2 May - 31 August (not Saturdays & Sundays), 2pm - 5pm, admission £4.00, children free.

Directions: The Woodland Garden is a 20 minute drive from Stornoway on the B895 to Tolsta and its beaches. Turn left in the village of Back, just past the Free Church. Garden also on the Stornoway-Back bus route.

Opening for: Bethesda Care Home and Hospice & Scotland's Gardens Scheme SCIO

25 RAASAY WALLED GARDEN

Isle of Raasay IV40 8PB
Raasay Community
T: 07939 106426 E: raasaywalledgarden@gmail.com
W: Raasay.com/the-walled-garden-raasay

Situated behind Raasay House, a 10 minute walk from the Ferry Terminal, is the Category A listed Walled Garden. Visited by Boswell & Johnson in 1773, the garden suffered neglect before coming into Community ownership. Ongoing restoration began in 2013 and the 1.43 acre garden now supplies vegetables, fruit, salad, herbs and cut flowers to the community and visitors. Features an orchard, rose beds, polytunnels, a fruit cage, wildflowers for pollinators and insects, and plenty of seats. We have a composting toilet for visitors' use. June & July provide the most colourful time and our main produce harvests take place from May to September. We run events during the year – please check our Facebook page for details. The garden isn't always staffed, so please contact for further details.

Open: 1 January - 31 December, 10am - 5pm, admission by donation. Plants for sale occasionally, and vegetables once/twice weekly during the season.

Directions: Take the Calmac Ferry to Raasay (20 minute journey) from Sconser, between Broadford and Portree on the Isle of Skye. The garden is an easy walk from the terminal and there is plenty to do and see on foot, although cars can also cross.

Opening for: Donation to SGS

26 SHANVALL

Glentruim, Newtonmore PH20 1BE
George and Beth Alder
T: 01540 673213 E: beth.alder@yahoo.co.uk

The garden is two thirds of an acre at 900 feet above sea level, surrounding a 19th-century cottage. On the south side of the River Spey, it has lovely views of the Creag Dubh and Creag Meagaidh mountains. There are ruined buildings of an old township within the garden. To the south is a garden of roses and perennials. Within a stone wall, there are fruit cages, a small orchard and organic vegetable beds which have been cultivated for about 200 years. The garden on the north slopes has trees, shrubs, herbaceous border, wildflowers, a pond and is rich with wildlife, including woodpeckers and red squirrels.

Inverness, Ross, Cromarty & Skye

Open: by arrangement 1 July - 15 August, admission by donation. Teas included.

Directions: Shanvall is on the minor road running along the south side of the Spey, linking the A9 south of Newtonmore at Glentruim and the A889 at Catlodge. The garden gate is on the right about one-and-a-half miles from the A9. Further details on request.

Opening for: Laggan and Newtonmore Church of Scotland

27 THE LOOKOUT
Kilmuir, North Kessock IV1 3ZG
David and Penny Veitch
T: 01463 731489 E: david@veitch.biz

A three-quarter-acre, elevated coastal garden, with incredible views over the Moray Firth, which is only for the sure-footed. This award-winning garden, featured on the *The Beechgrove Garden*, has been created out of a rock base with shallow pockets of ground, planted to its advantage to encourage all aspects of wildlife. There is a small, sheltered courtyard, raised bed vegetable area, pretty cottage garden, scree and rock garden, rose arbour, rhododendrons, flowering shrubs, bamboos, trees and lily pond with waterside plants.

Open: by arrangement 1 June - 30 September (Wednesdays & Thursdays), admission £4.00, children free. Teas available on request £5.00 per head. No dogs.

Directions: From Inverness, take the North Kessock left turn from the A9, and third left at the roundabout to go on the underpass, then sharp left onto Kilmuir Road. From Tore, take the slip road for North Kessock and immediately right for Kilmuir. Follow signs for *Kilmuir* (three miles) until you reach the shore. The Lookout is near the far end of the village with a large palm tree in front, surrounded by gravel.

Opening for: Alzheimer's Research UK

28 TORCROFT
Balnain, Glenurquhart IV63 6TJ
Barbara Craig
E: barbaramcraig@gmail.com

This garden is about three-quarters of an acre on a hillside overlooking Loch Meiklie in Glen Urquhart. It is a wild garden, with its own character and style. There are weeds and cardamine for the orange-tip butterflies, but most of all there are plants in profusion from acer, anemone and astrantia to veronicastrum, verbascum, weigela and water lilies. A natural stream comes into the garden and meanders into various small ponds. In the spring there are masses of bog primula of all types and colours. There is a fern bed, a rockery, herbs, wooded area, a stumpery and another pond nearby.

Open: 4 July - 25 July (Mondays only), 2pm - 5pm. Also open by arrangement 1 April - 31 October. Admission £3.00, children free.

Directions: From Inverness turn right at Drumnadrochit and go towards Cannich. After four miles, sign *Balnain*, there is a very sharp right-hand bend with a high retaining wall on the right. At the end of the wall take the turning to the right signposted *Torcroft Lodges*.

Opening for: Munlochy Animal Aid & Send a Cow

Kincardine & Deeside

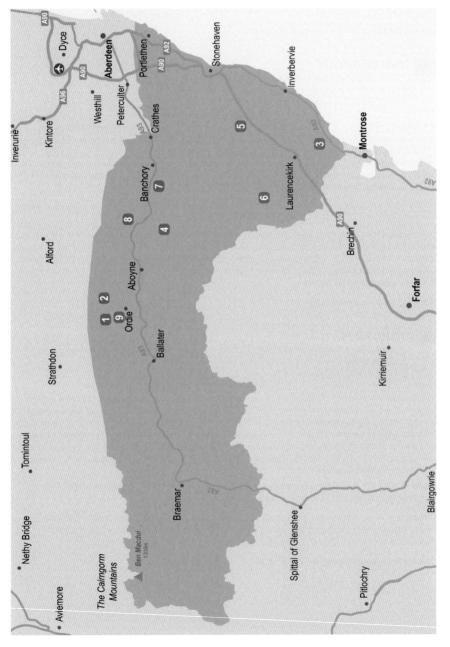

Kincardine & Deeside

OUR VOLUNTEER ORGANISERS

District Organisers:	Catherine Nichols	Westerton Steading, Dess, Aboyne AB34 5AY
	Julie Nicol	Cedarwood Lodge, Rhu-Na-Haven Road, Aboyne AB34 5JB
		E: info@scotlandsgardens.org
Area Organisers:	Wendy Buchan	Inneshewen, Dess, Aboyne AB34 5BH
	Gavin Farquhar	Ecclesgreig Castle, St Cyrus DD10 0DP
	Tina Hammond	Sunnybank, 7 Watson Street, Banchory AB31 5UB
	Liz Inglesfield	2 Earlspark Circle, Bieldside, Aberdeen AB15 9BW
	David & Patsy Younie	Bealltainn, Ballogie, Aboyne AB34 5DL
Treasurer:	Michael Buchan	Inneshewen, Dess, Aboyne AB34 5BH

GARDENS OPEN ON A SPECIFIC DATE

Ecclesgreig Castle, St Cyrus	Sunday, 6 March
Inchmarlo Retirement Village Garden, Inchmarlo, Banchory	Sunday, 22 May
Finzean House, Finzean, Banchory	Saturday, 4 June
Glensaugh, Glensaugh Lodge, Fettercairn, Laurencekirk	Sunday, 5 June
Kincardine Castle, Kincardine O'Neil	Sunday, 12 June
Dallachy, Logie Coldstone, Aboyne, Aberdeenshire	Saturday/Sunday, 18/19 June
Douneside House, Tarland	Sunday, 10 July
The Old Farmhouse, Milton of Logie, Dinnet, Aboyne	Saturday/Sunday, 30/31 July
Glenbervie House, Drumlithie, Stonehaven	Sunday, 7 August
Glensaugh, Glensaugh Lodge, Fettercairn, Laurencekirk	Sunday, 28 August

GARDENS OPEN BY ARRANGEMENT

Glenbervie House, Drumlithie, Stonehaven	1 May - 15 September

Kincardine & Deeside

1 DALLACHY
Logie Coldstone, Aboyne, Aberdeenshire AB34 5PQ
Graeme Law and Toby Johns
E: gandt5755@sky.com

A half-acre garden at 200m, with views to Morven and the hills, which has been developing from a blank canvas since 2016. It features several different areas including lawns with mixed borders, courtyard garden, scree garden, pond, small orchard/fruit garden and summer house. All are planted with a mixture of hardy trees, shrubs, perennials and bulbs to give year-round interest and to be wildlife friendly. There are several different seating areas to take advantage of the sun or shelter from the weather!

Open: Saturday/Sunday, 18/19 June, 10:30am - 4:30pm, admission £5.00, children free. Opened by timed bookings – please check Scotland's Gardens Scheme's website for details.

Directions: Take the A97 to Logie Coldstone, turn up the lane between the former church/war memorial and the old post office. Take the first left in front of 'Culharvie' onto unmade road, Dallachy is the third house on the right.

Opening for: The Seed Box Limited

2 DOUNESIDE HOUSE
Tarland AB34 4UD
The MacRobert Trust
W: www.dounesidehouse.co.uk

Douneside is the former home of Lady MacRobert, who developed these magnificent gardens in the early to mid-1900s. Ornamental borders, an Arts and Crafts themed terraced garden and water gardens surround a spectacular infinity lawn overlooking the Deeside hills. A walled garden supplies organic vegetables and cut flowers to Douneside House, which is now a multi-award winning hotel, and also houses a large ornamental greenhouse. A new arboretum displays over 130 trees amongst mown grass paths and there are many walking trails behind Douneside offering breathtaking views across the Howe of Cromar and beyond.

Open: Sunday 10 July, 2pm - 5pm, admission £5.00, children free. Concessions £3. There will be a local pipe band and raffle.

Directions: On the B9119 towards Aberdeen. Tarland one mile.

Opening for: Perennial

3 ECCLESGREIG CASTLE
St Cyrus DD10 0DP
Mr Gavin Farquhar
T: 01224 214301 E: enquiries@ecclesgreig.com
W: www.ecclesgreig.com

Ecclesgreig Castle, Victorian Gothic on a 16th-century core, is internationally famous as an inspiration for Bram Stoker's *Dracula*. The snowdrop walk (over 150 varieties of snowdrop) starts at the castle, meanders around the estate, along woodland paths and the pond, ending at the garden. In the Italian balustraded gardens, there is a 140-foot-long herbaceous border, classical statues and stunning shaped topiary with views across St Cyrus to the sea. Started from a derelict site, development continues. Also to be found in the grounds is the ancient well of St Cyrus.

Kincardine & Deeside

Open: Sunday 6 March, 1pm - 4pm for Snowdrops and Winter Walks, admission £4.00, children free.

Directions: *Ecclesgreig* will be signposted from the A92 Coast Road and from the A937 Montrose/Laurencekirk Road.

Opening for: Girlguiding Montrose District

4 FINZEAN HOUSE

Finzean, Banchory AB31 6NZ
Mr and Mrs Donald Farquharson

Finzean House was the family home of Joseph Farquharson, the Victorian landscape painter, and the garden was the backdrop for several of his paintings. The garden has lovely views over the historic holly hedge to the front of Clachnaben. There is a spring woodland garden, extensive lawns with herbaceous and shrub borders and a working cut-flower garden for late summer, alongside a recently restored pond area. A new vegetable garden was created in 2020. The garden is opening earlier in June this year so that visitors have a chance to enjoy the many azaleas and rhododendrons.

Open: Saturday 4 June, 2pm - 5pm, admission £5.00, children free.

Directions: On the B976, South Deeside Road, between Banchory and Aboyne.

Opening for: The Forget-Me-Not Club

5 GLENBERVIE HOUSE

Drumlithie, Stonehaven AB39 3YA
Mr and Mrs A Macphie

The nucleus of the beautiful present-day house dates from the 15th century with additions in the 18th and 19th centuries. There is a traditional Scottish walled garden on a slope with roses, herbaceous and annual borders along with fruit and vegetables. One wall is taken up with a Victorian-style greenhouse with many species of pot plants and climbers including peach and figs. A woodland garden by a burn is punctuated with many varieties of plants, primula to name but one.

Open: Sunday 7 August, 2pm - 5pm. Also open by arrangement 1 May - 15 September, apply in writing. Admission £5.00, children free. Please note some steep pathways and tree roots can make walking difficult in places. Gravel pathways are not accessible for electric wheelchairs. Please no dogs.

Directions: Drumlithie one mile. Garden is one-and-a-half miles off the A90.

Opening for: Scotland's Charity Air Ambulance

Kincardine & Deeside

6 **GLENSAUGH**
Glensaugh Lodge, Fettercairn, Laurencekirk AB30 1HB
Donald and Sue Barrie

Donald and Sue Barrie have been restoring the garden at Glensaugh Lodge for 16 years, bringing more of it back to life each year. A mixture of trees and shrubs provides year round interest while herbaceous planting provides colour into the autumn. Yew hedges and well-placed natural stone provide structure in the lower garden where a productive kitchen garden and polytunnel exist alongside informal borders and a sunken pond.

Open: Sunday 5 June & Sunday 28 August, 1:30pm - 4:30pm, admission £5.00, children free. No teas, but you are welcome to bring a picnic.

Directions: Three miles north of Fettercairn. Turn right off the B974 at Clatterin Brig and follow minor road signed *Drumtochty* for half a mile, then turn right into Glensaugh Farm. Follow beech avenue from the steading to Glensaugh Lodge.

Opening for: *Kincardine And Deeside Befriending*

Glensaugh

Kincardine & Deeside

7 INCHMARLO RETIREMENT VILLAGE GARDEN

Inchmarlo, Banchory AB31 4AL
Skene Enterprises (Aberdeen) Ltd
T: 01330 826242 E: info@inchmarlo-retirement.co.uk
W: www.inchmarlo-retirement.co.uk

Beautiful five-acre woodland garden filled with azaleas and rhododendrons beneath ancient Scots pines, Douglas firs and silver firs (some over 140 feet tall). Also beeches, rare and unusual trees including pindrow firs, Pere David's maple, Erman's birch and a mountain snowdrop tree. The Oriental Garden features a Karesansui, a dry slate stream designed by Peter Roger, a *RHS Chelsea* gold medal winner. The Rainbow Garden, within the keyhole-shaped purple *Prunus cerasifera* hedge, has been designed by Billy Carruthers of Binny Plants, an eight-times gold medal winner at Gardening Scotland and a regular at the RHS Chelsea Flower Show.

Open: Sunday 22 May, 1:30pm - 4:30pm, admission £5.00, children free.

Directions: From Aberdeen via North Deeside Road on the A93, one mile west of Banchory turn right at the main gate to the Inchmarlo Estate.

Opening for: Alzheimer Scotland & The Forget-Me-Not Club

8 KINCARDINE CASTLE

Kincardine O'Neil AB34 5AE
Edward and Rose Bradford

A superb series of gardens around a Victorian castle with great views across Deeside. Walled garden with a world-class laburnum walk, a mixture of herbaceous and shrub borders, vegetables and fruit trees. Extensive lawns, wildflower meadows and a thought-provoking Planetary Garden. A woodland garden with 120 varieties of rhododendrons and azaleas, many of recent planting, set amongst mature trees. A great day out.

Open: Sunday 12 June, 1:30pm - 5pm, admission £5.00, children free.

Directions: Kincardine O'Neil on the A93. Gates and lodge are opposite the village school.

Opening for: Christ Church, Kincardine O'Neil & Children 1st

9 THE OLD FARMHOUSE

Milton of Logie, Dinnet, Aboyne AB34 5LU
Roxanne Maris
E: roxannemaris@btconnect.com

A small garden of a third of an acre with big views, of *Morven* to the right and *Mount Keen* to the left. Situated on former farmland and surrounded by mature trees, the garden has been developed over the last ten years to include a 60 metre mixed-native hedge, stone dyke, small wildlife pond and year-round flowering borders as well as a sedum wildflower roof. The garden has been managed organically, specifically to encourage wildlife diversity and attract pollinating insects, as well as creating a haven for hedgehogs, squirrels and other garden visitors.

Open: Saturday/Sunday, 30/31 July, 10:30am - 4:30pm, admission £5.00, children free. Open by timed bookings. Please check Scotland's Gardens Scheme's website for details.

Directions: From the A93 at the centre of Dinnet, take the road signposted *Logie Coldstone & Strathdon*. Continue along this road for approximately two miles passing through Ordie. Turn left at the sign for Burn O Vat. Milton of Logie is located a short distance ahead on the right hand side.

Opening for: Children 1st & Maggie's

Kirkcudbrightshire

Sponsored by
⊕ Investec

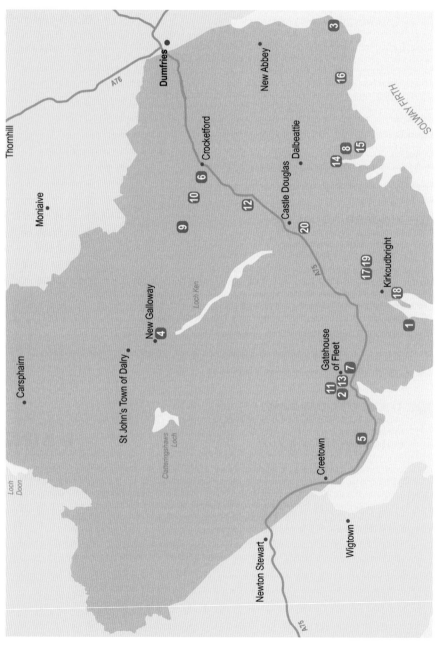

Kirkcudbrightshire

OUR VOLUNTEER ORGANISERS

District Organisers:	Theodora Stanning	Seabank, Merse Road, Dalbeattie DG5 4QH
	Julian Stanning	Seabank, Merse Road, Dalbeattie DG5 4QH
		Email: info@scotlandsgardens.org
Area Organisers:	Hedley Foster	Deer Park, Gatehouse of Fleet DG7 2DN
	May Lockhart	25 Victoria Park, Kirkcudbright DG6 4EN
	Norman McClure	142 Cotton Street, Castle Douglas DG7 1DG
	Lesley Pepper	Anwoth Old Schoolhouse, Gatehouse of Fleet DG7 2EF
	Audrey Slee	Holmview, Castle Douglas DG7 3RN
	George Thomas	Savat, Meikle Richorn, Dalbeattie DG5 4QT
District Photographers:	Stuart Littlewood	stu@f8.eclipse.co.uk
Treasurer:	Russell Allan	Braeburn, 6 Barcloy Mill, Dalbeattie DG5 4QL

GARDENS OPEN ON A SPECIFIC DATE

The Limes, Kirkcudbright	Sunday, 27 March
3 Millhall, Shore Road, Kirkcudbright	Sunday, 17 April
Balmaclellan House, Balmaclellan, Castle Douglas	Sunday, 24 April
Brooklands, Crocketford	Sunday, 1 May
Cally Gardens, Cally Avenue, Gatehouse of Fleet	Sunday, 8 May
Arbigland House, Kirkbean, Dumfries	Sunday, 15 May
The Limes, Kirkcudbright	Sunday, 22 May
Corsock House, Corsock, Castle Douglas	Sunday, 29 May
Threave Garden, Castle Douglas	Fri/Sat/Sun, 3/4/5 June
Seabank, The Merse, Rockcliffe	Sunday, 12 June
Clonyard Farm, Colvend, Dalbeattie	Sunday, 19 June
Four Gardens in Anwoth, Anwoth, Gatehouse of Fleet	Sunday, 26 June
Southwick House, Southwick	Sunday, 3 July
Crofts, Kirkpatrick Durham, Castle Douglas	Sunday, 24 July
Kings Grange House, Castle Douglas	Sunday, 31 July
Cally Gardens, Cally Avenue, Gatehouse of Fleet	Sunday, 14 August
3 Millhall, Shore Road, Kirkcudbright	Sunday, 4 September

Kirkcudbrightshire

GARDENS OPEN BY ARRANGEMENT

Stockarton, Kirkcudbright	1 January - 31 December
The Limes, Kirkcudbright	1 January - 31 December
Barholm Castle, Gatehouse of Fleet	1 February - 31 October
Anwoth Old Schoolhouse, Anwoth, Gatehouse of Fleet	15 February - 15 November
3 Millhall, Shore Road, Kirkcudbright	1 March - 31 October
Corsock House, Corsock, Castle Douglas	1 April - 30 June
Luckie Harg's, Anwoth, Gatehouse of Fleet, Castle Douglas	1 April - 31 August
Savat, Meikle Richorn, Dalbeattie	1 April - 31 October (Fridays - Mondays)
The Waterhouse Gardens at Stockarton, Kirkcudbright	1 May - 30 September
Brooklands, Crocketford	1 May - 30 September
Seabank, The Merse, Rockcliffe	28 May - 30 June
Kings Grange House, Castle Douglas	16 July - 13 August

Southwick House

Kirkcudbrightshire

1 3 MILLHALL
Shore Road, Kirkcudbright DG6 4TQ
Mr Alan Shamash
T: 01557 870352 E: shamash@freeuk.com

Impressive five-acre garden with a large collection of mature shrubs, including over 200 rhododendron species, many camellias, perennials, over 300 hydrangeas and many rare Southern Hemisphere plants. The garden has several interesting paths and is on a hillside running along the rocky shore of the Dee Estuary in Kirkcudbright Bay.

Open: Sunday 17 April, 2pm - 5pm and Sunday 4 September, 2pm - 5pm. Also open by arrangement 1 March - 31 October. Admission £5.00, children free.

Directions: On the B727 between Kirkcudbright and Borgue on the west shore of the Dee Estuary. Parking at Dhoon beach public car park, about three miles south of Kirkcudbright. There is a five-minute walk to the house. Please note there will be no vehicular access to 3 Millhall and all visitors should park at Dhoon Beach and walk up to the property.

Opening for: Kirkcudbright Hospital League Of Friends & Alzheimer's Research UK

3 Millhall

2 ANWOTH OLD SCHOOLHOUSE
Anwoth, Gatehouse of Fleet DG7 2EF
Mr and Mrs Pepper
T: 01557 814444 E: lesley.pepper@btinternet.com

Two acres of delightful cottage-style gardens behind the old schoolhouse and cottage in a picturesque setting opposite Anwoth Old Church (in ruins) and graveyard. Winding paths alongside a burn, informally planted with unusual woodland perennials and shrubs. Wildlife pond, fish pond, rock garden, vegetable garden, wildflower area and viewpoint.

Open: by arrangement 15 February - 15 November, admission £3.00, children free. Also open with **Four Gardens in Anwoth** on 26 June, 2pm - 5pm.

Directions: Driving west on the A75, take the Anwoth turn off about half a mile after Gatehouse of Fleet. Anwoth Church is about half a mile along the road and Anwoth Old Schoolhouse is a little further along, opposite Anwoth Old Church (in ruins).

Opening for: Dogs for Good

Kirkcudbrightshire

3 ARBIGLAND HOUSE

Kirkbean, Dumfries DG2 8BQ
Alistair Alcock and Wayne Whittaker
T: 01387 880764 E: alcockalistair@gmail.com
W: www.arbiglandhouseandgardens.co.uk

Arbigland House is an Adam-style 18th-century mansion surrounded by 24 acres of woodland gardens running down to a beach on the Solway Firth. The gardens date from the 18th century but the more formal areas were developed in the late 19th and early 20th centuries and are currently undergoing a programme of restoration and development. There are 200 year old trees lining the Broad Walk which runs down to the Solway and a huge variety of rhododendrons and azaleas. Within the woodland are a range of features including a stream-fed lake and a Japanese garden, with a more formal sundial garden and sunken rose garden, all in the process of renewal. Amongst these are a diverse collection of mature trees and shrubs.

Open: Sunday 15 May, 2pm - 5pm, admission £5.00, children free. Teas at John Paul Jones Museum.

Directions: Take the A710 to Kirkbean. In the village turn off towards Carsethorn and, after 200 yards, turn right and follow signs to *John Paul Jones Cottage*. After a mile or so, turn left at the T junction through white gates and down the drive through ornamental gates to Arbigland House.

Opening for: Absolute Classics

4 BALMACLELLAN HOUSE

Balmaclellan, Castle Douglas DG7 3PW
Alan and Fiona Smith
T: 01644 420227 Mob: 07769 680938 E: alan.smith12345@btinternet.com

The formal garden at Balmaclellan House sits within a six-acre woodland garden with many interesting maturing trees. This formal garden was created in 2011 on the site of a redundant tennis court. The design is based on the Balmaclellan Mirror, a very early iron age mirror made of bronze which was found nearby and is currently in the National Museum of Scotland. The mirror is represented by a raised pond with other decorative features on the original replicated by raised beds and granite setts. While the planting has been designed to give year-round colour the use of daffodils and tulips brings a vibrancy to the garden in early spring. A small wooden building dates back to 1896 and is where the resident Minister is said to have written his sermons. The woodland walks and lawned areas have stone seats at appropriate points to take in the lovely views over the Rhins of Kells.

Open: Sunday 24 April, noon - 4pm, admission £5.00, children free.

Directions: On the B7075, just off the A712 approximately 14 miles north of Castle Douglas and two miles from New Galloway.

Opening for: Glenkens Community And Arts Trust Limited

5 BARHOLM CASTLE

Gatehouse of Fleet DG7 2EZ
Drs John and Janet Brennan
T: 01557 840327 E: barholmcastle@gmail.com

Barholm Castle, a 16th-century tower, was restored from a ruin in 2006. The gardens surrounding the tower have been mostly developed from scratch and are now mature. There is a recently extended walled garden, with a gate designed by the artist blacksmith Adam Booth; a courtyard garden; a wooded ravine with huge hybrid rhododendrons from Benmore;

Kirkcudbrightshire

a pond and a large fernery with over 90 varieties of fern, including very large tree ferns; a large Victorian style greenhouse filled with succulents and tender perennials; and a large open garden with island beds of shrubs and perennials and a pond. Directly around the castle are rockeries and shrub borders. Views over Wigtown Bay are magnificent. The garden is planted for year-round colour, from February, when the castle ravine is a river of snowdrops, to October, when autumn colour is splendid.

Open: by arrangement 1 February - 31 October including for Snowdrops and Winter Walks, admission £5.00, children free.

Directions: Off the A75 at the Cairn Holy turn off, fork right three times up a steep narrow road for half-a-mile.

Opening for: Home-Start Wigtownshire

6 BROOKLANDS
Crocketford DG2 8QH
Mr and Mrs Robert Herries
T: Gardener, Holly: 07525 755178

Large old walled garden with a wide selection of plants, including some interesting shrubs and climbers and a kitchen garden. Mature woodland with many established rhododendrons and azaleas.

Open: Sunday 1 May, 2pm - 5pm. Also open by arrangement 1 May - 30 September. Admission £5.00, children free. Teas will be weather dependent.

Directions: Turn off the A712 Crocketford to New Galloway Road one mile outside Crocketford at the Gothic gatehouse (on the right travelling north).

Opening for: SGS and Beneficiaries

7 CALLY GARDENS
Cally Avenue, Gatehouse of Fleet DG7 2DJ
Kevin Hughes
T: 01557 815228 E: info@callygardens.co.uk
W: www.callygardens.co.uk

Cally Gardens and specialist Plant Centre is a treasure trove of rare and exotic hardy plants gathered worldwide. The towering 18th-century walls of the former kitchen and pleasure garden of Cally House provide shelter for informal gardens created by the famous plant collector Michael Wickenden. Plantsman Kevin Hughes took ownership in 2018 and has since brought his own large collection of magnolias, daphnes and trilliums and has also expanded on many existing plant taxa, notably paeonia, meconopsis and nerines. As an ecologist and environmentalist, Kevin has adopted a philosophy of gardening with wildlife and is creating a new grassland planting whilst making the entire garden pesticide free with notable increases in biodiversity.

Open: Sunday 8 May, 10am - 5pm and Sunday 14 August, 10am - 5pm. Admission £5.00, children free.

Directions: From Dumfries take the Gatehouse of Fleet turning off the A75, follow the B727 and turn left through the Cally Palace Hotel gateway from where the gardens are well signposted. A regular bus service will stop at the end of Cally Drive if requested.

Opening for: WWF-UK

Kirkcudbrightshire

8 CLONYARD FARM
Colvend, Dalbeattie DG5 4QW
Matthew and Pam Pumphrey
E: clonyard@btinternet.com

Informal garden around traditional stone buildings with views over pasture, wetland and a loch to mature mixed forest. There is an ornamental vegetable garden, and around the house, mixed plantings merge from sun to shade and woodland planting to provide all-year-round interest. The garden joins a wildflower meadow dominated by black knapweed and established yellow rattle. It features three species of native orchids and a former mill pond, a notable damselfly site. Both are maintained specifically to allow native wildlife and plants to thrive. There are meadow, wetland and woodland walks to two lochs and a crannog.

Open: Sunday 19 June, 2pm - 5pm, admission £5.00, children free.

Directions: On the north side of the A710 approximately four miles from the crossroads with the A711 in Dalbeattie, adjacent to Clonyard House Hotel and one mile from Colvend village. Parking at the Farm or Hotel as signposted on the day. There is a limited bus service on Sunday afternoon from Dalbeattie but current timetables should be checked. Clonyard Farm is a request stop.

Opening for: Peter Pan Moat Brae Trust & Birchvale Theatre

9 CORSOCK HOUSE
Corsock, Castle Douglas DG7 3DJ
The Ingall family
T: 01644 440250 E: jingall@hotmail.com

Corsock House garden includes an amazing variety of designed landscape, from a strictly formal walled garden, through richly planted woodlands full of different vistas, artfully designed water features and surprises to extensive lawns showing off the Bryce baronial mansion. This is an Arcadian garden with pools and temples, described by Ken Cox as 'perhaps my favourite of Scotland's many woodland gardens'.

Open: Sunday 29 May, 2pm - 5pm. Also open by arrangement 1 April - 30 June. Admission £5.00, children free.

Directions: Off the A75, Dumfries is 14 miles, Castle Douglas is ten miles, Corsock Village is half-mile on the A712.

Opening for: Corsock & Kirkpatrick Durham Church Of Scotland

10 CROFTS
Kirkpatrick Durham, Castle Douglas DG7 3HX
Mrs Andrew Dalton
T: 01556 650235 E: jenniedalton@mac.com

Victorian country-house garden with mature trees, a walled garden with fruit and vegetables and glasshouses, hydrangea garden and a pretty water garden. Delightful woodland walk, colourfully planted with bog plants, and a stream running through.

Open: Sunday 24 July, 2pm - 5pm, admission £5.00, children free.

Directions: A75 to Crocketford, then three miles on the A712 to Corsock and New Galloway.

Opening for: Corsock & Kirkpatrick Durham Church Of Scotland

Kirkcudbrightshire

11 FOUR GARDENS IN ANWOTH
Anwoth, Gatehouse of Fleet DG7 2EF
Gardeners of Anwoth

Anwoth House (NEW) Anwoth, Gatehouse of Fleet DG7 2EF (Major William Peto): Two acres of formal and woodland gardens surrounding a charming 18th century house. Recent developments have lead to the garden having distinct areas including large borders in the walled garden, a croquet lawn border, a cottage garden and a lochan with woodland stream and interesting wild flowers.
Anwoth Old Schoolhouse Anwoth, Gatehouse of Fleet DG7 2EF (Mr and Mrs Pepper): Two acres of delightful cottage-style gardens behind the old schoolhouse and cottage in a picturesque setting opposite Anwoth Old Church (in ruins) and graveyard. Winding paths alongside a burn, informally planted with unusual woodland perennials and shrubs. Wildlife pond, fish pond, rock garden, vegetable garden, wildflower area and viewpoint.
Bambastie (NEW) Anwoth, Gatehouse of Fleet DG7 2EF (Ute Weber): The garden is very much a work in progress. The site is on a south facing slope with dry stone walls inhabited by a variety of wildlife. The borders are planted with a colourful mix of perennials, wild flowers and grasses.
Bush O'Bield (NEW) Anwoth, Gatehouse of Fleet DG7 2EF (Paul and Caroline Chilcott): Newly created small garden with an aim to create privacy and shelter. The project commenced in 2016 and includes a range of shrubs, roses with perennial scented plants a particular favourite.

Open: Sunday 26 June, 2pm - 5pm, admission £5.00, children free. Parking will be in the field adjacent to Anwoth House and Teas in Anwoth Church.

Directions: Driving west on the A75, take the Anwoth turnoff about ½ a mile after Gatehouse of Fleet. Anwoth Church and Anwoth House are about ½ a mile along the road on the right and the other properties are nearby.

Opening for: Marie Curie

12 KINGS GRANGE HOUSE
Castle Douglas DG7 3EU
Christine and Peter Hickman
T: 07787 535889

An extensive garden surrounded by mature trees and shrubberies, with views to the south west over the surrounding countryside. Originally Victorian, the garden is being restored by the present owners with a colourful variety of herbaceous mixed borders, beds and rockeries, mainly to the front of the house. There are banks of daffodils and a carpet of white narcissus in the lawns and around the pergola in springtime.

Open: Sunday 31 July, 2pm - 5pm. Also open by arrangement 16 July - 13 August. Admission £5.00, children free.

Directions: Take the B794 north off the A75, two miles east of Castle Douglas. Kings Grange House is approximately one mile on the left.

Opening for: RNLI & Marie Curie

Kirkcudbrightshire

13 LUCKIE HARG'S

Anwoth, Gatehouse of Fleet, Castle Douglas DG7 2EF
Drs Carole and Ian Bainbridge
T: 01557 814141 E: luckiehargs@btinternet.com

A new and developing garden on the outskirts of Gatehouse. A rock and spring herbaceous garden with a wide range of alpines, Himalayan and New Zealand plants, rock garden, crevices, troughs, large alpine house and bulb frame. Under the extension new beds and woodland area are being developed. Small productive vegetable and fruit garden, plus a bluebell bank in May.

Open: by arrangement 1 April - 31 August, admission £5.00, children free.

Directions: From Gatehouse High Street, turn north onto Station Road, immediately west at the Fleet Bridge by The Ship Inn. After almost one mile turn left signed to *Anwoth Old Church*. Luckie Harg's is the first on the right after 400 yards. The nearest bus stop is on Gatehouse High Street, walk about 15 minutes to Luckie Harg's.

Opening for: Scottish Rock Garden Club

14 SAVAT

Meikle Richorn, Dalbeattie DG5 4QT
George Thomas
T: 01556 612863 Mob. 07866 392150 E: georgethomas6@icloud.com

A generally informal garden of about two-thirds of an acre with mature trees, exposed Dalbeattie granite and winding paths. The garden houses a unique summerhouse, artist Sue Thomas's studio and a greenhouse. Planting caters for sun to shade and dry to very moist, with shrubs – including rhododendrons, herbaceous and minimal summer bedding with an eye to keeping maintenance requirements to a minimum! There is a paved area around the house in which there are two water features, and may display potted plants.

Open: by arrangement 1 April - 31 October (Fridays to Mondays inclusive), admission £5.00, children free.

Directions: Leave Dalbeattie along the A710 south towards Kippford. After about 1.7 miles pass *Gorsebank* on the left and 200 yards further on turn right into a large lay-by. Enter the lane marked with cul de sac signs and proceed straight ahead along the paved road for about 500 yards. Limited parking is available at the property entrance. Savat is the sixth house on the left.

Opening for: SGS and Beneficiaries

Savat © George and Sue Thomas

Kirkcudbrightshire

15 SEABANK
The Merse, Rockcliffe DG5 4QH
Julian and Theodora Stanning
T: 01556 630244

This one-and-a-half-acre garden extends to the high water mark with westerly views across a wildflower meadow to the Urr Estuary, Rough Island and beyond. The house is flanked by raised beds, and overlooks a cottage style garden; peripheral plantings of mixed shrubs and perennials are interspersed with spring bulbs and summer annuals for all-year-round interest. There is a greenhouse with a range of succulents and tender plants. To the rear of the property is a new walled garden stocked with top and soft fruit, perennial vegetables (sea kale, asparagus and globe artichokes), a range of annual vegetables and flower borders. A further greenhouse is used for tomatoes and cucumbers, and has peaches growing against the back wall. A plantswoman's garden with a range of interesting and unusual plants.

Open: Sunday 12 June, 2pm - 5pm. Also open by arrangement 28 May - 30 June. Admission £5.00, children free.

Directions: Park in the public car park at Rockcliffe. Walk down the road about 50 yards towards the sea and turn left along The Merse, a private road. Seabank is the sixth house on the left.

Opening for: Marie Curie: DG5 Group

Seabank

16 SOUTHWICK HOUSE
Southwick DG2 8AH
Mr and Mrs R H L Thomas

The extensive gardens at Southwick House comprise three main areas. The first is a traditional formal walled garden with potager and large glasshouse producing a range of fruit, vegetables and cutting flowers. Adjacent to this is a hedged formal garden with herbaceous, shrub and rose beds centred around a lily pond, with roses being a notable feature. Outwith the formal gardens there is a large water garden with two connected ponds with trees, shrubs and lawns running alongside the Southwick Burn.

Open: Sunday 3 July, 2pm - 5pm, admission £5.00, children free.

Directions: On the A710 near Caulkerbush. Dalbeattie 7 miles, Dumfries 17 miles.

Opening for: Loch Arthur

Kirkcudbrightshire

17 STOCKARTON

Kirkcudbright DG6 4XS
Lt Col and Mrs Richard Cliff
T: 01557 330430

This garden was started in 1995 by Carola Cliff, a keen and knowledgeable plantswoman, and contains a collection of unusual shrubs and small trees, which are growing well. Her aim has been to create different informal gardens around a Galloway farm house, leading down to a lochan. Above the lochan there is a sweet cottage, used for holiday retreats, with its own interesting garden. In 1996 a three-acre arboretum was planted as a shelter belt and it now contains some rare oak trees.

Open: by arrangement 1 January - 31 December, admission £5.00, children free.

Directions: On the B727 Kirkcudbright to Gelston Road. Kirkcudbright three miles, Castle Douglas seven miles.

Opening for: Loch Arthur

Stockarton © Stuart Littlewood

18 THE LIMES

Kirkcudbright DG6 4XD
David and Carolyn McHale
E: carolyn.mchale@btinternet.com

This one-and-a-quarter-acre plantsman's garden has a variety of different plant habitats: woodland, dry sunny gravel beds, rock garden, crevice garden and mixed perennial and shrub borders. There is also a large productive vegetable garden. The McHales like to grow most of their plants from seed obtained through various international seed exchanges. You can expect to see a large number of unusual and exciting plants. The garden is full of colour with an abundance of spring flowers in March, and in late May and early June the meconopsis should be at their best.

Kirkcudbrightshire

Open: Sunday 27 March and Sunday 22 May, 2 - 5pm, and open by arrangement 1 January - 31 December. Admission £5.00, children free.

Directions: In Kirkcudbright go straight along St Mary Street towards Dundrennan. The Limes is on the right, about half a mile from the town centre crossroads, on the edge of the town.

Opening for: Friends Of Kirkcudbright Swimming Pool

---

19 THE WATERHOUSE GARDENS AT STOCKARTON
Kirkcudbright DG6 4XS
Martin Gould and Sharon O'Rourke
T: 01557 331266 E: waterhousekbt@aol.com
W: www.waterhousekbt.co.uk

One acre of densely planted, terraced, cottage-style gardens attached to a Galloway cottage. Three ponds surround the oak-framed eco-polehouse, The Waterhouse. Climbing roses, clematis and honeysuckles are a big feature as well as a pond-side walk. There are over 50 photos on their website. Featured on *The Beechgrove Garden* in 2007.

Open: by arrangement 1 May - 30 September, admission £5.00, children free.

Directions: On the B727 Kirkcudbright to Gelston/Dalbeattie road. Kirkcudbright is three miles and Castle Douglas is seven miles.

Opening for: Loch Arthur

---

20 THREAVE GARDEN
Castle Douglas DG7 1RX
National Trust for Scotland
T: 01556 502 575 E: threave@nts.org.uk
W: www.nts.org.uk/visit/places/threave-garden

The third year of the Threave Gardening Show coincides with the Queen's Platinum Jubilee celebrations. This three-day event with a jubilee theme at the home of the School of Heritage Gardening will offer the opportunity to gain advice and ideas from people who have innovated, transformed and developed these outstanding gardens. Exhibitors will be arranged throughout the main paths across the garden, displaying new plants, sculptures, tools and services from landscape design to garden maintenance. There will be talks and daily demonstrations on key horticultural skills and many opportunities to take tours of the garden and glasshouses. Threave House will be opening its doors to another flower 'extravaganza' which visitors can wonder at and admire. Food and drink will be supplied by Threave's catering team, with new venues throughout the garden. Don't miss out on Scotland's newest and most exciting garden festival.
Champion Trees: *Acer platanoides* 'Princeton Gold'; *Carpinus caroliniana; X Cuprocyparis leylandii* 'Picturesque' and a further 25 Scottish Champion Trees.

Open: Friday/Saturday/Sunday, 3/4/5 June, 10am - 5pm, admission £5.00, children free.

Directions: Off the A75, one mile west of Castle Douglas.

Opening for: The National Trust for Scotland: School of Heritage Gardening

Lanarkshire

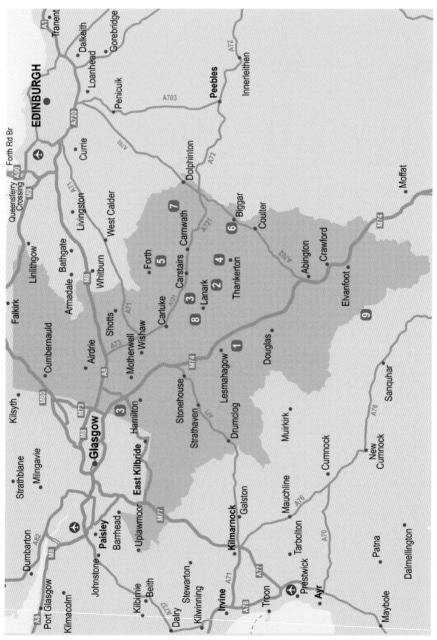

Lanarkshire

OUR VOLUNTEER ORGANISERS

District Organiser:	Vanessa Rogers	1 Larkspur Way, Carluke, Lanarkshire ML8 5TD E: info@scotlandsgardens.org
Area Organisers:	Nicky Eliott Lockhart	Stable House, Cleghorn Farm, Lanark ML11 7RW
District Photographer:	Alistair McNeill	57 Sheriflats Rd, Thankerton, Biggar ML12 6PA
Treasurer:	Sheila Munro Tulloch	Castlegait House, Lanarkshire ML10 6FF

GARDENS OPEN ON A SPECIFIC DATE

Cleghorn, Stable House, Cleghorn Farm, Lanark	Sunday, 6 March
Old Farm Cottage, The Ladywell, Nemphlar	Sunday, 10 April
Dippoolbank Cottage, Carnwath	Sunday, 19 June
Lindsaylands, Biggar	Sunday, 26 June
Little Sparta, Stonypath, Dunsyre	Tuesday, 28 June
Little Sparta, Stonypath, Dunsyre	Tuesday, 5 July
Old Manse Wild Garden, Old Manse, Wanlockhead	Saturday/Sunday, 9/10 July
Little Sparta, Stonypath, Dunsyre	Tuesday, 30 August
Little Sparta, Stonypath, Dunsyre	Tuesday, 6 September

GARDENS OPEN BY ARRANGEMENT

Carmichael Mill, Hyndford Bridge, Lanark	1 January - 31 December
Cleghorn, Stable House, Cleghorn Farm, Lanark	1 March - 31 March
Old Farm Cottage, The Ladywell, Nemphlar, Lanark	1 April - 30 September
Covington House, Covington Road, Thankerton, Biggar	1 June - 31 August
Auchlochan Walled Garden, New Trows Road, Lesmahagow	19 June - 31 October

Lanarkshire

1 AUCHLOCHAN WALLED GARDEN
New Trows Road, Lesmahagow, Lanarkshire ML11 0GS
MHA Auchlochan Garden Village
T: 01555 893592 E: auchlochan.enquiries@mha.org.uk

The Walled Garden at Auchlochan Garden Village was created at the turn of the century as a kitchen garden to service Auchlochan House. The garden, which is located within 50 acres of landscaped parkland and small lochan, has evolved over the years and now has interesting mixed planting, within a traditional framework. Around every corner you will find a mass of summer colour with lots of lovely shaded seating areas from which to appreciate the wide variety of plants on offer. The central walkway is of particular note. Adjacent to the garden is a large lily pond offering picturesque views of the terraces beyond.

Open: by arrangement 19 June - 31 October, admission £5.00, children free.

Directions: Exit the M74 at Junction 9 and follow signs to *Lesmahagow Village.* Once on the High Street take New Trows Road, opposite the Bank of Scotland, keep on this road for two miles. Follow the brown tourist signs to *Auchlochan Garden Village.*

Opening for: MHA Auchlochan

Auchlochan Walled Garden

2 CARMICHAEL MILL
Hyndford Bridge, Lanark ML11 8SJ
Chris, Ken and Gemma Fawell
T: 01555 665880 E: ken.fawell@btinternet.com

Gardens developed over the last 30 years surrounding the last workable water mill in Clydesdale. The water wheel will be rotating, river levels permitting. A large collection of over 200 different ornamental trees with shrubs and herbaceous plants, as well as a large vegetable and fruit garden. The mill lade (stream) flows through the centre, providing diverse habitats including candelabra primula in late May. Large collection of tulips and narcissi in early spring followed by glorious displays of flowering cherry and crab apple. Wildlife protection and enhancement are priorities. Also visible are archaeological remains of the medieval grain milling, flax processing and a foundry. (The bell in Carmichael village was made here.)

Open: by arrangement 1 January - 31 December, admission £5.00, children free.

Directions: Just off the A73 Lanark to Biggar road, a half-mile east of the Hyndford Bridge.

Opening for: Donation to SGS

Lanarkshire

3 **CLEGHORN**
Stable House, Cleghorn Farm, Lanark ML11 7RN
Mr and Mrs R Eliott Lockhart
T: 01555 663792 E: eliottlockhart.nicky@gmail.com
W: www.cleghornestategardens.com

Eighteenth-century garden gradually being returned to its former layout. Lawns with mature trees, shrubs, abundant snowdrops and a woodland walk along the valley, formed by 12th-century dams that were originally built to form fish ponds. The valley has been totally cleared in the last couple of years and the burn and snowdrops are now visible from both sides of the valley. Visitors are welcome to return when the daffodils are in flower.

Open: Sunday 6 March, 2pm - 5pm for Snowdrops and Winter Walks. Also open by arrangement 1 March - 31 March. Admission by donation.

Directions: Cleghorn Farm is situated two-miles north of Lanark off the A706.

Opening for: Marie Curie

4 **COVINGTON HOUSE**
Covington Road, Thankerton, Biggar ML12 6NE
Angus and Angela Milner-Brown
T: 01899 308024 E: angela@therathouse.com

Covington House stands within both traditional and formal gardens, including an 18th-century walled garden containing a potager, fruit cages and alpine garden. The owners have added touches of humour, with assorted sculpture. Can you find all the hidden serpents? A fernery and hosta garden can be found within one of two small areas of broadleaved woodland. The original glebe lands are managed as a wildflower meadow, best seen in June or July. Visitors are welcome to bring a picnic and sit in the meadow or on the lawns. Biodiversity is deliberately being allowed to flourish, in part to help the honeybee apiary near the house, but also to encourage moths, bumblebees and butterflies.

Open: by arrangement 1 June - 31 August, admission £5.00, children free.

Directions: One mile along Covington Road from Thankerton on the left.

Opening for: Bumblebee Conservation Trust

5 **DIPPOOLBANK COTTAGE**
Carnwath ML11 8LP
Mr Allan Brash

Artist's intriguing cottage garden. Vegetables are grown in small beds. There are herbs, fruit, flowers and a pond in woodland area with a treehouse and summerhouse. This is an organic garden that was mainly constructed with recycled materials. The highlight of your visit will be the stunning display of a Meconopsis cultivar, first discovered here a few years ago and now named Meconopsis 'Dippoolbank'.

Open: Sunday 19 June, 2pm - 6pm, admission £4.00, children free.

Directions: Off the B7016 between Forth and Carnwath near the village of Braehead on the Auchengray road. Approximately eight miles from Lanark. Well signposted.

Opening for: The Little Haven (Forth)

Lanarkshire

6 **LINDSAYLANDS**
Biggar ML12 6NR
Steve and Alison Crichton

Lindsaylands was designed by the well known Scottish architect William Leiper and although built in 1869 it incorporates a much older building. The garden which complements the, house features a collection of mature specimen trees set amongst extensive lawns. There are herbaceous borders, a beautiful Nepeta walkway, a working kitchen garden, greenhouses and woodland walks.

Open: Sunday 26 June, 1:30am - 5:30pm, admission £5.00, children free.

Directions: On Lindsaylands Road half a mile south west of Biggar.

Opening for: Scottish Autism & Cats Protection

7 **LITTLE SPARTA**
Stonypath, Dunsyre ML11 8NG
Laura Robertson
T: 07826 495677 E: contact@littlesparta.org.uk
W: www.littlesparta.org.uk

Little Sparta is Ian Hamilton Finlay's greatest work of art. Ian and Sue Finlay moved to the farm of Stonypath in 1966 and began to create what would become an internationally acclaimed garden across seven acres of a wild and exposed moorland site. Collaborating with stone carvers, letterers and other artists and poets, the numerous sculptures and artworks created by Finlay explore themes as diverse as the sea and its fishing fleets, our relationship to nature, classical antiquity, the French Revolution and the Second World War. Individual poetic and sculptural elements, in wood, stone and metal, are sited in relation to carefully structured landscaping and planting. Please note that there is a 700m uphill walk from the car park and livestock grazing in the fields. For visitors with limited mobility, it may be possible to book a space near the house; call the garden for details.

Open: Tuesday 28 June, Tuesday 5 July, Tuesday 30 August, and Tuesday 6 September, 1pm - 4pm. Admission £9.00, children aged three to fifteen £5.00. Book Tuesday openings via the Scotland's Gardens Scheme's website. Last entry 3pm.

Directions: Check www.littlesparta.org.uk/visit for directions.

Opening for: Little Sparta Trust

8 **OLD FARM COTTAGE**
The Ladywell, Nemphlar, Lanark ML11 9GX
Ian and Anne Sinclair
T: 01555 663345 M: 07833 204180 E: anniesinclair58@gmail.com

If you are visiting the Clyde Valley please take a short detour to visit this garden that sits on the Nemphlar Spur of the Clyde Walkway, less than two miles outside Lanark. There are many beautiful walks in this vicinity and you will be welcome to take a rest or bring a picnic to this green haven. Ian and Anne Sinclair have been developing the garden for over twenty years and, as Ian is an experienced beekeeper, the garden has evolved to attract wildlife and pollinating insects. The general planting consists of a wide variety of trees, bushes, spring bulbs and mixed borders. The wildlife garden also offers mown paths through grassed areas plus features such as a putting green, a summer-house, beetle banks and a pond. This delightful one-acre garden has always something of interest from springtime until autumn.

Lanarkshire

Open: Sunday 10 April, 11am - 4pm for daffodils. Also open by arrangement 1 April - 30 September, admission £4.00, children free. Other opening dates to be confirmed on Scotland's Gardens Scheme's website later in the season. Look our for a mid-August Fun Day with tents and tepees and an autumn plant sale. Gardening and walking groups are welcome by arrangement. Refreshments are available for an additional donation. There will be a season ticket available for £20, which allows five visits and you can bring a friend at no extra charge. In addition, the garden owners are offering the opportunity for small groups to have photographs taken for family birthdays or celebrations with the garden setting as a backdrop. Please contact the owners directly to arrange in advance.

Directions: Leave the A73 at Cartland Bridge (Lanark to Carluke Road) or the A72 (Clyde Valley Road) at Crossford. Both routes are well signposted. The garden is on the Nemphlar spur of the Clyde Walkway, just off the West Nemphlar Road on Ladywell Lane.

Opening for: Parkinsons Self Help Group

9 OLD MANSE WILD GARDEN
Old Manse, Wanlockhead, Biggar ML12 6UR
Callum Gough
T: 07717 768324 E: callum.gough@exel.net

Featured in the *Scotsman* and on *Border television*. It is recognised that gardening at 1530 feet is not easy but this fascinating garden is exceptional. Extending to about one acre, it is divided into many intriguing and sometimes quirky rooms, each one very different from the next and hugely biodiverse. The owner has an interest in permaculture and the garden is dedicated to providing habitats for wildlife (the entire ecosystem for some species), in particular amphibians and all types of insects including butterflies and bees. The garden is enjoyed all year round by people and wildlife alike.

Open: Saturday/Sunday, 9/10 July, noon - 5pm, admission £5.00, children free. Not suitable for visitors with limited mobility. Stout shoes recommended. In an area of great interest, the Mining museum in Wanlockhead has a Mine and Visitors' Centre.

Directions: Leave the M74 at Junction 13 follow signs to Abington, through the village signposted *Leadhills*. From the A76 Sanquhar/Thornhill road take the turn near Mennock signposted *Wanlockhead*. Buses available from Sanquhar and Lanark.

Opening for: Leadhills Reading Society & Scottish Mountain Rescue

Old Manse Wild Garden

Moray & Nairn

Sponsored by

Investec

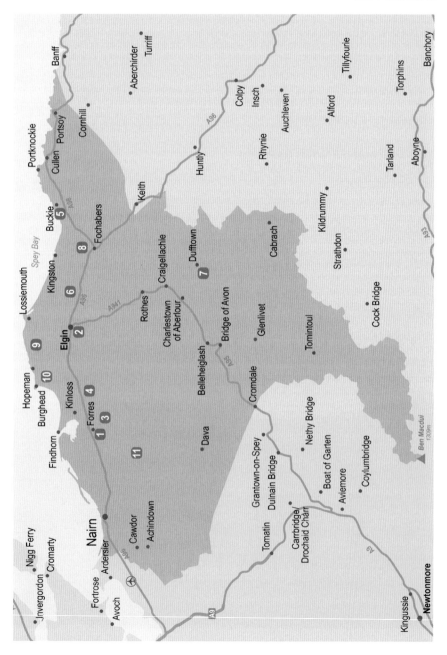

Moray & Nairn

OUR VOLUNTEER ORGANISERS

District Organiser:	James Byatt	Lochview Cottage, Scarffbanks, Elgin IV30 5PQ E: info@scotlandsgardens.org
Area Organisers:	Michael Barnett	Drumdelnies, Nairn IV12 5NT
	Lorraine Dingwall	10 Pilmuir Road West, Forres IV36 2HL
	David Hetherington	Haugh Garden, College of Roseisle IV30 5YE
	Gwynne Hetherington	Haugh Garden, College of Roseisle IV30 5YE
	Annie Stewart	33 Albert Street, Nairn IV12 4HF
Treasurer:	David Barnett	196 Findhorn, Forres IV36 3YN

GARDENS OPEN ON A SPECIFIC DATE

Gordonstoun, Duffus, near Elgin	Sunday, 26 June
Haugh Garden, College of Roseisle	Sunday, 26 June
Glebe House, Main Street, Urquhart	Sunday, 17 July
Gordon Castle Walled Garden, Fochabers, Moray	Sunday, 17 July
Haugh Garden, College of Roseisle	Sunday, 24 July
Cuthberts Brae, 84 Seatown, Buckie	Saturday/Sunday, 30/31 July
Glenrinnes Lodge, Dufftown, Keith, Banffshire	Sunday, 31 July
An-Grianan, Rafford, Forres	Saturday/Sunday, 20/21 August
55 South Guildry Street, Elgin	Saturday, 20 August

GARDENS OPEN REGULARLY

Gordon Castle Walled Garden, Fochabers, Moray	3 January - 31 December
Burgie Arboretum, Between Forres and Elgin	1 April - 31 October
Logie House, Dunphail, Forres	1 April - 31 December

GARDENS OPEN BY ARRANGEMENT

10 Pilmuir Road West, Forres	25 January - 11 March
Haugh Garden, College of Roseisle	1 May - 31 August
10 Pilmuir Road West, Forres	1 June - 1 August

Moray & Nairn

1 10 PILMUIR ROAD WEST
Forres IV36 2HL
Mrs Lorraine Dingwall
T: 01309 674634 E: fixandig@aol.com

Plantswoman's small town garden with over 300 cultivars of hostas, an extensive collection of hardy geraniums together with many other unusual plants. Managed entirely without the use of artificial fertilisers or chemicals, the owner encourages hedgehogs, toads and wild birds to control slugs. In early spring there are approximately 150 named snowdrops to be seen, some of which are very rare.

Open: by arrangement 25 January - 11 March for Snowdrops and Winter Walks. Also open by arrangement 1 June - 1 August. Admission £4.00, children free. There is a well stocked sales area.

Directions: From Tesco roundabout at Forres continue along Nairn Road. Take the first left onto Ramflat Road, then go right at the bottom and first left onto Pilmuir Road West.

Opening for: Macmillan Cancer Support

2 55 SOUTH GUILDRY STREET
Elgin IV30 1QN
Cate Bulmer
E: catebulmer@gmail.com

Located in the centre of Elgin, this, my very first garden, has been developing from a blank canvas since 2018, often with the aid of a head torch in between NHS shift work. Visitors describe it as a tranquil, lush and verdant secret sanctuary. Using hardy perennials mostly from local nurseries, this small space (60m2) includes tiny pockets of woodland, fern, bog, and sunny border areas in which I am continuously experimenting and building my knowledge. From the early trilliums, martagon lilies and irises, to the ligularia and crocosmia of late summer, to feel completely enveloped in the energy of plants is the perfect antidote to stress and anxiety. I would love for others to enjoy it too, and beginners to be inspired by what can be created with little knowledge in a small town garden, using our fantastic local nurseries.

Open: Saturday 20 August, noon - 5pm, admission £3.00, children free.

Directions: From the west follow the A96 into Elgin and turn right onto the A941 at the second roundabout. From the east, again follow the A96 through the town and turn left onto the A941. You can park in Lidl's car park and the garden is a few minutes walk up South Guildry Street on the right. Parking is also available at Moray College, also a short walk away. Elgin station is almost opposite the street, so it is easily accessible by train, or a 15 minute walk from Elgin bus station. There is one disabled parking space close by on South Guildry Street. The garden has gravel paths and two steps.

Opening for: Doctors' Support Network

3 AN-GRIANAN
Rafford, Forres IV36 2RT
Susan and Howard Stollar
T: 07843 795053 E: susan.mccrone@gmail.com

Delightful, four-acre garden. There are beautiful herbaceous borders which will appeal to the beginner and connoisseur alike; a herb area and rockery, as well as a mature orchard, organic vegetable garden and polytunnel which supply the owners with fresh food all year round. Enjoy a tranquil walk through semi-mature woodland and enjoy the abundant birdsong and the sight of the wild flowers growing freely in the meadow and wooded areas.

Moray & Nairn

Open: Saturday/Sunday, 20/21 August, 11am - 3pm, admission £5.00, children free.

Directions: Head out of Forres on St Leonards Road towards Rafford. In Lower Rafford, take the sharp right for Dallas Dhu Distillery. An-Grianan is approximately three quarters of a mile along this road on the right.

Opening for: Guide Dogs & Rangjung Yeshe Gomde Trust: Scotland

4 BURGIE ARBORETUM
Between Forres and Elgin IV36 2QU
Hamish Lochore
T: 01343 850231 E: hamish@burgie.org

A rare opportunity to see a sizeable woodland garden/arboretum in its infancy. It has a good collection of rhododendrons, Sorbus, alder, birch and Tilia but also includes many unusual trees from around the world. The arboretum is zoned into geographic areas and species type. It includes a Japanese Garden, bog garden, bog wood, loch and quarry garden. First created in 2005 and is ongoing. Most plants are grown from hand-collected seed and propagated in the Georgian greenhouse.

Open: 1 April - 31 October, 8am - 5pm, admission £4.00, children free.

Directions: A96 between Forres and Elgin. Four miles east of Forres. Six miles west of Elgin. Sign to *Burgie Mains* along the A96 is set in wrought iron decorated with horses and cattle. South off the main road and one mile to the Woodland Garden car park.

Opening for: Sandpiper Trust

Burgie Arboretum

Moray & Nairn

5 CUTHBERTS BRAE

84 Seatown, Buckie AB56 1JS
Elizabeth and Malcolm Schofield
T: 07878 486093 E: malcolmsgsp@gmail.com
W: www.instagram.com/cuthbertsbrae_garden

Gardeners' World Magazine, **Readers' Garden of the Year 2020, Judges' Choice Winner.** *'In the small seaside town of Buckie in the north east Moray Coast, what was once a wild hill, overgrown with brambles, has now been transformed into a beautiful colourful haven for all to admire.'* – Gardeners' World Magazine. The garden is sited on a steep hill with a small flat terrace with gravel garden wrapping around the house. The path then takes you down the bank into a terraced cottage garden that is a magnet for bees, butterflies and other wildlife. As you continue into the newer section of the garden you discover the greenhouse, rabbit enclosure and veg beds. *'This garden is a really good lesson in what you can achieve in inhospitable conditions with limited knowledge and money.'* – Alan Titchmarsh.

Open: Saturday/Sunday, 30/31 July, 2pm - 5pm, admission £4.00, children free.

Directions: Arriving from the Tesco road turn left at the Town Square. Take the next right. Use the car park at the *Seatown* sign. Follow the signage to our garden. The garden is a short walk (five minutes) from the Town Square.

Opening for: Scottish Association For Mental Health

Cuthberts Brae

Moray & Nairn

6 GLEBE HOUSE
Main Street, Urquhart IV30 8LG
Melanie Collett
E: mel.collett2015@outlook.com

Early 19th-century formal walled garden of the former manse by Alexander Forteath, also incorporating a unique doocot in its construction of clay dab. The garden consists of colourful herbaceous borders within the walled garden and box hedge symmetry. A wide variety of roses together with an orchard and kitchen garden area to the south.

Open: Sunday 17 July, 2pm - 4:30pm, admission £5.00, children free.

Directions: Off the main street in Urquhart, find the walled entrance at the end of the street. Follow parking signs.

Opening for: The Royal Air Force Benevolent Fund

7 GLENRINNES LODGE
Dufftown, Keith, Banffshire AB55 4BS
Mrs Kathleen Locke
T: 01340 820384
W: www.glenrinnes.com

The garden and policies surrounding Glenrinnes Lodge are typical of a Victorian lodge. There is a semi-formal garden that lends itself to quiet reflection with stunning views up Glenrinnes. A walled kitchen garden, with a large, heated greenhouse, supplies plants, cut flowers and fruit and vegetables. There is also a newly-developed herbaceous border displaying vibrant colours through the use of perennial and half-hardy plantings. There are delightful walks in the meadow around the pond and into the woodland; watch out for red squirrels! Some major works have been undertaken recently which include the Baltic wheel labyrinth and much of the garden is still a 'work in progress'. In keeping with the rest of the estate, Glenrinnes Lodge is gardened following organic principles.

Open: Sunday 31 July, 2pm - 5pm, admission £5.00, children free.

Directions: In the centre of Dufftown at the Clock Tower take the B9009 road to Tomintoul for about one mile. After passing Dufftown Golf Club on your right there is a lane to the left, which leads to two stone pillars to Glenrinnes Lodge.

Opening for: Alzheimer's Research UK

Glenrinnes Lodge © Damon Powell

Moray & Nairn

8 GORDON CASTLE WALLED GARDEN

Fochabers, Moray IV32 7PQ
Angus and Zara Gordon Lennox
T: 01343 612317 E: info@gordoncastlescotland.com
W: www.gordoncastle.co.uk

At almost eight acres in size, Gordon Castle has one of the oldest and largest walled gardens in Britain. Lovingly restored to its former glory with a modern design by award-winning designer Arne Maynard, this beautiful garden is overflowing with vegetables, fruit, herbs, and cut flowers. The onsite cafe has a 'Plant, Pick, Plate' ethos using wonderful fresh produce grown in the garden. There is a children's natural play area and shop.

Open: Sunday 17th July, adults £8.00 and children £4.00. Also open 1 April - 31 October 10am - 4pm at the same price. From November to March 10am - 4pm, adult entry is £4.00 and children, £2.00.

Directions: The main entrance is at the western end of the village of Fochabers, just off the A96, nine miles east of Elgin and 12 miles west of Keith.

Opening for: Gordon Lennox Fochabers Trust: Sunday 17 July

Gordon Castle Walled Garden

9 GORDONSTOUN

Duffus, near Elgin IV30 5RF
Gordonstoun School
E: principalpa@gordonstoun.org.uk
W: www.gordonstoun.org.uk

Gordonstoun is famous for educating the Royal family, but its history dates much further back, including the 18th century Georgian home of the first marquis of Huntly. The school gardens consist of formal herbaceous borders, an ornamental lake and an apple orchard. Visitors will also be given a guided tour of the extensive school grounds including the unique 'Round Square' former farm building (now boarding house) which has an unusual echo and can stroll down the 'silent walk' to the 17th century kirk where former students including HRH Prince Philip would have worshipped.

Open: Sunday 26 June, 2pm - 5pm, admission £8.00, children free.

Directions: Entrance off B9012, four miles from Elgin at Duffus village.

Opening for: SGS and Beneficiaries

Moray & Nairn

10 HAUGH GARDEN
College of Roseisle IV30 5YE
Gwynne and David Hetherington
T: 01343 835790

Within our previously unmaintained two-acre hidden garden, we have created four different environments. Our mature woodland, with informal pond and 18th century farmhouse ruin, is filled with birdsong, insects and wildlife. Walks meander through early flowering snowdrops followed by hellebores, tulips and narcissi. Extensive herbaceous borders enclosing the lawns and orchard display vibrant colours. Various paths wind their way through young pine and birch woodland underplanted with shrubs and meadow areas. Lastly, our organic vegetable beds, soft fruit and polytunnel keep us self-sufficient all year round.

Open: Sunday 26 June & Sunday 24 July, 2pm - 5pm. Also open by arrangement 1 May - 31 August. Admission £5.00, children free.

Directions: From Elgin take the A96 west, then the B9013 Burghead Road to the crossroads at the centre of College of Roseisle. The garden is on the right, enter from the Duffus Road. Car parking at the village hall off Kinloss road. Drop off and disabled parking is available at the house.

Opening for: CHAS & Alzheimer Scotland

11 LOGIE HOUSE
Dunphail, Forres IV36 2QN
Alasdair and Panny Laing
E: panny@logie.co.uk
W: www.logie.co.uk

Originally a traditional formal garden, Logie House walled garden has been developed since 1991 with emphasis on trees, shrubs and hardy perennials, giving all-year-round interest. The meandering burn and dry stone walls support the creation of a wide variety of planting habitats from dry sunny banks to damp shady areas. Many of the unusual plants are propagated for sale in the Garden Shop at Logie Steading. Also features woodland and river walks.

Open: 1 April - 31 December, 10am - 5pm, admission £2.00, children free.

Directions: Six miles south of Forres off the A940. Follow signs to *Logie Steading*.

Opening for: Donation to SGS

Logie House

Peeblesshire & Tweeddale

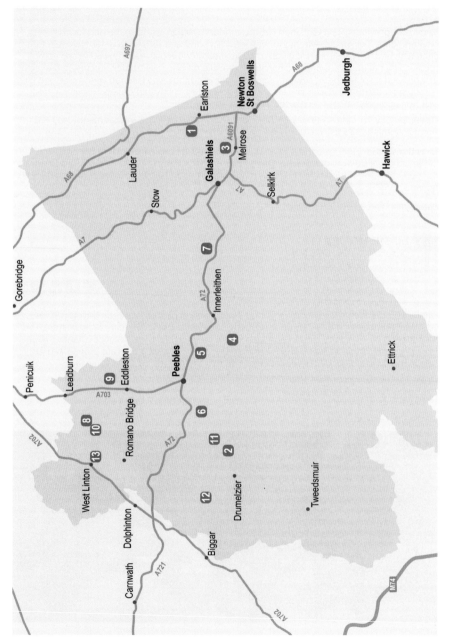

Peeblesshire & Tweeddale

OUR VOLUNTEER ORGANISERS

District Organiser:	Lesley McDavid	Braedon, Medwyn Road, West Linton EH46 7HA E: info@scotlandsgardens.org
Deputy District Organiser::	John Bracken	Gowan Lea, Croft Road, West Linton EH46 7DZ
Area Organisers:	Jennifer Barr Jenny Litherland	Allerly, Gattonside, Melrose TD6 9LT Laidlawstiel House, Clovenfords TD1 1TJ

GARDENS OPEN ON A SPECIFIC DATE

Kirkton Manor House, Peebles	Wednesdays, 16 February - 27 April
Kailzie Gardens, Kailzie Gardens	Sunday, 6 March
Quercus Garden Plants, Whitmuir Farm, West Linton	Sunday, 29 May
Laidlawstiel House, Clovenfords, Galashiels	Thursday, 2 June
Lamancha Community Hub Plant Sale, Old Moffat Road, Lamancha	Sunday, 5 June
Stobo Japanese Water Garden, Stobo Farm, Stobo	Sunday, 5 June
The Potting Shed, Broughton Place, Broughton, Biggar	Wednesdays, 8 June - 6 July
West Linton Village Gardens, West Linton	Sunday, 12 June
Laidlawstiel House, Clovenfords, Galashiels	Wednesday, 15 June
Portmore, Eddleston	Wednesdays, 6 July - 31 August
Carolside, Earlston	Saturday, 16 July
Glen House, Glen Estate, Innerleithen	Sunday, 17 July
Kailzie Gardens, Kailzie Gardens	Sunday, 24 July
Gattonside Village Gardens, Gattonside	Sunday, 31 July
Quercus Garden Plants, Whitmuir Farm, West Linton	Sunday, 21 August
Laidlawstiel House, Clovenfords, Galashiels	Wednesday, 31 August
Dawyck Botanic Garden, Stobo	Sunday, 9 October
Stobo Japanese Water Garden, Stobo Farm, Stobo	Sunday, 9 October

GARDENS OPEN BY ARRANGEMENT

Kirkton Manor House, Peebles	1 May - 14 July
The Potting Shed, Broughton Place, Broughton, Biggar	1 May - 31 October
Portmore, Eddleston	1 June - 31 August

Peeblesshire & Tweeddale

1 CAROLSIDE

Earlston TD4 6AL
Mr and Mrs Anthony Foyle
T: 01896 849272 E: info@carolside.com
W: www.carolside.com

A traditional and romantic garden set in a beautiful 18th century landscape, comprising lawns, shrubberies, mixed borders, a secret garden, winter garden, herb and hidden garden and an apple orchard of wild flowers. The oval walled garden contains herbaceous borders, fruits, vegetables, parterres and an historically important collection of roses. Carolside is best known for its roses, soft delicate herbaceous planting and design of rooms. Kenneth Cox in his book *Scotland for Gardeners* describes Carolside as 'one of Scotland's finest private gardens'. National Plant Collection: Pre 19th century Gallica Roses.

Open: Saturday 16 July, 11am - 5pm, admission £6.00, children free. Dogs on leads in the park only.

Directions: One mile north of Earlston on the A68. Entrance faces south. Garden accessible by bus, ask to get off at Carolside gate.

Opening for: Marie Curie

2 DAWYCK BOTANIC GARDEN
Stobo EH45 9JU
A Regional Garden of the Royal Botanic Garden Edinburgh
T: 01721 760254
W: www.rbge.org.uk/dawyck

Dawyck is a regional garden of the Royal Botanic Garden Edinburgh which had its 350th anniversary in 2020. Stunning collection of rare trees and shrubs. With over 300 years of tree planting, Dawyck is a world-famous arboretum with mature specimens of Chinese conifers, Japanese maples, Brewer's spruce, the unique Dawyck beech and sequoiadendrons from North America which are over 150 feet tall. Bold herbaceous plantings run along the burn. Range of trails and walks. Fabulous autumn colours.
National Plant Collection: *Larix* spp. and *Tsuga* spp.
Champion Trees: Numerous.

Open: Sunday 9 October, 10am - 5pm, admission details can be found on the garden's website.

Directions: Eight miles south west of Peebles on the B712.

Opening for: Donation to SGS

3 GATTONSIDE VILLAGE GARDENS
Gattonside TD6 9NP
The Gardeners of Gattonside
T: 07500 869041 E: jenbarr@gmx.com

A group of varied village gardens situated on a south facing slope with views across the River Tweed to Melrose. Visit Allerly, the former home of David Brewster which has espalier apple trees thought to have been gifted by Sir Walter Scott of Abbotsford. Also, stop by the small garden of a dahlia enthusiast. The garden also features a pond with fish. This year take the short walk over the chain bridge to visit gardens of Melrose and walk back for teas in Gattonside. Accessible by wheelchair for most of gardens.

Open: Sunday 31 July, 2pm - 5pm, admission £5.00, children free.

Peeblesshire & Tweeddale

Directions: Short walk from Melrose over the chain bridge. Twenty-minute walk along the River Tweed from Tweedbank Railway Station. By car access off the A68 signposted *Gattonside*. Parking at Allerly.

Opening for: Borders Carers Centre & The Fragile X Society

4 GLEN HOUSE

Glen Estate, Innerleithen EH44 6PX
The Tennant family
T: 01896 830210 E: info@glenhouse.com
W: www.glenhouse.com

Surrounding the outstanding Scots Baronial mansion designed by David Bryce in the mid-19th century, Glen House gardens are laid out on shallow terraces overhanging the glen itself. It offers one of the loveliest designed landscapes in the Borders. The garden expands from the formal courtyard through a yew colonnade, and contains a fine range of trees, long herbaceous border and a pool garden with pergola, all arranged within the curve of slopes sheltering the house.

Open: Sunday 17 July, 1pm - 4pm, admission £5.00, children free.

Directions: Follow the B709 out of Innerleithen for approximately two-and-a-half miles. Right turn at signpost for *Glen Estate*.

Opening for: WFGA

Glen House © Kathy Henry

Peeblesshire & Tweeddale

5 KAILZIE GARDENS

Kailzie Gardens EH45 9HT
Susan and Steve Plag
T: 01721 720682
W: kailziegardens.com

Kailzie Gardens sits at the heart of the Tweed Valley just a mile east of Peebles occupying a beautiful position on the River Tweed. At its heart lies the stunning walled garden with plantings of many unusual shrubs, laburnum arches, an enchanting rose garden and spectacular herbaceous borders and one of the best examples of a Mackenzie and Moncur glasshouse still in existence, filled with fuschias, pelargoniums and exotics. The garden also features prize winning show vegetables. The surrounding woodlands have one of the best laid arboretums in Scotland with champion trees and specimens (including the oldest Larch) providing 15 acres of captivating woodland and burnside walks and spectacular vistas. Champion Trees: Larch planted 1725.

Open: Sunday 6 March, 10am - 4pm for Snowdrops and Winter Walks; admission £5.00, children free. Also open Sunday 24 July, 10am - 4pm; admission £6.50, children free. See website for other opening times.

Directions: A mile east of Peebles on the B7062.

Opening for: Tweed Togs SCIO

6 KIRKTON MANOR HOUSE

Peebles EH45 9JH
Mrs Rosemary Thorburn
T: 01721 740220 E: rpthorburn@icloud.com

Kirkton Manor House has a delightful, three-acre, informal country garden set in the beautiful Manor Valley. It enjoys spectacular open views and calling curlews from its riverside position. Bluebells flank the impressive entrance leading to a new shrub border. Stone steps continue through to terraced slopes filled with bulbs, roses and hellebores providing height, interest and fragrance. Grass paths meander along the burn where blue and white camassia, meconopsis, and ligularia thrive in this sunny meadow environment. Later, in June, sisyrinchiums, irises, orchids and many flowering shrubs and roses are abundant. The natural woodland includes many interesting trees.

Open: From 16 February till end of March (Wednesdays only), 1pm - 4pm for Snowdrops and Winter Walks. Also open in April (Wednesdays only), 1pm - 4pm. And open by arrangement 1 May - 14 July. Admission £5.00, children free.

Directions: Turn off the A72 west of Neidpath Castle, signposted to *Kirkton Manor*. After crossing the River Tweed, enter a garden gate which is a mile downhill, opposite a *Beware Horses* sign.

Opening for: SGS and Beneficiaries

Peeblesshire & Tweeddale

7 **LAIDLAWSTIEL HOUSE**
Clovenfords, Galashiels TD1 1TJ
Mr and Mrs P Litherland

Walled garden containing herbaceous border, fruit, and vegetables in raised beds. There are colourful rhododendrons and azaleas as well as splendid views down to the River Tweed.

Open: Thursday 2 June, Wednesday 15 June & Wednesday 31 August, 2pm - 5pm, admission £5.00, children free.

Directions: On the A72 between Clovenfords and Walkerburn turn up the hill signposted for *Thornielee*. The house is on the right at the top of the hill.

Opening for: *Young Lives vs Cancer*

Laidlawstiel House © Kathy Henry

8 **LAMANCHA COMMUNITY HUB PLANT SALE**
Old Moffat Road, Lamancha EH46 7BD
Mike Madden
T: 07774 609547 E: hello@lamanchahub.org.uk

A small community garden with shrubs for year-round interest, and herbaceous and cottage garden borders. It is currently in the process of being developed as an organic demonstration garden, following the recent installation of a Keder house, rainwater collection and composting areas.

Open: Sunday 5 June, 10am - 1pm, admission by donation.

Directions: Three miles south of the Leadburn Junction on the A701.

Opening for: *Lamancha Hub*

Peeblesshire & Tweeddale

9 PORTMORE
Eddleston EH45 8QU
Mr and Mrs David Reid
T: 07825 294388
W: www.portmoregardens.co.uk

Lovingly created by the current owners over the past 30 years; the gardens surrounding the David Bryce-designed mansion house contain mature trees and offer fine views of the surrounding countryside. Large walled garden with box-edged herbaceous borders is planted in stunning colour harmonies, potager, rose garden, pleached lime walk and ornamental fruit cages. The Victorian glasshouses contain fruit trees, roses, geraniums, pelargoniums and a wide variety of tender plants. There is also an Italianate grotto and water garden with shrubs and meconopsis. The woodland walks are lined with rhododendrons, azaleas and shrub roses. Starred in *Good Gardens Guide* and featured in Kenneth Cox's book *Scotland for Gardeners* and on *The Beechgrove Garden*.

Open: 6 July - 31 August (Wednesdays only), 1pm - 5pm. Also open by arrangement 1 June - 31 August. Admission £6.00, children free. Self-service refreshments for Wednesday openings. Homemade cream teas for groups over 15 people by prior arrangement.

Directions: Off the A703 one mile north of Eddleston. Bus 62.

Opening for: *Love Learning Scotland SCIO: Gorgie Farm, Edinburgh*

10 QUERCUS GARDEN PLANTS
Whitmuir Farm, West Linton EH46 7BB
Rona Dodds
T: 01968 660708 E: quercusgardenplants@gmail.com
W: www.quercusgardenplants.co.uk

We are a small, independent nursery growing and selling a wide range of happy, healthy plants propagated from our nursery gardens. At just under two acres, these gardens were started in 2015 to show visitors and customers what can be grown in our conditions here on a north-west-facing hill at 850 feet above sea level. Explore our herb garden, scented garden, wildlife garden and all the other inspirational smaller borders. New areas are being developed to include prairie-style planting of grasses and perennials. Many of the plants seen in the gardens are available to buy in the nursery.

Open: Sunday 29 May, 10am - 5pm. Also open Sunday 21 August, 10am - 5pm. Admission by donation. A percentage of plant sales on these dates will be donated to Scotland's Garden Scheme and Breast Cancer Now. The 16mm narrow gauge garden railway will be running from 2pm.

Directions: On the A701, four miles south of the Leadburn junction or two miles north of West Linton.

Opening for: *Breast Cancer Now*

Peeblesshire & Tweeddale

11 **STOBO JAPANESE WATER GARDEN**
Stobo Farm, Stobo EH45 8NX
E: enquiries@stobofarmestate.com

This is a mature, secluded woodland garden created in the early 1900s. Its most prominent feature is the constant presence of water that adds to the tranquility of the garden throughout the seasons, beginning with the drama of a waterfall at its head through a cascade of ponds, punctuated along the way by stepping stones and bridges. The garden was brought to life when Japanese style was the height of fashion – hence its cherry trees, maples, and iconic Japanese lanterns, 'tea house' and humpback bridge. The azaleas and rhododendrons provide a spectacular display in the spring while autumn brings the unmistakable scent of burnt sugar from the Katsura and the colour changes from greens to stunning deep reds and yellows. Limited disabled access due to gravel paths and steps. Visitors are advised to wear appropriate footwear.

Open: Sunday 5 June, 2pm - 5pm. Also open Sunday 9 October, 2pm - 5pm. Admission £5.00, children free.

Directions: Off the B712. (Peebles/Broughton road) via *Stobo Castle* entrance. Bus 91.

Opening for: Charity to be confirmed

12 **THE POTTING SHED**
Broughton Place, Broughton, Biggar ML12 6HJ
Jane and Graham Buchanan-Dunlop
T: 01899 830574 E: buchanandunlop@btinternet.com

A one-acre garden begun from scratch in 2008, on an exposed hillside at 900 feet. It contains herbaceous plants, climbers, shrubs and trees – all selected for wind resistance and ability to cope with the poor, stony soil. There are usually fine views to the Southern Uplands.

Open: 8 June - 6 July (Wednesdays only), 11am - 5pm. Also open by arrangement 1 May - 31 October. Admission £5.00, children free.

Directions: Signposted from the main A701 Edinburgh – Moffat Road, immediately north of Broughton village.

Opening for: Macmillan Cancer Support: Borders General Hospital

13 **WEST LINTON VILLAGE GARDENS**
West Linton EH46 7EW
West Linton Village Gardeners
T: 01968 660669 E: j.bracken101@gmail.com

A varied selection of gardens, approximately 1,000 feet above sea level, with acidic soil, high rainfall and low winter temperatures. Srongarbh, an Arts and Crafts house (the house is not open) has a large well established garden dating from the 1930s, surrounded by woodland, with many trees and shrubs within the garden. Others have interesting herbaceous borders and borrowed landscapes, a cutting garden and mixed planting to attract wildlife.

Open: Sunday 12 June, 2pm - 5pm, admission £5.00, children free. Tickets, teas and plants will be available at the Graham Institute in the centre of the village. A minibus will run between the gardens which are uphill and have very limited parking.

Directions: About 15 miles south west of Edinburgh, take the A701 or the A702 and follow signs. Bus 101 or 102 to Gordon Arms Hotel.

Opening for: Ben Walton Trust & Borders General Hospital, Margaret Kerr Unit

Perth & Kinross

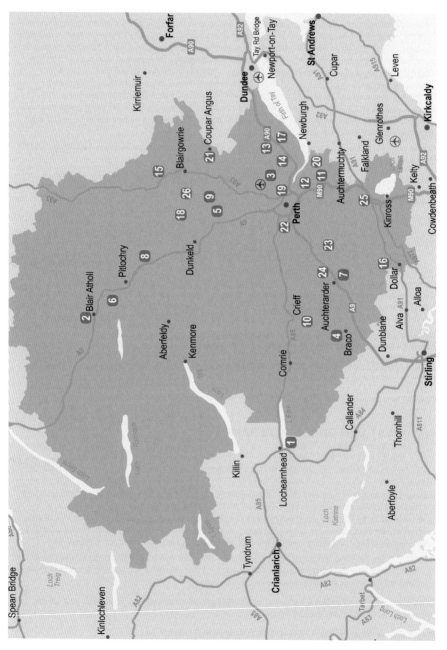

Perth & Kinross

OUR VOLUNTEER ORGANISERS

District Organiser:	Alex Lindsay	19 St Serf's Place, Auchterarder PH3 1QS E: info@scotlandsgardens.org
Area Organisers:	Gill Boardman	16, Acremoar Drive, Kinross KY13 8RE
	Jane Gallier	The Old Farmhouse, Dunning Road Auchterarder PH3 1DU
	Henrietta Harland	Easter Carmichael Cottage, Forgandenny Road, Bridge of Earn PH2 9EZ
	Elizabeth Mitchell	Woodlee, 28 St Mary's Drive, Perth PH2 7BY
	Judy Norwell	Dura Den, 20 Pitcullen Terrace, Perth PH2 7EQ
	Kareen Robertson	2 The Orchard, Bridge of Earn, Perthshire PH2 9DX
	Fiona Stewart	7 Craigend Cottages, Craigend, Perth PH2 8PX
	Mary Jane Thompson	Mosspark House, Rumbling Bridge, Kinross KY13 0QE
	Heather Wood	Mill of Forneth, Forneth, Blairgowrie PH10 6SP
District Photographers:	Carolyn Bell	carolynbell@gmail.com
	Mike Bell	docmike@hotmail.co.uk
	Camelia Hudema	camelia.hudema@gmail.com
Treasurer:	Michael Tinson	Parkhead House, Parkhead Gardens, Burghmuir Road, Perth PH1 1JF

GARDENS OPEN ON A SPECIFIC DATE

Princeland House, Blairgowrie Road, Coupar Angus, Blairgowrie	Sats/Suns, 19 February to 12 March
Cloan, by Auchterarder	Sunday, 20 February
Megginch Castle, Errol	Sunday, 10 April
Fingask Castle, Rait	Sunday, 1 May
Cloan, by Auchterarder	Sunday, 22 May
Bradystone House, Murthly	Thursdays, 2 June to 11 August
Mill of Forneth, Forneth, Blairgowrie	Sunday, 5 June
Cloan, by Auchterarder	Saturday/Sunday, 11/12 June
The Bield at Blackruthven, Blackruthven House, Tibbermore	Saturday, 11 June
Blair Castle Gardens, Blair Atholl	Saturday, 2 July
Cloan, by Auchterarder	Sunday, 31 July
Mount Tabor House, Mount Tabor Road, Perth	Sunday, 7 August
Drummond Castle Gardens, Muthill, Crieff	Sunday, 7 August

Perth & Kinross

GARDENS OPEN REGULARLY

Glenericht House Arboretum, Blairgowrie	1 Jan - 24 Dec & 26 - 30 Dec
Fingask Castle, Rait	24 January - 3 March (Mons & Thurs)
Braco Castle, Braco	1 February - 31 October
Glendoick, Glencarse, Perthshire	1 April - 31 May
Ardvorlich, Lochearnhead	1 May - 5 June

GARDENS OPEN BY ARRANGEMENT

Eastbank Cottage, Perth Road, Abernethy	1 April - 30 June
The Old Farmhouse, Dunning Road, Auchterarder	1 April - 31 July
The Pond Garden, The Pond, Milnathort	1 April - 30 June
Bonhard House, Perth	1 April - 31 October
Hollytree Lodge, Muckhart, Dollar	1 April - 31 October
Craigowan, Ballinluig	10 April - 31 July
Delvine, Murthly	17 April - 16 October
The Steading at Clunie, The Steading	30 April - 23 May
Carig Dhubh, Bonskeid, Pitlochry	1 May - 30 September
Pitcurran House, Abernethy	1 May - 1 September
Fehmarn, Bridge of Earn	15 May - 30 September
The Crofts, Perth Road, Dunning	1 June - 31 July
The Steading at Clunie, The Steading	11 June - 9 July
The Pond Garden, The Pond, Milnathort	1 August - 7 November

The Pond Garden

Perth & Kinross

1 **ARDVORLICH**
Lochearnhead FK19 8QE
Mr and Mrs Sandy Stewart
T: 01567 830335

Beautiful hill garden featuring over 170 different species of rhododendrons and many hybrids, grown in a glorious setting of oaks and birches on either side of the Ardvorlich Burn.

Open: 1 May - 5 June, 9am - dusk, admission £5.00, children free. The paths are quite steep and rough in places and boots are advisable, especially when wet.

Directions: On South Loch Earn Road three miles from Lochearnhead, five miles from St Fillans.

Opening for: *The Ghurka Welfare Trust*

2 **BLAIR CASTLE GARDENS**
Blair Atholl PH18 5TL
Blair Charitable Trust
T: 01796 481207 E: office@blair-castle.co.uk
W: www.blair-castle.co.uk

Blair Castle stands as the focal point in a designed landscape of some 2,500 acres within a Highland estate. Hercules Garden is a walled enclosure of about nine acres recently restored to its original 18th-century design with landscaped ponds, a Chinese bridge, contemporary plantings, vegetables and an orchard of more than 100 fruit trees. The glory of this garden in summer is the herbaceous border, which runs along the 275 yard south-facing wall. A delightful sculpture trail incorporates contemporary and 18th-century sculpture as well as eight new works, letter-carving on stone from the *Memorial and Commemorative Arts* charity's 'Art and Memory Collection'. Diana's Grove is a magnificent stand of tall trees including grand fir, Douglas fir, larch and wellingtonia running along the Banvie Burn, with the 12th-century ruins of St Bride's Church on the far bank.

Open: Saturday 2 July, 9:30am - 4:30pm, admission details can be found on the garden's website.

Directions: Off the A9, follow signs to *Blair Castle, Blair Atholl*.

Opening for: *Donation to SGS*

Perth & Kinross

3 BONHARD HOUSE
Perth PH2 7PQ
Stephen and Charlotte Hay
T: 07990 574570 E: stephenjohnhay@me.com

Traditional 19th-century garden of five acres approached through an avenue of magnificent oaks. Mature trees, six classified by the National Tree Register as 'remarkable', including a handsome monkey puzzle, sequoias, Douglas fir and a variety of hollies. Grassy paths wind around ponds, rockeries, shrubbery and smaller trees, providing some splendid perspectives. Rhododendron and azalea beds. Pinetum on a knoll behind the house contains 25 species; beehives and productive kitchen garden. Shifting of garden emphasis to habitat. First fruits of rewilding visible. Orchard in process of extension. Possible sighting of red squirrels. Plentiful and varied birdlife.

Open: by arrangement 1 April - 31 October, admission £5.00, children free. Groups welcome to enquire.

Directions: On A94 just under a mile north of Perth take right turn, signed *Murrayshall Hotel*. After approximately one mile take entrance right marked *Bonhard House*, at a sharp left turn. From Balbeggie turn left, signposted for *Bonhard*, one mile north of Scone. Turn right in half a mile, pass any sign for *Bonhard Nursery*, and enter drive at sharp right turn.

Opening for: Freedom from Fistula Foundation

4 BRACO CASTLE
Braco FK15 9LA
Mr and Mrs M van Ballegooijen
T: 01786 880437

A 19th-century landscaped garden with a plethora of wonderful and interesting trees, shrubs, bulbs and plants. An old garden for all seasons that has been extensively expanded over the last 33 years. The partly walled garden is approached on a rhododendron and tree-lined path featuring an ornamental pond. Spectacular spring bulbs, exuberant shrub and herbaceous borders and many ornamental trees are all enhanced by the spectacular views across the park to the Ochils. From snowdrops through to vibrant autumn colour, this garden is a gem. Look out for the embothrium in June, hoheria in August, eucryphia in September and an interesting collection of rhododendrons and azaleas with long flowering season.

Open: 1 February - 31 October, 10am - 5pm. Snowdrops and Winter Walks February to early March, admission £5.00, children free.

Directions: Take a one-and-a-half-mile drive from the gates at the north end of Braco Village, just west of the bridge on the A822. Parking at the castle is welcome.

Opening for: The Woodland Trust Scotland

5 BRADYSTONE HOUSE
Murthly PH1 4EW
Mrs James Lumsden
T: 01738 710308 E: pclumsden@me.com

A small, intimate cottage garden converted from a derelict farm steading to create a unique and tranquil setting. The sunny courtyard is imaginatively planted with interesting perennials, clematis and roses. There is a small, productive kitchen garden and a newly planted orchard with free-roaming hens and ducks. The small woodland garden is underplanted with ornamental shrubs.

Perth & Kinross

Open: 2 June - 11 August (Thursdays only), 11am - 4pm. Admission £5.00, children free. An interesting and varied selection of plants are available for sale. Dogs on leads please.

Directions: From south/north follow the A9 to Bankfoot, then signs to *Murthly*. At the crossroads in Murthly take the private road to Bradystone.

Opening for: Scotland's Charity Air Ambulance

Bradystone House © Mike Nicoll

6 CARIG DHUBH
Bonskeid, Pitlochry PH16 5NP
Jane and Niall Graham-Campbell
T: 01796 473469 E: niallgc@btinternet.com

'I don't know how Niall and Jane manage to grow their splendid meconopsis on the sand and rock of their garden but they do, most successfully.' In this stunning situation, when not admiring the views, you will find wonderful primulas, cardiocrinum and meconopsis, all interspersed between beautiful shrubs and other herbaceous plants. Look up and in July you will see roses flowering 40 feet up in the tree. This is a gem of a garden and you will be welcomed by Niall and Jane Graham-Campbell with all their expert knowledge.

Open: by arrangement 1 May - 30 September, admission £5.00, children free.

Directions: Take the old A9 between Pitlochry and Killiecrankie, turn west on the Tummel Bridge Road B8019, Carig Dhubh is three-quarters of a mile on the north side of the road.

Opening for: Earl Haig Fund Poppy Scotland

Perth & Kinross

7 CLOAN
by Auchterarder PH3 1PP
Neil Mitchison
T: 07958 155831 E: niall@fastmail.co.uk

Two acres of wild garden, with a wide variety of rhododendrons and azaleas, and an impressive collection of trees, including metasequoia, cryptomeria, *Acer cappadocicum*, *Sequoia sempervirens*, *Quercus robur* 'Filicifolia', liriodendron, several Japanese maples, magnificent beech and Scots pine trees, and extensive yew topiary; also an acre of walled garden with embothriums, *Acer griseum*, liquidambar, several sorbus varieties, parrotia and a large herbaceous border. Fine views of Strathearn from the front of the house.

Open: Sunday 20 February, 10am - 3pm for Snowdrops and Winter Walks. Also open Sunday 22 May, Saturday/Sunday, 11/12 June and Sunday 31 July, 11am - 5pm. Admission £4.00, children free.

Directions: From A823, just south of A9, follow small road heading north east, signposted *Duchally*. Continue for approximately two-and-a-half miles, turn right at sign *Coulshill*. Continue just under half a mile. Follow signs for car parking.

Opening for: Tiphereth Limited: Camphill Scotland

8 CRAIGOWAN
Ballinluig PH9 0NE
Ian and Christine Jones
T: 01796 482244 E: i.q.jones@btinternet.com

This is a specialist garden with a major collection of rhododendrons put together over the last 40 years; initially, mainly species from Glendoick following the plant hunting and discoveries of Peter Cox and the late Sir Peter Hutchison and others. In the last 20 years there have been added noteworthy hybrids sourced from Glendoick and the major English nurseries. Each year further additions are made and earlier introductions which have outgrown their original or secondary planting spot are moved to new locations. With growth rates tending to increase, this is a major exercise but the result is a constantly changing garden and more plants are developing into a spectacular presentation. Other plant types include magnolias, ornamental acers and a collection of unusual trees. There are areas of more formal beds where there is a large collection of meconopsis, lilies including cardiocrinum with roughly a hundred flowering each year. The rhododendron flowering period lasts from January to August but the best months are April, May and June. There is adjoining woodland which is being replanted with trees free of disease risk and with the larger rhododendrons which have outgrown the more formal areas. In June and July two large herbaceous borders give summer colour and interest.

Open: by arrangement 10 April - 31 July, admission £5.00, children free.

Directions: From north or south A9 to Ballinluig junction. Follow sign for *Tulliemet* and *Dalcapon*. Pass the filling station and Ballinluig Hotel. Turn right following the *Tulliemet/ Dalcapon* sign; this is a steep narrow road so take care. About a half mile up the road take a left turning with fields on either side and Craigowan is the first house on the left about a half mile along. Park on paviours adjoining house.

Opening for: LUPUS UK

Perth & Kinross

9 DELVINE

Murthly PH1 4LD
Mr and Mrs David Gemmell
E: gemmell.david@googlemail.com

If you love something unusual, you must come and see the Millennium Project Arboretum developed over 20 years and the Water Gardens set in a beautiful, wild and secluded setting, surrounded by fine and very old trees. You can wander among collections of different bamboos, shrub roses, birches and other special trees. In the spring you will see swans and geese nesting. There are also inquisitive guinea fowl, and if you are really lucky, you might be able to see kingfishers, otters and beavers. This is a very special place even in the rain.

Open: by arrangement 17 April - 16 October, admission £5.00, children free. Surfaces are level grass, but may be muddy for wheelchair users. Boots or waterproof shoes are a must if it's wet. Dogs on leads, please.

Directions: On the A984, seven miles east of Dunkeld, four miles south west of Blairgowrie.

Opening for: ABF The Soldiers' Charity

10 DRUMMOND CASTLE GARDENS

Muthill, Crieff PH7 4HN
Grimsthorpe & Drummond Castle Trust Ltd
T: 01764 681433
W: www.drummondcastlegardens.co.uk

Activities and events for a great family day out. The gardens of Drummond Castle were originally laid out in 1630 by John Drummond, second Earl of Perth. In 1830 the parterre was changed to an Italian style. One of the most interesting features is the multi-faceted sundial designed by John Mylne, Master Mason to Charles I. The formal garden is said to be one of the finest in Europe and is the largest of its type in Scotland.

Open: Sunday 7 August, 1pm - 5pm, admission details can be found on the garden's website.

Directions: Entrance two miles south of Crieff on Muthill road (A822).

Opening for: BLESMA

11 EASTBANK COTTAGE

Perth Road, Abernethy PH2 9LR
Mike and Elsa Thompson
T: 01738 850539 E: mikestuartthompson@hotmail.com

Traditional Scottish cottage, a third-of-an-acre garden, walled and bounded by a small burn to the east. Erythroniums, varieties of wood anemones, trillium, a fine display of clematis, rhododendrons and azaleas. Altogether a little haven in the country.

Open: by arrangement 1 April - 30 June, admission by donation.

Directions: When coming from Perth, drive to the Abernethy *30 mph* sign. A layby is on the left. The gate has the property name on it. Bus 36 stops very close by.

Opening for: SGS and Beneficiaries

Perth & Kinross

12 FEHMARN

Bridge of Earn PH2 9AH
Mr and Mrs Gimblett
T: 01738 813653 E: gimblettsmill@aol.com

This medium size garden, battling with wind and clay, is inspirational. Full of colour and interest for almost every month of the year, it is at its best from May to early autumn. Flowing lawns and curving paths lead from one 'garden-room' to another with a seat in each. Dry shady woodland, water, herbaceous borders, roses, clematis, shrubs, dozens of pots, alpine gardens in containers, and a small very colourful jewel garden in a dark corner. Well worth visiting.

Open: by arrangement 15 May - 30 September, admission £5.00, children free. Small groups welcome.

Directions: From the north and south, take the exit on the M90 for Bridge of Earn and follow the road into the village. Go ahead at the mini-roundabout and take the first right into Old Edinburgh Road. At the T junction turn right and go straight on for about half a mile. Turn right by a group of bungalows. Fehmarn is first on the right.

Opening for: Parkinsons UK

Fehmarn © Camelia Hudema

Perth & Kinross

13 FINGASK CASTLE

Rait PH2 7SA
Mr and Mrs Andrew Murray Threipland
T: 01821 670777 ext 2 E: andrew@fingaskcastle.com
W: www.fingaskcastle.com

Scotland's surrealist garden: spectacular topiary staggers across the garden bumping into stone globes, marble balls, statues and a figure of Alice (in Wonderland). Other literary and historical characters are scattered among the 17th-century pleasure gardens. Bonnie Prince Charlie and his father are said to have approached the castle up the long yew avenue known as 'The King's Walk'. A 15-minute walk takes you down to the dell beneath the castle and St Peter's Well – a stopping place for medieval pilgrims on their way to the bones of the saintly Queen Margaret at Dunkeld Cathedral. Return via a Chinese bridge, Gabriel's bridge, an iron age fort, along a stream, past Sir Stuart's House, and back to the castle via the Old Orchard. There are large drifts of snowdrops, daffodils and flowering shrubs in season.
Champion Trees: *Pinus wallichiana* (Bhutan Pine) and the handsome remnants of what was the largest walnut in Scotland.

Open: 24 January - 3 March (Mondays & Thursdays), 10am - 4pm for Snowdrops and Winter Walks Admission £3.00, children free. Also open Sunday 1 May, 1pm - 4pm. Admission £4.00, children free. Homemade Teas on 1 May only.

Directions: Half-way between Perth and Dundee. From the A90 follow signs to *Rait* until small crossroad, turn right and follow signs to *Fingask*.

Opening for: All Saints Episcopal Church & Fingask Follies

Fingask Castle

Perth & Kinross

14 GLENDOICK

Glencarse, Perthshire PH2 7NS
Cox Family
T: 01738 860260 E: manager@glendoick.com
W: www.glendoick.com

Glendoick's gardens and garden centre with its award-winning café is the ideal spring day out in April and May. In 2019, Glendoick celebrated 100 years since Euan Cox returned from Burma with the first rhododendron seeds to be grown and planted in the gardens. Glendoick Gardens boast a unique collection of plants from three generations of Cox plant-hunting expeditions in China and the Himalaya. Enjoy one of the finest collections of rhododendrons and azaleas and other acid-loving plants in the woodland garden and the gardens surrounding the house. Many of the plants have been introduced from the wild or bred by the Cox family and the gardens boast a vast range of plants from as far afield as Chile, Tasmania and Tibet. There are fine waterfall views in the woodland gardens. The award-winning Glendoick Garden Centre has one of Scotland's best selections of plants including their world-famous rhododendrons and azaleas as well as a gift shop and cafe.

Open: 1 April - 31 May, 10am - 4pm, admission £5.00, children free. Tickets must be purchased from the Garden Centre before your drive up to the garden. For group bookings email: jane@glendoick.com. Groups should pay by single cheque made out to Glendoick Gardens Ltd. Any restaurant bill needs to be paid separately. We can offer guided tours for keen gardening groups only. Visiting at other times by appointment, please email: gardencentre@glendoick.com.

Directions: Follow the *brown* signs to Glendoick Garden Centre off A90 Perth – Dundee road. Gardens are a half mile behind the Garden Centre. After buying tickets at the Garden Centre, please drive up and park at the gardens (free parking).

Opening for: Donation to SGS

15 GLENERICHT HOUSE ARBORETUM

Blairgowrie PH10 7JD
Mrs Mary McCosh
T: 01250 872092 E: m.mccosh123@gmail.com

Spectacular collection of Victorian-planted trees and shrubs which are centred around a Grade 'A' listed suspension bridge (1846). Ninety-two tree varieties, mostly conifers including a top Douglas fir which is 171 feet and still growing, also a collection of younger trees. In late May and June you will be able to view the wonderful daffodils and the rhododendrons in flower.

Open: 1 January - 24 December & 26 December - 30 December, dawn – dusk, admission £4.00, children free. Honesty box for payment. Bridge is not open to visitors.

Directions: Off the A93, the Lodge House is four miles north of Blairgowrie on the right-hand side of the A93 when coming from Blairgowrie. Follow the avenue towards the bridge and the parking area is beside the river.

Opening for: Sands

Perth & Kinross

16 HOLLYTREE LODGE

Muckhart, Dollar FK14 7JW
Liz and Peter Wyatt
T: 07973 374687 E: elizwyatt@aol.com

A tranquil one-acre garden, divided by internal hedges into 'rooms' as featured in *Country Homes & Interiors* in January 2018. Highlights include a small Japanese garden, mini orchard, naturalised spring bulbs and wildflowers, rill and wildlife pond, mixed herbaceous borders, a good collection of rhododendrons and azaleas, a variety of unusual trees and shrubs, snow gum, *Metasequoia glyptostroboides*, Persian ironwood and acers, many producing spectacular autumn colours. We aim to garden organically working with nature, complementing our beekeeping interests.

Open: by arrangement 1 April - 31 October, admission £5.00, children free. Always worth a call if you are in the area outwith these dates.

Directions: Approximately 100 yards from the A91 (between Dollar and Milnathort) down the small lane directly opposite the entrance to the Inn at Muckhart.

Opening for: Coronation Hall, Muckhart

17 MEGGINCH CASTLE

Errol PH2 7SW
Giles Herdman and Catherine Drummond-Herdman
T: 01821 642222 E: info@megginch.com
W: megginchcastle.com

Come and wander through our hosts of golden daffodils under the ancient trees and avenues of Megginch. Head through the charming, cobbled courtyard where you will find a vibrant outdoor market with local producers showcasing their products from milk and honey to meat and vegetables. (NeighbourFood.co.uk/markets/megginch-castle/30). On into the walled garden where there is a collection of daffodils from the renowned collectors, Duncan and Kate Donald from Croft 16 Daffodils. There will be archery in the orchard where you can also have a chat with Gavin and his bees, walk back past some of the apple and pear trees that make up our two National Collections and wander under the tallest yew trees in Scotland! National Plant Collection: Scottish cider apples, Scottish Heritage apples and pears. Champion Trees: *Acer palmatum*.

Open: Sunday 10 April, noon - 4pm, admission £5.00, children free. Homemade Teas in the Camellia House. You're welcome to bring your own picnic lunch.

Directions: Ten miles from Perth and Dundee directly off the A90, Perth-bound carriageway, 600 yards after the Errol/Rait flyover, on the left hand side, 300 yards after *Beware Pedestrians Crossing* sign, or signed entrance just before the level crossing in Errol Station.

Opening for: The Inspiration Orchestra

Perth & Kinross

18 MILL OF FORNETH
Forneth, Blairgowrie PH10 6SP
Mr and Mrs Graham Wood
E: gaw@forneth-mill.co.uk

Built on the site of a former watermill on the Lunan Burn, originally laid out in the 1970s by James Aitken, the Scottish landscape designer and naturalist. The sheltered four-acre garden has a range of mature trees, including a Himalayan blue cedar, large rhododendrons, azaleas and a wide range of shrubs. The former mill lade feeds rocky waterfalls and a lily pond. Planting includes established perennials with seasonal colours, many bulbs, primulas and heathers, plus a vegetable garden on the site of an old tennis court and a new wildflower meadow.

Open: Sunday 5 June, 2pm - 5pm, admission £5.00, children free.

Directions: Take the A923 Dunkeld to Blairgowrie road. Six miles east of Dunkeld turn south onto a minor road signposted Snaigow and Clunie. Mill of Forneth is the first gate on the left-hand side. PLEASE NOTE: Due to wet weather conditions there may be limited safe meadow parking on site (exceptions will be made for people with mobility problems).

Opening for: Tayside Mountain Rescue Association (SCIO)

19 MOUNT TABOR HOUSE
Mount Tabor Road, Perth PH2 7DE
Mr and Mrs John McEwan

Mature terraced town garden originally laid out in the late 19th century, but constantly evolving. A sheltered and peaceful garden surrounded by mature trees and hedges with well filled herbaceous borders. There is a cascade of ponds filled with carp and other wildlife and lots of places to sit in the sun and relax.

Open: Sunday 7 August, noon - 4:30pm, admission £5.00, children free.

Directions: From Dundee Road in Perth at Isle of Skye Hotel, turn right into Manse Road, over the mini-roundabout and into Mount Tabor Road.

Opening for: The Katie McKerracher Trust

Mount Tabor House

Perth & Kinross

20 PITCURRAN HOUSE

Abernethy PH2 9LH
The Hon Ranald and Mrs Noel-Paton
T: 01738 850933 E: patricianp@pitcurran.com

This end-of-village garden was created 17 years ago. It includes an interesting combination of trees, rare shrubs and herbaceous plants including azaleas, rhododendrons, tree peonies, trilliums and veratrum. Also a rose pergola, eucryphias and a large west-facing hydrangea border for the later summer. Above the pond there is a good collection of pink- and white-barked birches and an embryonic arboretum.

Open: by arrangement 1 May - 1 September, admission £6.00, children free.

Directions: South east of Perth. From M90 (exit nine) take A912 towards Glenfarg, go left at roundabout onto A913 to Abernethy. Pitcurran House is at the far eastern end of the village. Buses run through Abernethy from Perth and surrounding districts.

Opening for: Juvenile Diabetes Research Foundation Limited

21 PRINCELAND HOUSE

Blairgowrie Road, Coupar Angus, Blairgowrie PH13 9AU
Helen and Alistair Carmichael
T: 07864778170 E: carmichaelhf@hotmail.com

Sited on the edge of Coupar Angus, the wider grounds of Princeland House garden are currently under active renovation and replanting by Mrs Carmichael. There is a wooded area around the drive and entrance with an extended area of beautiful and different snowdrops planted in drifts among mature trees.

Open: Saturdays and Sundays, 19 February to 12 March, 10am - 2pm for Snowdrops and Winter Walks. Admission by donation. There is partial wheelchair access from the drive, but smaller paths in woodland may be uneven. Dogs on leads please.

Directions: From the outskirts of Coupar Angus, take the A94 Blairgowrie Road from the mini roundabout junction with the A923, to the junction with School Road. Parking on the street is available for visitors, except for those with disabilities and mobility difficulties, who can park by the house. Entry to Princeland House is on the corner of School Road, past a lodge cottage on the left of the entrance.

Opening for: Shelter Scotland

Princeland House

Perth & Kinross

22 **THE BIELD AT BLACKRUTHVEN**
Blackruthven House, Tibbermore PH1 1PY
The Bield Christian Co Ltd
T: 01738 583238 E: info@bieldatblackruthven.org.uk

The Bield is set in extensive grounds with well maintained lawns, hedges, flower meadow and specimen trees. A labyrinth is cut into the grass of the old orchard and there is a wheelchair-friendly labyrinth. Traditional walled garden with colourful, richly stocked borders and lawns, plus cut-flower garden, Healing Garden, glasshouse, trained fruit trees and organic vegetable plot. Walk through extensive woodland and visit the old curling pond. Southton Smallholding is a social enterprise ten minutes walk away, featuring vegetable plots, polytunnels and a number of animals (not staffed on the day).

Open: Saturday 11 June, 2pm - 5pm, admission £5.00, children free.

Directions: From Dundee or Edinburgh, follow signs for *Glasgow, Stirling* and *Crianlarich* which lead onto the Perth bypass. Head west on the A85 signed to *Crieff/Crianlarich* to West Huntingtower. Turn left at the crossroads to *Madderty/Tibbermore*. Entrance is left after a half-mile passing the gate lodge on your right. Parking signed to right at the steading.

Opening for: Southton Smallholding

23 **THE CROFTS**
Perth Road, Dunning PH2 0SF
Lorna and Alistair Radbourne
T: 01764 684452 E: lradbourne@btinternet.com

The garden of a watercolour and stained glass artist; small, welcoming, natural and full of year-round interest. Old roses and honeysuckle round the windows, a gravel garden, small lawn surrounded by trees, shrubs and flowers and a greenhouse tucked away near the studio. Small sculptures nestle among the plants or appear in the gravel. Under apple trees in the wild garden is a beautiful drystone curving seat, and on the cottage roof, a flock of fan and straight tail white doves bask in the sun. Sit quietly for five minutes in this garden and feel your cares slip away.

Open: by arrangement 1 June - 31 July, admission £3.00, children free.

Directions: From Dunning take the B934 towards Forteviot and Bridge of Earn. The Crofts is behind the last house on the right up a gravel drive. Limited parking.

Opening for: Perth Autism Support SCIO

24 **THE OLD FARMHOUSE**
Dunning Road, Auchterarder PH3 1DU
Jane and Nigel Gallier
T: 01764 662471 E: thegalliers@msn.com

A garden of approximately one acre with herbaceous borders, a gravel garden, vegetable garden, trained fruit trees in half-wine barrels, wild areas under-planted with bulbs, and woodland areas, with other areas still being developed. As you approach the house, look out for our kamikaze hens. The garden is not always immaculate; a well-ordered winter garden and a floriferous summer garden.

Open: by arrangement 1 April - 31 July 10.30am - 4.30pm, admission £5.00, children free.

Directions: From the A9, take the A824 and halfway between Auchterarder and Aberuthven take the B8062 at Grand Eagles and head towards Dunning. We are on the left just before the A9 bridge.

Opening for: ABF The Soldiers' Charity

Perth & Kinross

25 **THE POND GARDEN**
The Pond, Milnathort KY13 0SA
Fay Young & Ray Perman
T: 07767 407396 E: fay@fayyoung.org
W: www.fayyoung.org/category/pond-cottage

A wild woodland and wetland garden supporting birds, bees, butterflies, red squirrels, swans and other less visible wildlife. Enticing paths lead through seasonal highlights: snowdrops, daffodils, bluebells, foxgloves and ferns. Fine old beeches and oaks mark the boundary of the former Victorian estate. Since the mid 1990s we have rebuilt the derelict cottage and planted a mixed species hedgerow and native trees, adding spring and autumn colour. Stone features gather moss, and waterside benches welcome you to rest by the pond.

Open: by arrangement 1 April - 30 June. Also open by arrangement 1 August - 7 November. Admission £5.00, children free.

Directions: From the North, take the M90 south from Perth and exit at Junction 7 (Milnathort). Turn left into Milnathort Village and at the mini roundabout in the centre of the village turn left signed for *Path of Condie* up Wester Loan, then North Street. At the top of the hill, past the church on your left, you will cross the motorway again. Carry straight on for half-a-mile.

Opening for: SGS and Beneficiaries

26 **THE STEADING AT CLUNIE**
The Steading PH10 6SG
Jean and Dave Trudgill
T: 01250 884263 E: davetrudgill@googlemail.com

The Steading at Newmill is situated on the Lunan Burn midway between Lochs Clunie and Marlee. The policies include paths that extend for 800 metres along the Lunan, a small, colourful cottage garden and six acres of woodland, ponds and a wildflower meadow. The policies are open to visit in the spring when there is a profusion of primroses, wood anemones and then bluebells in the wooded areas. In the meadow snake's head fritillary flowers first, followed by a carpet of cowslips and cuckoo flowers. We open again in early summer when 14 species of native orchids start to flower in the meadow. This is more than in any other small meadow in Britain and includes rarities such as marsh helleborine, bee orchid and the two species of butterfly orchids.

Open: by arrangement 30 April - 23 May. Also open by arrangement 11 June - 9 July. Admission £4.50, children free. There are narrow paths, bridges and flowing water in the garden. We have friendly hens, hence no dogs.

Directions: Three miles west of Blairgowrie on the A923. About 600 metres west of the Kinloch Hotel take the track on the left, just after a mobile phone mast and a breeze-block wall.

Opening for: Save the Children UK

Renfrewshire

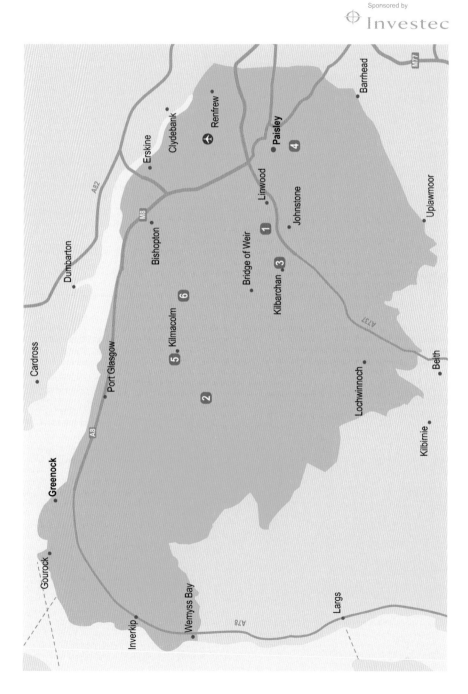

Renfrewshire

OUR VOLUNTEER ORGANISERS

District Organiser:	Alexandra MacMillan	Langside Farm, Kilmacolm PA13 4SA E: info@scotlandsgardens.org
Area Organisers:	Helen Hunter Barbara McLean	2 Bay Street, Fairlie, North Ayrshire KA29 0AL 49 Middlepenny Road, Langbank, PA14 6XE
Treasurer:	Jean Gillan	Bogriggs Cottage, Carlung KA23 9PS

GARDENS OPEN ON A SPECIFIC DATE

SGS Kilmacolm Plant Sale, Outside Kilmacolm Library, Kilmacolm	Saturday, 30 April
Highwood, off Lochwinnoch Road, Kilmacolm	Sunday, 15 May
Perch Corner, 25 Stanely Crescent, Paisley	Sunday, 22 May
Wraes, Corseliehill Road, nr Houston	Sunday, 12 June
No 14 – A Village Garden, 14 Taylor Avenue, Kilbarchan	Sunday, 19 June
Craig Hepburn Memorial Garden, Stirling Drive, Linwood	Wednesday/Thursday, 22/23 June

GARDENS OPEN BY ARRANGEMENT

Wraes, Corseliehill Road, nr Houston	1 May - 1 September

Highwood

Renfrewshire

1 CRAIG HEPBURN MEMORIAL GARDEN
Stirling Drive, Linwood PA3 3NB
Linwood High School
T: 01505 336146 E: gw07hindelesley@glow.sch.uk
W: facebook.com/welovegardening14

The Craig Hepburn Memorial Garden and Outdoor Learning Centre is located in Linwood High School. Our original garden with an outdoor classroom has been expanded to include community raised beds, an orchard, greenhouse and presentation area. We work with all years in the school reconnecting them to the natural world, whether through growing in our organic garden, encouraging biodiversity or learning about sustainability. Winners of the *Cultivation Street* competition 2020.

Open: Wednesday (3pm - 6pm)/Thursday (4pm - 6pm), 22/23 June, admission £3.50, children free.

Directions: Exit the M8 at St James Interchange and take the A737. Take the exit for Linwood onto the A761, follow to Clippens Road and then Stirling Drive. Accessible by McGill's buses.

Opening for: Teenage Cancer Trust

2 HIGHWOOD
off Lochwinnoch Road, Kilmacolm PA13 4TF
Dr Jill Morgan

A beautiful woodland walk around 50 acres of native bluebells, primroses and wild garlic in a delightful setting bordering the Green Water river with tumbling waterfalls. Great outdoor space for children to run and explore and splash in the burn (under supervision). A haven of tranquility only three miles from the centre of Kilmacolm.

Open: Sunday 15 May, 2pm - 5pm, admission £4.00, children free. Stout footwear is recommended as the footpath is uneven and can be muddy in inclement weather. Dogs are welcome on a lead. Fantastic opportunity for lovers of wildflowers and photography.

Directions: Take the B786 Lochwinnoch road out of Kilmacolm and continue for approximately two miles. From Lochwinnoch take the B786 Kilmacolm road for approximately six miles. Then follow the yellow *SGS* signs.

Opening for: Orkidstudio

3 NO 14 – A VILLAGE GARDEN
14 Taylor Avenue, Kilbarchan, Renfrewshire PA10 2LS
Nigel and Catriona Scriven

Last opened in 2016, this third-of-an-acre village garden in a setting with a borrowed landscape, has been improved and enhanced over that time with an extended border, vegetable garden, pond and established orchard. Planted so there is always something out or in flower through the year. June will be a good time to enjoy the David Austin roses, irises and Kalmia, the wildflower strip and summer annuals.

Open: Sunday 19 June, 2pm - 5pm, admission £3.50, children free.

Directions: From A737 travelling west, take the Kilbarchan turning, drive through the village, up Shuttle Street and Taylor Avenue is on the left. From A737 travelling east, take Howwood turning, through the village towards Johnstone, left at mini-roundabout, pass the bus depot and Milliken Park rail station, to the mini-roundabout and left into Kilbarchan, then as above through the village. From A761 Bridge of Weir, take the *Kilbarchan* road. As you enter Kilbarchan, Taylor Avenue is the second turning on the right. Look out for *SGS* signage. McGills Bus 38 from Glasgow/Paisley stops near Taylor Avenue. National cycle route 7 goes through Kilbarchan.

Opening for: Scottish Wildlife Trust Ltd & St Vincents Hospice Limited

Renfrewshire

4 PERCH CORNER

25 Stanely Crescent, Paisley PA2 9LF
Bob and Elaine Moffett

Perch Corner is a large, south-facing garden extending to over half an acre with formal areas and woodland paths. The garden overlooks Stanely Reservoir and beyond to the Gleniffer Braes. Planting consists of a vibrant array of mature shrubs and rare trees, which are more often found in extensive west coast gardens, including a range of magnolias, camellias, rhododendrons, azaleas and acers. Specimens include *Davidia Involucrata*, tulipa, copper beeches and cornus. Children are welcome to explore in the woodland area and garden.

Open: Sunday 22 May, 2pm - 5pm, admission £4.00, children free.

Directions: From the M8 take exit 28a and follow signs for *RAH Hospital*. Continue on Corsebar Road past the hospital to Moredun Road. Right onto Stanely Road, first right to Stanely Avenue. Continue and bear left at the postbox. Look for the *SGS* signs. From the south, take the B775 down Gleniffer Braes. First left after the Jet petrol station onto Stanely Avenue then as above. From Barrhead take the B774 to Paisley, left at the Splash carwash onto Glenburn Road. Follow Glenburn Road to the end, turn right onto Gleniffer Road, then as above.

Opening for: Parkinsons UK

5 SGS KILMACOLM PLANT SALE

Outside Kilmacolm Library, Kilmacolm PA13 4LE
Scotland's Gardens Scheme

Spring plant sale in the middle of Kilmacolm.

Open: Saturday 30 April, 10am - noon, donations welcome.

Directions: The plant sale will be held at the Cross outside the Library and Cargill Centre in the middle of Kilmacolm. Accessible by McGill's buses.

Opening for: Pancreatic Cancer Scotland

6 WRAES

Corseliehill Road, nr Houston PA6 7HU
Tim and Jo Mack
T: 07985 156555 E: jomack22@gmail.com

Tranquil seven-acre garden developed since 2012, with far-reaching rural views. Only surviving historic 1860 wood planted by Lady Anne Spiers of Houston House for the Wraes, currently undergoing renovation with extensive new tree planting. Formal garden with raised herbaceous borders, woodland walk with 100 different rhododendron species and hybrids. Pond, burnside and cliffside walks, peaceful woodland walk with plentiful seating areas to relax and enjoy the views and tranquility. A great space for children to run and explore (under supervision). In 2020 a new apple and pear orchard, wildflower meadow and grass maze were planted

Open: Sunday 12 June, 2pm - 5pm. Also open by arrangement 1 May - 1 September. Admission £5.00, children free.

Directions: From Houston follow Barochan Road towards Langbank B789 for about a mile, turn left down Corseliehill Road. From Kilmacolm leave the village on Houston Road, past the golf course, turn left down Corseliehill Road for about a mile. Follow the yellow *SGS* signs.

Opening for: Breast Cancer Care

Roxburghshire

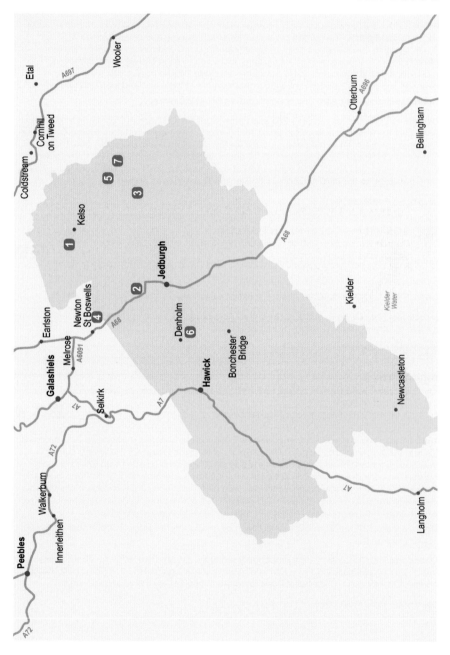

Roxburghshire

OUR VOLUNTEER ORGANISERS

District Organiser: Penny Wright   info@scotlandsgardens.org

Area Organisers: Julie Golding
                       Jane Robinson

District Photographer: Malcolm Ross

Treasurer: Vacant

GARDENS OPEN ON A SPECIFIC DATE

West Leas, Bonchester Bridge	Sunday, 5 June
Morebattle Village Gardens, Kelso	Sunday, 3 July
West Leas, Bonchester Bridge	Sunday, 7 August
Yetholm Village Gardens, Town Yetholm	Date to be advised

GARDENS OPEN REGULARLY

Monteviot, Jedburgh	1 April - 31 October
Floors Castle and Gardens, Kelso	9 April - 30 September
Stable House, Maxton, St Boswells, Melrose	1 May - 31 October (Mondays only)

GARDENS OPEN BY ARRANGEMENT

Thirlestane, Kelso	31 March - 31 October
West Leas, Bonchester Bridge	1 April - 31 December
Stable House, Maxton, St Boswells, Melrose	1 May - 31 October

Roxburghshire

1 FLOORS CASTLE AND GARDENS
Kelso TD5 7SF
The Duke of Roxburghe
T: 01573 223333
W: www.floorscastle.com

The gardens are situated within the grounds of Floors Castle. Meander through to the formal Millennium Parterre and soak up the spectacular visions of colour, texture and the most delicious scents around the four herbaceous borders in one of the finest Victorian kitchen gardens in Scotland. Features include, perennial gardens, fruit cage, Tapestry Garden and glasshouse access as well as the Terrace Cafe, Apple Shed Gift Shop and Deli and children's play area. Explore the grounds, which offer woodland and riverside walks from Easter to the end of September.

Open: 9 April - 30 September, 10:30am - 5pm, admission details can be found on the garden's website.

Directions: Floors Castle can be reached by following the A6089 from Edinburgh; the B6397 from Earlston; or the A698 from Coldstream. Go through Kelso, up Roxburgh Street to the Golden Gates.

Opening for: Donation to SGS

Floors Castle and Gardens

Roxburghshire

 2 **MONTEVIOT**
Jedburgh TD8 6UQ
Marquis and Marchioness of Lothian
T: 01835 830380
W: www.monteviot.com

A series of differing gardens displaying rose and herbaceous plants surrounded by foliage plants. A water feature linked by bridges and falls passes through the Dene Garden and Water Garden. The Garden of Persistent Imagination is planted with rose and clematis beside paths which meander across a bridge and under the Moonstone Gate, past the Dali-style clock.

Open: 1 April - 31 October, noon - 5pm, admission £6.00, children under 16 free. Card payments preferred.

Directions: Turn off A68, three miles north of Jedburgh on to B6400. After one mile turn right.

Opening for: Donation to SGS

3 **MOREBATTLE VILLAGE GARDENS**
Kelso TD5 8QU
The Gardeners of Morebattle

The attractive village of Morebattle lies seven miles south of Kelso in the foothills of the Cheviot range. It has an appealing range of colourful gardens to visit, formal and informal, large and small, looked after by enthusiastic gardeners. Wellbank, a former manse, is part of the quiet gardens movement. Outwith the village centre is a large cottage garden and two gardens of about an acre developed at a former farm steading, with extensive views of the Eildon Hills and beyond. The Granary has recently established stone terraces with shrub, vegetable and herbaceous beds. The Steading is a wildlife friendly organic garden which is aiming for self sufficiency in fruit and vegetables. It has a small meadow, ponds, orchard and vegetable areas, and informal rose and herbaceous borders. The open gardens are listed below.
21 Mainsfield Avenue (NEW) TD5 8QW (Liz Watson)
4 Renwick Gardens (NEW) TD5 8QB (Helen Cessford)
Caleb's Cottage (NEW) TD5 8QU (Sandra Redhead)
Mainsfield (NEW) TD5 8QW (Jane McIntyre):
The Granary (NEW) TD5 8QU (Roger Henderson)
The Steading (NEW) TD5 8QU (Ms Helen Kemp)
Wellbank (NEW) TD5 8QN (Matilda Hall)

Open: Sunday 3 July, 10:30am - 5pm, admission £5.00, children free.

Directions: Morebattle is seven miles south of Kelso and 10 miles east of Jedburgh. It is on the B6401 between Yetholm and Kalemouth. There is parking in the village and at the Granary.

Opening for: Friends of the Earth Scotland & Médecins Sans Frontières

Roxburghshire

4 STABLE HOUSE
Maxton, St Boswells, Melrose TD6 0EX
Ian Dalziel
T: 01835 824262 E: imd4@mac.com

An enclosed private garden around converted stables with a sunny courtyard. The garden extends to over half an acre and includes mixed borders in sun and shade, a wildflower meadow, a plant house and a hot border. A crevice garden with alpine plants has been enlarged over the winter. The garden was featured in the *Border Life* programme on ITV Border in January 2021.

Open: 1 May - 31 October (Mondays only), 2pm - 5pm. Also open by arrangement 1 May - 31 October. Admission £4.00, children free.

Directions: Two minutes from the A68 on the A699 to Kelso.

Opening for: Sight Scotland

5 THIRLESTANE
Kelso TD5 8PD
Catherine Ross and John Wylie
T: 01573 420487

Thirlestane is a large, informal garden, with some rough ground and long grass. It previously opened as one of the Yetholm gardens, but since then a nine-acre wood has been planted. This young woodland has a wide mix of trees, including some specimen trees, with fine autumn colour in October. There are two ponds and a burn. An orchard has about 50 varieties of apples and other fruit trees. Beech hedges enclose prairie planting in a formal setting. There is an enclosed flower garden, raised beds for vegetables and colour-themed planting.

Open: by arrangement 31 March - 31 October, admission £5.00, children free. Please feel free to bring a picnic to enjoy in the garden.

Directions: Thirlestane is near Yetholm, not to be confused with Thirlestane, Lauder. Do not follow SatNav, it will try to take you to Lochside. From Kelso, take the B6352 towards Yetholm for about six miles. Continue past a cottage on the edge of the road. Thirlestane is next on the left, opposite the road to Lochside. From Yetholm, take the road to Kelso for about two miles. After a very sharp corner, Thirlestane is on the right.

Opening for: Macmillan Cancer Support

6 WEST LEAS
Bonchester Bridge TD9 8TD
Mr and Mrs Robert Laidlaw
T: 01450 860711 E: ann@johnlaidlawandson.co.uk

The visitor to West Leas can share in an exciting and dramatic project on a grand scale, still in the making. At its core is a passion for plants, allied to a love and understanding of the land in which they are set. Collections of perennials and shrubs, many in temporary holding quarters, lighten up the landscape to magical effect. New lily pond and woodland planting added in 2019 and a new courtyard garden is under construction.

Open: Sunday 5 June, 2pm - 5pm. Also open Sunday 7 August, 2pm - 5pm. And open by arrangement 1 April - 31 December. Admission £4.00, children free. Teas for the specific date openings will be served in Bedrule Village Hall, Bonchester Bridge, Hawick TD9 8TE

Directions: Signposted off the Jedburgh/Bonchester Bridge Road.

Opening for: Macmillan Cancer Support: Borders Appeal

Roxburghshire

Thirlestane

 **YETHOLM VILLAGE GARDENS**
Town Yetholm TD5 8RL
The Gardeners of Yetholm Village

The villages of Town Yetholm and Kirk Yetholm are situated at the north end of the Pennine Way, close to the Bowmont Water in the dramatic setting of the foothills of the Cheviots. A variety of gardens will be open, each with their own unique features and style, reflecting distinctive horticultural interests. The short walking distance between the majority of the gardens provides magnificent views of the surrounding landscape.

Open: Further details and date will be available via the Scotland's Gardens Scheme website.

Directions: Equidistant between Edinburgh and Newcastle and south of Kelso in the Scottish Borders. Take the B6352 to Town Yetholm. Ample parking is available along the High Street.

Opening for: Charity to be confirmed

Stirlingshire

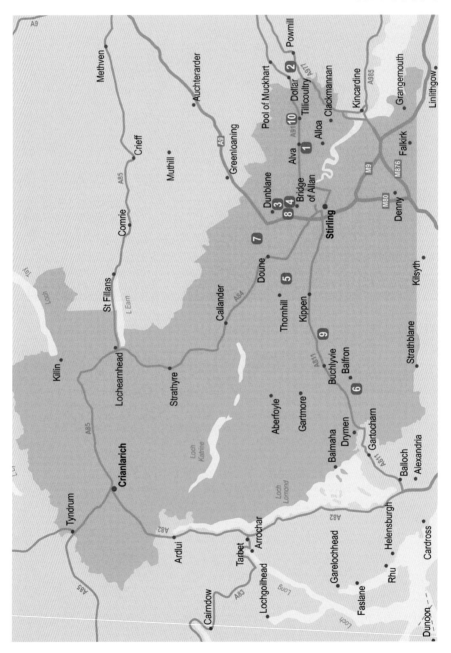

Stirlingshire

OUR VOLUNTEER ORGANISERS

District Organisers:	Graham Silcocks	Craigrennie, Queen Street, Doune FK16 6DP
District Administrator:	Jo Dormer	
Area Organisers:	Sylvia Broomfield	
	Clare Giles	Carselea Farm, Blair Drummond FK9 4UP
	Morna Knottenbelt	Gardener's Cottage, Killearn G63 9QB
	Rosemary Leckie	Auchengarroch, Bridge of Allan FK9 4DX
	Ann Shaw	Plaka, Bridge of Allan FK9 4LY
Treasurer:	David Ashton	Westmore Shiel, Cauldhame, Kippen FK8 3JB

GARDENS OPEN ON A SPECIFIC DATE

Kilbryde Castle, Dunblane	Sunday, 22 May
Bridge of Allan Gardens, Bridge of Allan	Sunday, 29 May
Tillicoultry Parish Church Community Garden, Tillicoultry	Sunday, 3 July
60 Greenhead, Alva, Clackmannanshire	Sunday, 7 August
Ault Wharrie, Ardnablane, Dunblane	Sunday, 14 August
Coldoch, Blairdrummond, Stirling	Sunday, 18 September

GARDENS OPEN BY ARRANGEMENT

Thorntree, Arnprior	1 February - 31 October
Kilbryde Castle, Dunblane	1 March - 30 September
Milseybank, Bridge of Allan	1 May - 31 May
Arndean, by Dollar	9 May - 5 June
Gardener's Cottage Walled Garden, Ballochruin Road, Killearn	15 June - 15 October

Stirlingshire

1 60 GREENHEAD
Alva, Clackmannanshire FK12 5HH
Lynn Cameron

A delightful hidden garden in Alva behind the primary school. Divided into 'rooms' with themes, two being Mediterranean and Oriental, there is extensive planting and clever use of pots throughout. Recycled materials are much in evidence, especially in the 'cosy' corner with a fireplace. There is a wide variety of shrubs, perennials and annuals as well as vegetables and fruit. There is a pond and a small wildlife area. There is also a 'folly' created during the lockdown of 2020. An inspiration for those trying to garden in a small space. We would ask that all children are to be accompanied.

Open: Sunday 7 August, 2pm - 5pm, admission £5.00, accompanied children free.

Directions: Signposted from the A91. Please park with consideration for other houses in the area.

Opening for: Stirling Baptist Church & CAP: Forth Valley Debt Centre

2 ARNDEAN
by Dollar FK14 7NH
Johnny and Katie Stewart
T: 07940530499 E: johnny@arndean.co.uk

Opening for more than 40 years, this is a beautiful mature garden extending to 15 acres including the woodland walk. There is a formal herbaceous part, a small vegetable garden and an orchard. In addition, there are flowering shrubs, abundant and striking rhododendrons and azaleas as well as many fine specimen trees. There is a tree house for children.

Open: by arrangement 9 May - 5 June, admission £5.00, children free.

Directions: Arndean is well signposted off the A977.

Opening for: Marie Curie

3 AULT WHARRIE
Ardnablane, Dunblane FK15 0NU
Bill Carman and Celia Aitken
E: Bill.f.carman@gmail.com

Ault Wharrie was formerly the Masonic Home in Dunblane. The extensive grounds have been redesigned and replanted over the last five years. These have benefitted from the shelter provided by mature trees and there are many flowering shrubs including rhododendron, camellia and magnolia. A parterre, a rockery and a large pond are all complemented by colourful herbaceous borders with a good mixture of plants including dahlias interspersed with annuals.

Open: Sunday 14 August, 2pm - 5pm, admission £5.00, children free. Please note that not all the garden is open to the public and the owners request that visitors obey any 'no entry' signs.

Directions: From the Fourways roundabout in Dunblane take the Glen Road, then the second left into Leewood Road. Continue and follow the *yellow* signs into Ardnablane. Take the first right beside a lodge and follow the directions given about parking. Overflow parking is on Leewood Road. The garden is about a 20 minute walk from Dunblane station.

Opening for: Strathcarron Hospice

Stirlingshire

4 BRIDGE OF ALLAN GARDENS
Bridge of Allan FK9 4DX
The Gardeners of Bridge of Allan
T: 07906838205 E: r.leckie44@btinternet.com

Bridge of Allan is an attractive village north of Stirling with the River Allan running through. There will be a selection of larger and smaller gardens on show, with various species of rhododendrons and azaleas, trees and shrubs and plants and flowers. Some of the gardens have water features, another has a Japanese 'Karesansui' dry stream and pond with a turtle island. One of the gardens, developed on a steep slope, shows 'rooms' designed with a variety of plants and shrubs. Many gardens feature sculptures. After the successful opening last year, we are delighted that the Bridge of Allan allotments will open again this year showing a variety of fruit, vegetables and flowers.

1 Anne Drive FK9 4RE (John and Elizabeth Rankin)
101a Henderson Street FK9 4HH (Rachel and Ronnie McEwan)
9 Mayne Avenue FK9 4QU (Donald and Nancy McLean)
Auchengarroch 16 Chalton Road FK9 4DX (Rosemary Leckie)
Plaka 5 Pendreich Road FK9 4LY (Malcolm and Ann Shaw)
Bridge of Allan Allotments Cornton Road FK9 4DA (The Gardeners of Bridge of Allan Allotments)

Open: Sunday 29 May, 1pm - 5pm, admission £5.00, children free. Entrance tickets and maps will be available from the Village Garden beside the Church in Keir Street, where there will also be a plant sale. Additional gardens may be open: further details can be found on Scotland's Gardens Scheme website. Tea and scones may be served in the Church.

Directions: Gardens will be signposted from the village.

Opening for: Artlink Central Ltd & St Saviours Episcopal Church: Bridge Of Allan

Ault Wharrie © Ann Shaw

Stirlingshire

5 COLDOCH

Blairdrummond, Stirling FK9 4XD
David & Kim Stewart and Tim Black
T: 01786 841217

The garden at Coldoch is sheltered by belts of mature woodland on three sides and looks south over the Carse of Stirling. The parterre courtyard garden and border have replaced the old farm buildings and lead on to a kitchen garden created by using the three old walls of an earlier rose garden. The less formal areas include a stream, a pond, paddocks and woodland. The drives are lined with old oaks and sycamores mixed with new trees from Eastern Europe, Central Asia and some fine, mature cherry trees.

Open: Sunday 18 September, 2pm - 5pm, admission £5.00, children free.

Directions: Signed from the A84. Take the A873 for Aberfoyle, after just under one mile turn left on to Coldoch Road, B8031 and continue for approximately half a mile. Wrought iron gates on the left mark the entrance.

Opening for: St Modocs Episcopal Church

6 GARDENER'S COTTAGE WALLED GARDEN

Ballochruin Road, Killearn G63 9QB
Morna Knottenbelt
T: 01360 551682 E: mornaknottenbelt@hotmail.com

The walled garden, acquired in 2013 by the present owners, has been planted with extensive herbaceous borders, box hedging, roses and many unusual plants. There is a White Garden, a long shrub border with primulas and gentians and a former fernery with a collection of salvias and peach and pear trees. June is a good time to visit when the roses are in bloom and borders with lupins, peonies and other perennials are in flower. By late summer, the borders have argyranthemums as well as dahlias, Michaelmas daisies, rudbeckias and blue aconitums. The Celtic Cross Garden was planted in May 2021 with a range of new plants including echinaceas, cardoons, lobelias, anthemis and lavender for mid to late summer colour. There are fine views of the Campsie Hills and the garden is surrounded by the conifers of the Designed Landscape of Carbeth.

Open: by arrangement 15 June - 15 October, admission £5.00, children free. The garden owners welcome visitors at short notice (the day before planned visits) and small numbers and individuals are welcome.

Directions: Follow SatNav to G63 0LF, which is Carbeth Home Farm. We are the next entrance below the farm. Turn left on to the gravel road and follow yellow *SGS* signs.

Opening for: The British Horse Society: Scotland

7 KILBRYDE CASTLE

Dunblane FK15 9NF
Sir James and Lady Campbell
T: 01786 824897 E: carolaandjames@googlemail.com
W: www.kilbrydecastle.com

Kilbryde Castle gardens cover some 12 acres and are situated above the Ardoch Burn and below the castle. The gardens are split into three parts: formal, woodland and wild. Natural planting (azaleas, rhododendrons, camellias and magnolias) is found in the woodland garden. There are glorious snowdrops, spring bulbs, and autumn colour provided by clematis and acers. Some new plantings for additional late summer/autumn colour were added in 2017.

Stirlingshire

Open: Sunday 22 May, 11am - 5pm. Also open by arrangement 1 March - 30 September. Admission £5.00, children free. A Plant Fair is being planned for 22 May. Refreshments will also be available.

Directions: Three miles from Dunblane and Doune, off the A820 between Dunblane and Doune. On Scotland's Gardens Scheme open days the garden is signposted from the A820.

Opening for: Leighton Library Trust

Gardener's Cottage Walled Garden © Morna Knottenbelt

Stirlingshire

8 MILSEYBANK

Bridge of Allan FK9 4NB
Murray and Sheila Airth
T: 07799036367 E: smairth@hotmail.com

Wonderful and interesting sloping garden with outstanding views, terraced for ease of access. Woodland with bluebells, rhododendrons, magnolias and camellias, and many other unusual plants, including a big variety of meconopsis. This is a true plantsman's garden with quiet corners to sit, admire and reflect. A garden to inspire you and give you ideas to take home. National Plant Collection: Meconopsis.

Open: by arrangement 1 May - 31 May, admission £5.00, children free.

Directions: Situated on the A9, one mile from junction 11, M9 and a quarter-of-a-mile from Bridge of Allan. Milseybank is at the top of the lane at Lecropt Nursery, 250 yards from the Bridge of Allan train station.

Opening for: Strathcarron Hospice

9 THORNTREE

Arnprior FK8 3EY
Mark and Carol Seymour
T: 01786 870710 E: carolseymour666@gmail.com
W: www.thorntreebarn.co.uk

After the difficulties of 2020/2021, this year Thorntree is opening by arrangement only, but they are looking forward to welcoming visitors. Carol will happily walk round the garden with you or you can wander on your own. The garden continues to evolve and cotoneasters by the saltire beds have been cut back which means the four flower beds are no longer hidden behind a hedge! Also, the view past the summerhouse can be seen and the Annabelle hydrangea has popped up now that there are fewer branches above it. It is an inspiring garden to visit at any time of the year. From the garden you can see panoramic views from Ben Lomond to Doune, watching the Forth meander down the bottom of the valley. Please note: plants are always available for sale as part of the trainee experience under the WRAGS scheme.

Open: by arrangement 1 February - 31 October, admission £5.00, children free.

Directions: On the A811, to Arnprior, then take the Fintry Road; Thorntree is second on the right.

Opening for: Forth Driving Group RDA SCIO

Stirlingshire

10 ## TILLICOULTRY PARISH CHURCH COMMUNITY GARDEN
Dollar Road, Tillicoultry, Clackmannanshire FK13 6PD
Mrs E Nicolson
T: 01259 750040 or 07593166706 E: eleanornicolson@yahoo.co.uk
W: www.tillicoultryparishchurch.co.uk

A former orchard to the Manse of Tillicoultry Parish Church, this garden has been developed by a group of enthusiastic volunteers, from a derelict and unloved piece of ground into a much-loved haven for the local community. It is used for moments of quiet contemplation, for young children where they can explore safely and freely, for youth groups and for all members of the community. This space is a comfort and an inspiration to all who visit and it is a testimony to what can be achieved when a community comes together.

Open: Sunday 3 July, 2pm - 5pm, admission £5.00, children free.

Directions: Located on the A91 - Dollar Road - next to Tillicoultry Parish Church. There is plenty of parking space to the rear of the church. The nearest bus stop is 'Cemetery stop' on X53 Kinross service from Stirling (approx 39 minutes).

Opening for: Tillicoultry Parish Church of Scotland

Tillicoultry Parish Church Community Garden

Wigtownshire

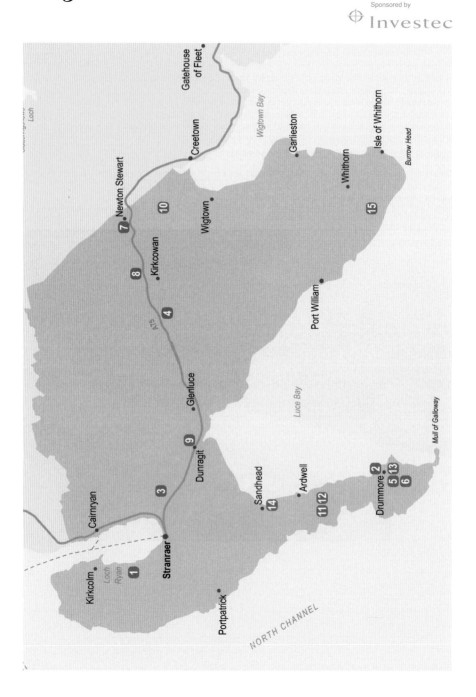

Wigtownshire

OUR VOLUNTEER ORGANISERS

District Organiser:	Ann Watson	Doonholm, Cairnryan Road, Stranraer DG9 8AT Email: info@scotlandsgardens.org
Area Organisers:	Colin Belton	Amulree, 8 Mill Street, Drummore DG9 9PS
	Teri Birch	The Old Manse, Gruisey House, Sandhead DG9 9JT
	Eileen Davie	Whitehills House, Minnigaff DG8 6SL
	Mary Gladstone	Craichlaw, Kirkcowan DG8 0DQ
	Shona Greenhorn	Burbainie, Westwood Avenue DG9 8BT
	Annmaree Mitchell	Cottage 2, Little Float, Sandhead DG9 9LD
District Photographer:	Stuart Littlewood	Tayvallich, West Port, New Galloway DG7 3SB

GARDENS OPEN ON A SPECIFIC DATE

Logan Botanic Garden, Port Logan, by Stranraer	Sunday, 22 May
Logan House Gardens, Port Logan, by Stranraer	Sunday, 22 May
Damnaglaur House with The Homestead and Mid Curghie, Drummore	Sunday, 5 June
Castle Kennedy and Gardens, Stranraer	Sunday, 12 June
Woodfall Gardens, Glasserton	Saturday/Sunday, 18/19 June
Aldouran Wetland Garden, Kirkland Bank, Leswalt	Saturday, 25 June
Woodfall Gardens, Glasserton	Sunday, 10 July
Amulree, 8 Mill Street, Drummore	Saturday/Sunday, 16/17 July
Damnaglaur House, Drummore	Saturday/Sunday, 16/17 July
Rawson Garden, 1, High Drummore Cottages, Drummore	Saturday/Sunday, 16/17 July

GARDENS OPEN REGULARLY

Glenwhan Gardens, Dunragit, by Stranraer	1 January - 31 December
Castle Kennedy	Check the garden's website for opening details

GARDENS OPEN BY ARRANGEMENT

Craichlaw, Kirkcowan, Newton Stewart	1 January - 31 December
Fernlea Garden, Corvisel Road, Newton Stewart	1 April - 30 September
Liggat Cheek Cottage, Baltersan, Newton Stewart	1 April - 30 September
Glasnick Smithy/House on Stilts, Glasnick Smithy, Newton Stewart	1 April - 30 September
The Old Manse, Sandhead	1 May - 30 September
Damnaglaur House, Drummore	1 May - 31 October
Rawson Garden, 1, High Drummore Cottages, Drummore	1 June - 30 September

Wigtownshire

1 ALDOURAN WETLAND GARDEN
Kirkland Bank, Leswalt DG9 0LJ
The Volunteers at Aldouran Wetland Garden
W: aldouran.org

Aldouran Glen, which means 'Glen of the Otter', is a unique blend of colourful community gardens, a natural water area with reed beds and a wild woodland with all-access trails, fairy doors and fantasy artwork including a nine foot Gruffalo.

Open: Saturday 25 June, dawn – dusk, admission by donation.

Directions: The garden lies off Glen Road on the outskirts of the village of Leswalt, three miles from Stranraer on the A718. It is well signposted and can also be accessed by bus from Stranraer, being a stop on the Stranraer-Kirkcolm service.

Opening for: Aldouran Wetland Garden Leswalt

2 AMULREE
8 Mill Street, Drummore, Stranraer DG9 9PS
Mr Colin Belton and Mrs Gabrielle Reynolds
T: 0789 909 2070 E: gabygardeners@btinternet.com

Amulree is home to two complete plantaholics who probably should start taking their own advice and stop collecting quite so many plants! Starting from a blank canvas in 2017 the garden now consists of a sunny terrace with displays of half-hardy and tender plants, exuberantly planted borders separated by serpentine grass patches, a small vegetable patch, a glasshouse and a 'wild' bit. Amulree contains many unusual plants including a National Plant Collection. National Plant Collection: *Nicotiana* species.

Open: Saturday/Sunday, 16/17 July, 10am - 4pm, admission £5.00, children free. Opening with Damnaglaur House and Rawson Garden, where refreshments will be available; all three gardens can be visited for £10.00.

Directions: Follow A716 signposted *Drummore and Mull of Galloway*. At the T junction in Drummore turn right. Amulree is on the left, a few doors up from the shop. Bus route 407 from Stranraer.

Opening for: Charity to be confirmed

3 CASTLE KENNEDY AND GARDENS
Stranraer DG9 8SJ
The Earl and Countess of Stair
T: 01581 400225
W: www.castlekennedygardens.com

Romantically situated, these famous 75 acres of landscaped gardens are located on an isthmus surrounded by two large natural lochs. At one end, the ruined Castle Kennedy overlooks a beautiful herbaceous walled garden with Lochinch Castle at the other end. With over 300 years of planting, there is an impressive collection of rare trees, rhododendrons, exotic shrubs and many spectacular Champion Trees. The stunning snowdrop walks, daffodils, spring flowers, rhododendron and magnolia displays and herbaceous borders make this a 'must visit' garden throughout the year.
Champion Trees: 95 in total; including 12 British, 30 Scottish, 44 for Dumfries and Galloway and 9 trees described as 'otherwise remarkable'.

Wigtownshire

Open: Sunday 12 June, 10am - 5pm, admission details can be found on the garden's website. Castle Kennedy is also open through the season and admission details for all openings can be found on their website.

Directions: On the A75, five miles east of Stranraer. The nearest train station is in Stranraer. On a local bus route.

Opening for: Home-Start Wigtownshire

4 CRAICHLAW

Kirkcowan, Newton Stewart DG8 0DQ
Mr and Mrs Andrew Gladstone
T: 01671 830208 E: craichlaw@aol.com

Formal garden with herbaceous borders around the house. Set in extensive grounds with lawns, lochs and woodland. A path around the main loch leads to a water garden returning past a recently planted arboretum in the old walled garden. The best times to visit the garden are early February for snowdrops, May to mid-June for the water garden and rhododendrons, and mid-June to August for herbaceous borders.

Open: by arrangement 1 January - 31 December, admission £5.00, children free. We have Snowdrops and Winter Walks from February to mid-March.

Directions: Take the B733 for Kirkcowan off the A75 at the Halfway House eight miles west of Newton Stewart. Craichlaw House is the first turning on the right.

Opening for: SGS and Beneficiaries

Craichlaw

Wigtownshire

5 DAMNAGLAUR HOUSE
Drummore, Stranraer DG9 9QN
Frances Collins
T: 01776 840636/ 07884 435353

Since moving into Damnaglaur House in 1991, its owners have totally transformed the garden, putting in a series of 'semi-terraces' and, following the planting of wind-defeating shrubs, they were able to introduce many special herbaceous plants and trees. Just short of half-an-acre, the garden has slowly evolved into one which feels substantially larger because of its design; the gravel paths weave their way through many hidden corners to come upon countless gems. The views from the garden are stunning, down to Drummore, across Luce Bay and in the far distance, to the Galloway Hills. An archway, arbour and pergola give extra height for the planting. Seating around the garden gives visitors a chance to sit and enjoy their surroundings, especially close to the pond with its numerous fish and trickling waterfall. Various areas have been replanted in 2021.

Open: Saturday/Sunday, 16/17 July, 12:30pm - 4pm. Also open by arrangement 1 May - 31 October. Admission £4.00, children free. Also opening as a group with The Homestead and Mid Curghie on Sunday 5 June; and with Amulree and Rawson Garden on 16/17 July, when all three gardens may be visited for £10.00.

Directions: From Drummore, follow signs to the *Mull of Galloway* for a mile on the B7041 to junction with B7065; Damnaglaur is on the right.

Opening for: British Red Cross: Yemen Appeal

6 DAMNAGLAUR HOUSE WITH THE HOMESTEAD AND MID CURGHIE
Drummore, Stranraer DG9 9QN
Frances Collins, Agnes McClymont and Carol Rennison

Damnaglaur House Drummore, Stranraer DG9 9QN (Frances Collins): See garden details under Damnaglaur House opening.
Mid Curghie (NEW) Kirkmalden DG9 9QR (Agnes McClymont): When we moved here in 2008, the garden was mainly laid in grass with no beds to speak of. We created new borders, starting as purely herbaceous, then introduced evergreen shrubs for more year round interest. The garden slopes down to a small orchard with a burn running alongside.
The Homestead (NEW) Drummore DG9 9QN (Carol Rennison): With a panoramic view over farmland to Luce Bay and the Galloway Hills beyond, The Homestead's one-third-acre garden has developed over the last 12 years. Lawns, gravel garden and shrubs dominate with self-sown alchemilla, violets and valerian growing profusely. Pots and containers highlight certain areas, while driftwood furniture and features made from beach findings adding to the still changing look. It is a lovely garden to sit and contemplate. Even better with the homemade cakes available on the Open Day.

Open: Sunday 5 June, 12:30pm - 4pm, admission £9.00, children free for all three gardens. Individual garden visits £4.00 per garden, children free. Homemade teas at The Homestead.

Directions: Damnaglaur House and The Homestead: from Drummore, follow signs to the *Mull of Galloway* for a mile on the B7041 to junction with B7065; Damnaglaur is on the right.
Mid Curghie heading along the A716 to Drummore, travel along beside the 'sea wall' then take the first right up through the Glen and Mid Curghie is at the top.

Opening for: British Red Cross: Yemen Appeal

Wigtownshire

7 **FERNLEA GARDEN**
Corvisel Road, Newton Stewart DG8 6LW
Mrs Jenny Gustafson
T: 07909 951 885/ 01671 638273 E: jennygustafson2@hotmail.com

A secluded town garden of a third of an acre, created in 2006 to complement a new house. There are many rare and unusual trees and shrubs. Two herbaceous borders, one with hot colours and the other pastels. A Chinese-inspired corner, small pond, fruit trees including a Galloway pippin apple and soft fruit. The upper part of the garden is hidden behind a tall beech hedge, where there is a summer house and adjacent woodland planting.

Open: by arrangement 1 April - 30 September, admission £4.50, children free. Plants for sale.

Directions: Turn right at the roundabout on the A75 if coming from Dumfries direction. Go left at the cattle market (opposite Crown Hotel), first through road on the right.

Opening for: The Woodland Trust Scotland

8 **GLASNICK SMITHY/HOUSE ON STILTS**
Glasnick Smithy, Newton Stewart, Dumfries and Galloway DG8 0ED
Ms Liz Stansbridge
T: 07789 792549 E: lizstansbridge@yahoo.com

Glasnick Smithy is the iconic 'House on Stilts' on the A75. I have been developing this acre of land over the last 13 years into a beautiful and productive garden. There is a large pond, areas of woodland in different stages of development, herbaceous borders, fruit pockets, polytunnel, vegetable and flower cutting gardens and sitting areas. I use the 'no dig' method pioneered by Charles Dowding and aim for abundance while still leaving room for wildlife.

Open: by arrangement 1 April - 30 September, admission £5.00, children free. Due to limited parking, viewing is by prior arrangement only. Plant sales, vegetables and flowers available seasonally.

Directions: From Newton Stewart roundabout head on the A75 towards Stranraer, Glasnick Smithy is four and a half miles on the right.

Opening for: Marie Curie

9 **GLENWHAN GARDENS**
Dunragit, by Stranraer DG9 8PH
Tessa Knott
T: 07787 990702
W: www.glenwhangardens.co.uk

Described as one of the most beautiful gardens in Scotland, Glenwhan Gardens is situated at 300 feet and overlooks Luce Bay and the Mull of Galloway, with clear views to the Isle of Man. Forty years ago there was wild moorland, but now, following considerable dedication and vision, you can see glorious collections of plants from around the world. There is colour in all seasons and the winding paths, well-placed seats and varied sculptures, set around small lakes, add to the tranquil atmosphere. There is a 17-acre moorland wildflower walk, the chance to see red squirrels and a well-marked Tree Trail.

Open: 1 January - 31 December, 10am - 5pm, admission by donation. Admission to Gardens at entrance.

Directions: Seven miles east of Stranraer, one mile off the A75 at Dunragit (follow brown *VisitScotland* and yellow SGS arrows).

Opening for: Scotland's Gardens Scheme SCIO

Wigtownshire

10 LIGGAT CHEEK COTTAGE

Baltersan, Newton Stewart DG8 6AX
Philip and Jennifer Bradley
T: 01671 402639 E: bradley@liggat.plus.com

The garden is approximately half-an-acre and includes a small woodland and shaded area with ferns, hostas, trilliums, erythroniums and many other shade-loving plants. The rest of the garden is divided into informal 'rooms' with large borders containing herbaceous perennials, shrubs, conifers, grasses, etc. There is one south-facing bed devoted to less hardy plants including agaves, yuccas, cordylines, aeoniums and tetrapanax. The garden was featured in an episode of *The Beechgrove Garden* on 5 September 2019.

Open: by arrangement 1 April - 30 September, admission £4.00, children free. Teas and plants may be available by prior request.

Directions: From Newton Stewart roundabout (A75) towards Wigtown (A714) *Scotland's National Book Town*. Approximately two miles from the roundabout on the right, above Baltersan Farm on the left.

Opening for: Euan Macdonald Centre for Motor Neurone Disease Research

Liggat Cheek Cottage

Wigtownshire

11 **LOGAN BOTANIC GARDEN**
Port Logan, by Stranraer DG9 9ND
A Regional Garden of the Royal Botanic Garden Edinburgh
T: 01776 860231 E: logan@rbge.org.uk
W: www.rbge.org.uk/logan

Logan Botanic Garden lies at the south western tip of Scotland, unrivalled as 'Scotland's Most Exotic Garden'. Warmed by the Gulf Stream, a remarkable collection of southern hemisphere plants flourish, making this a plantsman's paradise. Logan enjoys an almost subtropical climate where the Garden's avenues and borders feature a spectacular and colourful array of half-hardy perennials. The Garden is warmed by the Gulf Stream which enables plants from Australia, New Zealand, South and Central America and Southern Africa to thrive. Voted 'Best Garden in the UK' 2021, Logan promises a delightful day out for all'.
National Plant Collection: *Gunnera, Leptospermum, Griselinia, Clianthus* and *Sutherlandia.*
Champion Trees: *Polylepis* and *Eucalyptus.*

Open: Sunday 22 May, 10am - 5pm, admission details can be found on the garden's website.

Directions: Ten miles south of Stranraer on the A716 then two-and-a-half miles from Ardwell village.

Opening for: Board Of Trustees Of The Royal Botanic Garden Edinburgh

12 **LOGAN HOUSE GARDENS**
Port Logan, by Stranraer DG9 9ND
Mr and Mrs Andrew Roberts

A mature woodland garden of 20 acres with fine species of rhododendrons, champion trees and plants from the Southern Hemisphere.
Champion Trees: 7 UK and 11 Scottish.

Open: Sunday 22 May, 2pm - 4:30pm, admission £5.00, children free. Dogs on a lead are welcome to have a walk round the garden.

Directions: On the A716, 13 miles south of Stranraer, two-and-a-half miles from Ardwell Village. The garden is situated next door to Logan Botanic Gardens.

Opening for: Port Logan Hall

Wigtownshire

13 RAWSON GARDEN

1, High Drummore Cottages, Drummore, Stranraer DG9 9QL
Beverley Darville
E: darvy@sky.com

Rawson Garden is a large cottage garden with a stunning sea view. The garden is divided into different parts, including a self-contained Bothy. It has a plethora of shrubs, flowers, pine trees, bamboo, palm trees and a small waterfall with a burn that runs through the garden. There are three tiers to the garden separated by paths and steps, with patios and a large decking area. Seating is interspersed throughout the garden and this year the owners have added some garden sculptures and bird houses. A wonderful garden to explore and somewhere to sit and admire the gorgeous view.

Open: Saturday/Sunday, 16/17 July, 12:30pm - 4pm. Also open by arrangement 1 June - 30 September. Admission £4.00, children free. The garden is opening with Damnaglaur House and Amulree on 16/17 July, when all three gardens may be visited for £10.00, and refreshments will be available at Rawson Garden and Damnaglaur House. Accommodation available at The Bothy and Rawson Cottage; email darvy@sky.com for more information.

Directions: From Stranraer, head out to Drummore and Mull of Galloway on the A716. 16 miles from Stranraer, follow signs through Drummore for Mull of Galloway, come up the hill past the farm building on the right, follow the road round and Rawson Garden is the first cottage on the right after farm and a pair of big green gates.

Opening for: NSPCC

Rawson Garden

14 THE OLD MANSE

Sandhead, Stranraer DG9 9JT
Mrs Teri Birch
T: 01776 830455 E: birchteri@gmail.com

Recently designed, landscaped and replanted by the current owners who are keen to develop the garden to its full potential. Comprising about half an acre, the garden is surrounded by stone walls and has a burn running through it. Recent projects include a formal parterre, a rose garden, herbaceous borders and rockeries. The planting is creative and thoughtful, using grasses, bulbs, annuals, herbaceous perennials and alpines to make full use of the temperate climate enjoyed in this location. Current projects include developing a shady woodland area.

Wigtownshire

Open: by arrangement 1 May - 30 September, admission £5.00, children free.

Directions: From Stranraer take A716 south following signs for Drummore; past Sandhead, look for a tourist sign for Kirkmadrine Stones and Clachanmore and turn immediately right. The Old Manse is on the corner on the right (known locally as 'Doctors' Corner'). A bus service is available from Stranraer and stops at Doctors' Corner.

Opening for: Board Of Trustees Of The Royal Botanic Garden Edinburgh

15 WOODFALL GARDENS
Glasserton DG8 8LY
Ross and Liz Muir
E: woodfallgardens@btinternet.com
W: www.woodfall-gardens.co.uk

This lovely three-acre 18th-century triple walled garden has been thoughtfully restored to provide year-round interest. It contains many mature trees and shrubs, including some less common species, herbaceous borders and shrub roses which surround the foundations of original greenhouses, grass borders, a parterre, extensive beds of fruit and vegetables, a herb garden and a small woodland walk. This unusual garden is well worth a visit.

Open: Saturday/Sunday, 18/19 June, 10:30am - 4:30pm and Sunday 10 July, 10:30am - 4:30pm. Admission £5.00, children free. Please check the garden's website for further openings.

Directions: Two miles south west of Whithorn at junction of A746 and A747 (directly behind Glasserton Church).

Opening for: Whithorn Primary School

Woodfall Gardens

SUBSCRIBE

to Scottish Field and receive a FREE bottle of Arran Malt*

Perfect for those who love all things Scottish

Save 25% on the cover price only £10.69 per quarter delivered direct to your door.

Call **01778 392014** and quote **Garden22** or go to **scottishfield.co.uk/subscriptions**

Relax and enjoy our major monthly gardening features from Antoinette Galbraith and photos from Ray Cox, plus gardening news and much more.

James Byatt BSc (Hons) MLD

Garden & Estate Cartography

www.jamesbyatt.com
07796 591197
enquiries@jamesbyatt.com

Lochview Cottage Scarffbanks
Pitgaveny, Elgin
Moray IV30 5PQ

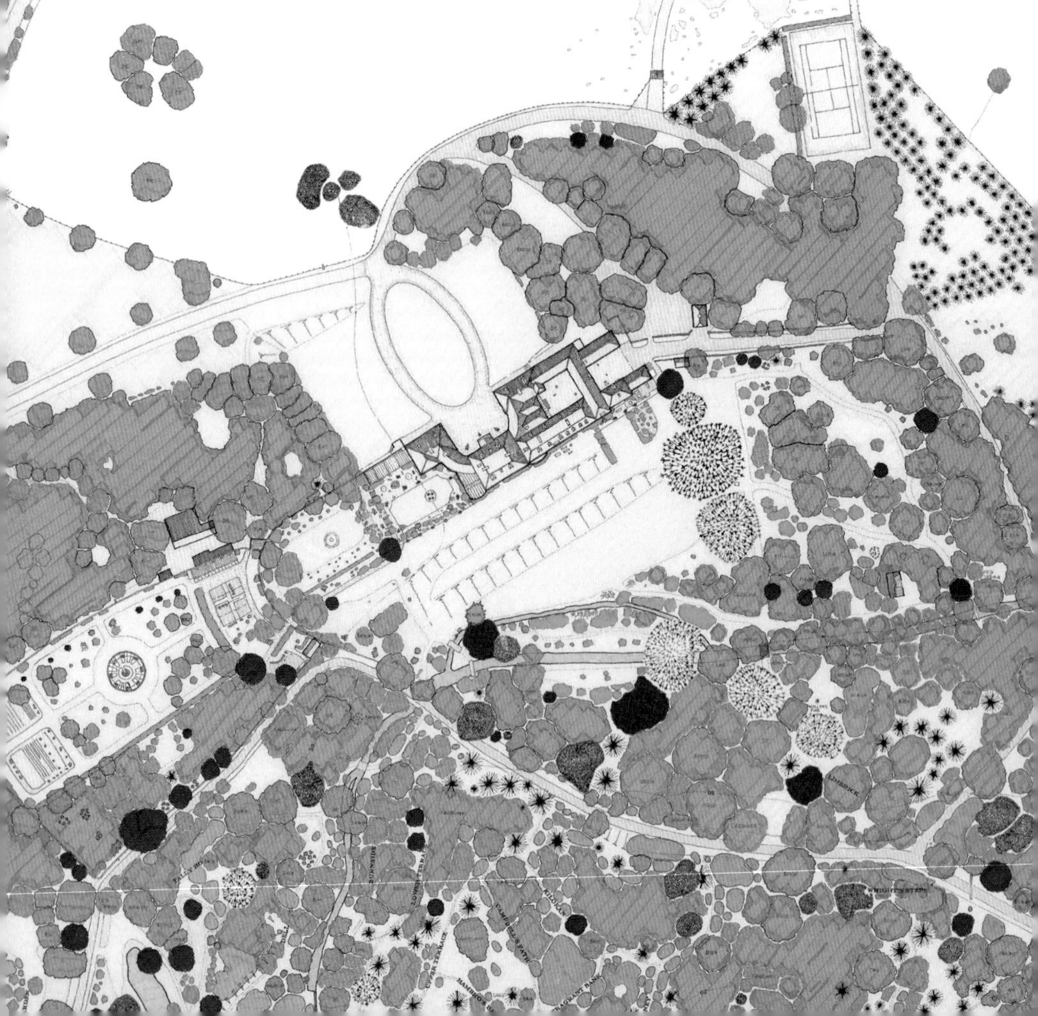

Award-Winning
Professional
Garden & Landscape
Photography
www.andreajones.co.uk

RHS
Membership

Bloom with an RHS membership

JOIN TODAY
rhs.org.uk/join

Becoming an RHS member supports our work as a charity

SAVE **25%** WHEN YOU PAY BY DIRECT DEBIT*

*Terms and conditions apply

Gardens open on a specific date

DATE TO BE ADVISED

Edinburgh, Midlothian and West Lothian
Dumfriesshire
Roxburghshire

Bonnington House by Jupiter Artland, Wilkieston
Portrack, The Garden of Cosmic Speculation, Holywood
Yetholm Village Gardens, Town Yetholm

FEBRUARY

Tuesday 1 February
Angus & Dundee

Dunninald Castle, Montrose

Sunday 6 February
Angus & Dundee
Fife

Dunninald Castle, Montrose
NEW Millfield Garden, Millfield House, Falkland

Monday 7 February
Angus & Dundee

Dunninald Castle, Montrose

Tuesday 8 February
Angus & Dundee

Dunninald Castle, Montrose

Thursday 10 February
East Lothian

Shepherd House, Inveresk, Musselburgh

Sunday 13 February
Angus & Dundee
Fife

Dunninald Castle, Montrose
NEW Millfield Garden, Millfield House, Falkland

Monday 14 February
Angus & Dundee

Dunninald Castle, Montrose

Tuesday 15 February
Angus & Dundee
East Lothian

Dunninald Castle, Montrose
Shepherd House, Inveresk, Musselburgh

Wednesday 16 February
Peeblesshire & Tweeddale

Kirkton Manor House, Peebles

Thursday 17 February
East Lothian

Shepherd House, Inveresk, Musselburgh

Saturday 19 February
East Lothian
Perth & Kinross

Shepherd House, Inveresk, Musselburgh
NEW Princeland House, Blairgowrie Road, Coupar Angus

Sunday 20 February
Angus & Dundee
Dumfriesshire
East Lothian
Fife
Perth & Kinross
Perth & Kinross

Dunninald Castle, Montrose
Craig, Langholm
Shepherd House, Inveresk, Musselburgh
NEW Millfield Garden, Millfield House, Falkland, Fife
NEW Princeland House, Blairgowrie Road, Coupar Angus
Cloan, by Auchterarder

Monday 21 February
Angus & Dundee   Dunninald Castle, Montrose

Tuesday 22 February
Angus & Dundee   Dunninald Castle, Montrose
East Lothian   Shepherd House, Inveresk, Musselburgh

Wednesday 23 February
Peeblesshire & Tweeddale   Kirkton Manor House, Peebles

Thursday 24 February
East Lothian   Shepherd House, Inveresk, Musselburgh

Saturday 26 February
Perth & Kinross   NEW Princeland House, Blairgowrie Road, Coupar Angus

Sunday 27 February
Angus & Dundee   Dunninald Castle, Montrose
Fife   NEW Millfield Garden, Millfield House, Falkland, Fife
Perth & Kinross   NEW Princeland House, Blairgowrie Road, Coupar Angus

Monday 28 February
Angus & Dundee   Dunninald Castle, Montrose

MARCH
....

Wednesday 2 March
Peeblesshire & Tweeddale   Kirkton Manor House, Peebles

Saturday 5 March
Perth & Kinross   NEW Princeland House, Blairgowrie Road, Coupar Angus

Sunday 6 March
Fife   NEW Auchtertool House, Auchtertool, Fife
Kincardine & Deeside   Ecclesgreig Castle, St Cyrus
Lanarkshire   Cleghorn, Stable House, Cleghorn Farm, Lanark
Peeblesshire & Tweeddale   Kailzie Gardens, Kailzie Gardens
Perth & Kinross   NEW Princeland House, Blairgowrie Road, Coupar Angus

Wednesday 9 March
Peeblesshire & Tweeddale   Kirkton Manor House, Peebles

Thursday 10 March
Angus & Dundee   Lawton House, Inverkeilor, by Arbroath

Friday 11 March
Angus & Dundee   Lawton House, Inverkeilor, by Arbroath

Saturday 12 March
Angus & Dundee   Lawton House, Inverkeilor, by Arbroath
Perth & Kinross   NEW Princeland House, Blairgowrie Road, Coupar Angus

Sunday 13 March
Angus & Dundee   Lawton House, Inverkeilor, by Arbroath

Wednesday 16 March
Peeblesshire & Tweeddale   Kirkton Manor House, Peebles

Wednesday 23 March
Peeblesshire & Tweeddale   Kirkton Manor House, Peebles

Saturday 26 March
Fife   Willowhill, Forgan, Newport-on-Tay

Sunday 27 March
Kirkcudbrightshire   The Limes, Kirkcudbright

Monday 28 March
Fife   Willowhill, Forgan, Newport-on-Tay

Wednesday 30 March
Peeblesshire & Tweeddale   Kirkton Manor House, Peebles

APRIL

Sunday 3 April
East Lothian   Winton Castle, Pencaitland
Fife   Teasses Gardens, near Ceres

Tuesday 5 April
Angus & Dundee   Primula Garden at Reswallie, Reswallie, Forfar

Wednesday 6 April
Peeblesshire & Tweeddale   Kirkton Manor House, Peebles

Thursday 7 April
Angus & Dundee   Inchmill Cottage, Glenprosen, near Kirriemuir
Angus & Dundee   Primula Garden at Reswallie, Reswallie, Forfar

Sunday 10 April
Aberdeenshire   Auchmacoy, Ellon
Aberdeenshire   Westhall Castle, Oyne, Inverurie
Edinburgh, Midlothian & West Lothian   Kevock Garden, 16 Kevock Road, Lasswade
Fife   Cambo Spring Plant & Garden Market, Kingsbarns
Perth & Kinross   Megginch Castle, Errol
Lanarkshire   Old Farm Cottage, The Ladywell, Nemphlar

Tuesday 12 April
Angus & Dundee   Primula Garden at Reswallie, Reswallie, Forfar

Wednesday 13 April
Peeblesshire & Tweeddale   Kirkton Manor House, Peebles

Thursday 14 April
Angus & Dundee   Primula Garden at Reswallie, Reswallie, Forfar
East Lothian   Humbie Dean, Humbie

Saturday 16 April
Angus & Dundee   10 Menzieshill Road, Dundee
East Lothian   NEW A Blackbird Sings, 20 Kings Park, Longniddry

Sunday 17 April
Angus & Dundee   10 Menzieshill Road, Dundee
Berwickshire   Harlaw Farmhouse, Eccles near Kelso, Roxburghshire
Kirkcudbrightshire   3 Millhall, Shore Road, Kirkcudbright

Tuesday 19 April
Angus & Dundee
Primula Garden at Reswallie, Reswallie, Forfar

Wednesday 20 April
Peeblesshire & Tweeddale
Kirkton Manor House, Peebles

Thursday 21 April
Angus & Dundee
Primula Garden at Reswallie, Reswallie, Forfar
East Lothian
Shepherd House, Inveresk, Musselburgh
Inverness, Ross, Cromarty & Skye
Dundonnell House, Little Loch Broom, Wester Ross

Saturday 23 April
East Lothian
Shepherd House, Inveresk, Musselburgh
Edinburgh, Midlothian & West Lothian
101 Greenbank Crescent, Edinburgh
Edinburgh, Midlothian & West Lothian
Spring Temple Gardens, The Mill House, Temple
Fife
Willowhill, Forgan, Newport-on-Tay

Sunday 24 April
Dumfriesshire
The Old Mill, Keir Mill, Thornhill
East Lothian
Shepherd House, Inveresk, Musselburgh
Edinburgh, Midlothian & West Lothian
101 Greenbank Crescent, Edinburgh
Edinburgh, Midlothian & West Lothian
Moray Place and Bank Gardens, Edinburgh
Fife
South Flisk, Blebo Craigs, Cupar
Kirkcudbrightshire
Balmaclellan House, Balmaclellan, Castle Douglas

Monday 25 April
Fife
Willowhill, Forgan, Newport-on-Tay

Tuesday 26 April
Angus & Dundee
Primula Garden at Reswallie, Reswallie, Forfar
East Lothian
Shepherd House, Inveresk, Musselburgh

Wednesday 27 April
Peeblesshire & Tweeddale
Kirkton Manor House, Peebles

Thursday 28 April
Angus & Dundee
Primula Garden at Reswallie, Reswallie, Forfar
East Lothian
Shepherd House, Inveresk, Musselburgh

Saturday 30 April
Angus & Dundee
NEW Colliston Castle, Colliston, Arbroath
Edinburgh, Midlothian & West Lothian
41 Hermitage Gardens, Edinburgh
Renfrewshire
SGS Kilmacolm Plant Sale, Outside Kilmacolm Library

MAY

Sunday 1 May
Angus & Dundee
NEW Colliston Castle, Colliston, Arbroath
Edinburgh, Midlothian & West Lothian
Newliston, Kirkliston
Kirkcudbrightshire
Brooklands, Crocketford
Perth & Kinross
Fingask Castle, Rait

Tuesday 3 May
Angus & Dundee
Primula Garden at Reswallie, Reswallie, Forfar
East Lothian
Shepherd House, Inveresk, Musselburgh

Wednesday 4 May
Edinburgh, Midlothian & West Lothian
Newliston, Kirkliston

Thursday 5 May

Angus & Dundee	Inchmill Cottage, Glenprosen, near Kirriemuir
Angus & Dundee	Primula Garden at Reswallie, Reswallie, Forfar
East Lothian	Shepherd House, Inveresk, Musselburgh
Edinburgh, Midlothian & West Lothian	Newliston, Kirkliston

Friday 6 May

Edinburgh, Midlothian & West Lothian	Newliston, Kirkliston

Saturday 7 May

Edinburgh, Midlothian & West Lothian	Dr Neil's Garden, Duddingston Village
Edinburgh, Midlothian & West Lothian	Greentree, 18 Green Hill Park, Edinburgh
Edinburgh, Midlothian & West Lothian	Newliston, Kirkliston

Sunday 8 May

East Lothian	Tyninghame House and The Walled Garden, Dunbar
Edinburgh, Midlothian & West Lothian	Dr Neil's Garden, Duddingston Village
Edinburgh, Midlothian & West Lothian	Newliston, Kirkliston
Kirkcudbrightshire	Cally Gardens, Cally Avenue, Gatehouse of Fleet

Tuesday 10 May

Angus & Dundee	Primula Garden at Reswallie, Reswallie, Forfar
East Lothian	Shepherd House, Inveresk, Musselburgh

Wednesday 11 May

Edinburgh, Midlothian & West Lothian	Newliston, Kirkliston

Thursday 12 May

Angus & Dundee	Primula Garden at Reswallie, Reswallie, Forfar
East Lothian	Humbie Dean, Humbie
East Lothian	Longwood, Humbie
East Lothian	Shepherd House, Inveresk, Musselburgh
East Lothian	Stobshiel House, Humbie
Edinburgh, Midlothian & West Lothian	Newliston, Kirkliston

Friday 13 May

Angus & Dundee	Balhary Walled Garden, Balhary, Alyth, Blairgowrie
Edinburgh, Midlothian & West Lothian	Newliston, Kirkliston

Saturday 14 May

Aberdeenshire	Cruickshank Botanic Garden, 23 St Machar Drive, Aberdeen
Angus & Dundee	10 Menzieshill Road, Dundee
Angus & Dundee	Balhary Walled Garden, Balhary, Alyth, Blairgowrie
Argyll & Lochaber	Knock Newhouse, Lochgair
Ayrshire & Arran Cumnock	Netherthird Community Garden, Craigens Road, Netherthird,
East Lothian	NEW A Blackbird Sings, 20 Kings Park, Longniddry
Edinburgh, Midlothian & West Lothian	Newliston, Kirkliston
Edinburgh, Midlothian & West Lothian	Redcroft, 23 Murrayfield Road, Edinburgh

Sunday 15 May

Angus & Dundee	10 Menzieshill Road, Dundee
Argyll & Lochaber	Knock Newhouse, Lochgair
Argyll & Lochaber	Strachur Flower & Woodland Gardens, Strachur
Berwickshire	NEW Broomhill Villa, 4 Edinburgh Road, Greenlaw
Dumfriesshire	Dalswinton House, Dalswinton
Dunbartonshire	NEW Hillcroft with Stonecroft, Rhu, Helensburgh
Edinburgh, Midlothian & West Lothian	Newliston, Kirkliston
Edinburgh, Midlothian & West Lothian	Redcroft, 23 Murrayfield Road, Edinburgh
Fife	Lindores House, by Newburgh
Kirkcudbrightshire	Arbigland House, Kirkbean, Dumfries
Renfrewshire	Highwood, off Lochwinnoch Road, Kilmacolm

Tuesday 17 May
Angus & Dundee   Primula Garden at Reswallie, Reswallie, Forfar
East Lothian   Shepherd House, Inveresk, Musselburgh

Wednesday 18 May
Edinburgh, Midlothian & West Lothian   Newliston, Kirkliston

Thursday 19 May
Angus & Dundee   Primula Garden at Reswallie, Reswallie, Forfar
East Lothian   Shepherd House, Inveresk, Musselburgh
Edinburgh, Midlothian & West Lothian   Newliston, Kirkliston

Friday 20 May
Edinburgh, Midlothian & West Lothian   Newliston, Kirkliston

Saturday 21 May
Argyll & Lochaber   NEW Achamore Gardens, Isle of Gigha
Edinburgh, Midlothian & West Lothian   Newliston, Kirkliston

Sunday 22 May
Angus & Dundee   Dalfruin, Kirktonhill Road, Kirriemuir
Argyll & Lochaber   Ardno, Cairndow
Argyll & Lochaber   Braevallich Farm, by Dalmally
Argyll & Lochaber   Strachur Flower & Woodland Gardens, Strachur
Dumfriesshire   Drumpark, Irongray
Dunbartonshire   Ross Priory, Gartocharn
Edinburgh, Midlothian & West Lothian   Newliston, Kirkliston
Fife   NEW Strathkinness Community Garden and Orchard, Bonfield Rd
Fife   Blebo Craigs Village Gardens, Blebo Craigs, Cupar
Fife   Kirklands, Saline
Fife   South Flisk, Blebo Craigs, Cupar
Glasgow & District   NEW Heart of Scotstoun Community Gardens,
                                            64 Balmoral St, Glasgow
Kincardine & Deeside   Inchmarlo Retirement Village Garden, Inchmarlo, Banchory
Kirkcudbrightshire   The Limes, Kirkcudbright
Perth & Kinross   Cloan, by Auchterarder
Renfrewshire   NEW Perch Corner, 25 Stanely Crescent, Paisley
Stirlingshire   Kilbryde Castle, Dunblane
Wigtownshire   Logan Botanic Garden, Port Logan, by Stranraer
Wigtownshire   Logan House Gardens, Port Logan, by Stranraer

Tuesday 24 May
Angus & Dundee   Primula Garden at Reswallie, Reswallie, Forfar
East Lothian   Shepherd House, Inveresk, Musselburgh

Wednesday 25 May
Edinburgh, Midlothian & West Lothian   Newliston, Kirkliston
Inverness, Ross, Cromarty & Skye   House of Gruinard, Laide, by Achnasheen

Thursday 26 May
Angus & Dundee   Primula Garden at Reswallie, Reswallie, Forfar
East Lothian   Shepherd House, Inveresk, Musselburgh
Edinburgh, Midlothian & West Lothian   Newliston, Kirkliston

Friday 27 May
Edinburgh, Midlothian & West Lothian   Newliston, Kirkliston
Inverness, Ross, Cromarty & Skye   Gorthleck House Garden, Stratherrick

Saturday 28 May

Aberdeenshire	Leith Hall Plant Sale, Huntly
Angus & Dundee	Trio of Gardens on Glamis Drive, 3, 10 & 12 Glamis Drive, Dundee
Caithness, Sutherland, Orkney & Shetland	Amat, Amat Lodge
Edinburgh, Midlothian & West Lothian	Newliston, Kirkliston
Fife	Willowhill, Forgan, Newport-on-Tay
Inverness, Ross, Cromarty & Skye	Gorthleck House Garden, Stratherrick

Sunday 29 May

Angus & Dundee	Trio of Gardens on Glamis Drive, 3, 10 & 12 Glamis Drive, Dundee
Caithness, Sutherland, Orkney & Shetland	Amat, Amat Lodge
East Lothian	Congalton House, North Berwick
East Lothian	Fairnielaw, Athelstaneford, North Berwick
Edinburgh, Midlothian & West Lothian	Newliston, Kirkliston
Fife	NEW Auchtertool House, Auchtertool, Fife
Fife	Earlshall Castle, Leuchars
Glasgow & District	Kilsyth Gardens, Allanfauld Road, Kilsyth
Inverness, Ross, Cromarty & Skye	Gorthleck House Garden, Stratherrick
Kirkcudbrightshire	Corsock House, Corsock, Castle Douglas
Peeblesshire & Tweeddale	Quercus Garden Plants, Whitmuir Farm, West Linton
Stirlingshire	Bridge of Allan Gardens, Bridge of Allan

Monday 30 May

Fife	Willowhill, Forgan, Newport-on-Tay
Inverness, Ross, Cromarty & Skye	Gorthleck House Garden, Stratherrick

Tuesday 31 May

Angus & Dundee	Primula Garden at Reswallie, Reswallie, Forfar
East Lothian	Shepherd House, Inveresk, Musselburgh
Inverness, Ross, Cromarty & Skye	Gorthleck House Garden, Stratherrick

JUNE

Wednesday 1 June

Edinburgh, Midlothian & West Lothian	Newliston, Kirkliston
Fife	Gardener's Cottage, Crombie Point, Shore Road, Crombie
Inverness, Ross, Cromarty & Skye	Gorthleck House Garden, Stratherrick

Thursday 2 June

Angus & Dundee	Inchmill Cottage, Glenprosen, near Kirriemuir
Angus & Dundee	Primula Garden at Reswallie, Reswallie, Forfar
East Lothian	Shepherd House, Inveresk, Musselburgh
Edinburgh, Midlothian & West Lothian	Newliston, Kirkliston
Fife	Gardener's Cottage, Crombie Point, Shore Road, Crombie
Inverness, Ross, Cromarty & Skye	Dundonnell House, Little Loch Broom, Wester Ross
Inverness, Ross, Cromarty & Skye	Gorthleck House Garden, Stratherrick
Peeblesshire & Tweeddale	Laidlawstiel House, Clovenfords, Galashiels
Perth & Kinross	Bradystone House, Murthly

Friday 3 June

Aberdeenshire	Airdlin Croft, Ythanbank, Ellon
Edinburgh, Midlothian & West Lothian	Newliston, Kirkliston
Inverness, Ross, Cromarty & Skye	Gorthleck House Garden, Stratherrick
Kirkcudbrightshire	Threave Garden, Castle Douglas

Saturday 4 June

Aberdeenshire	Airdlin Croft, Ythanbank, Ellon
Edinburgh, Midlothian & West Lothian	Newliston, Kirkliston
Inverness, Ross, Cromarty & Skye	Gorthleck House Garden, Stratherrick
Kincardine & Deeside	Finzean House, Finzean, Banchory
Kirkcudbrightshire	Threave Garden, Castle Douglas

Sunday 5 June

Aberdeenshire	Airdlin Croft, Ythanbank, Ellon
Argyll & Lochaber	Ardverikie with Aberarder, Kinloch Laggan, Newtonmore
Dumfriesshire	Westerhall, Bentpath, Langholm
Dunbartonshire	Geilston Garden, Main Road, Cardross
Edinburgh, Midlothian & West Lothian	Dean Gardens, Edinburgh
Inverness, Ross, Cromarty & Skye	Gorthleck House Garden, Stratherrick
Kincardine & Deeside	Glensaugh, Glensaugh Lodge, Fettercairn, Laurencekirk
Kirkcudbrightshire	Threave Garden, Castle Douglas
Peeblesshire & Tweeddale	NEW Lamancha Community Hub Plant Sale, Old Moffat Road
Peeblesshire & Tweeddale	Stobo Japanese Water Garden, Stobo Farm, Stobo
Perth & Kinross	Mill of Forneth, Forneth, Blairgowrie
Roxburghshire	West Leas, Bonchester Bridge
Wigtownshire	NEW Damnaglaur House with The Homestead and Mid
Curghie, Drummore, Stranraer	

Tuesday 7 June

Angus & Dundee	Primula Garden at Reswallie, Reswallie, Forfar
East Lothian	Shepherd House, Inveresk, Musselburgh

Wednesday 8 June

Fife	Gardener's Cottage, Crombie Point, Shore Road, Crombie
Peeblesshire & Tweeddale	The Potting Shed, Broughton Place, Broughton, Biggar

Thursday 9 June

Angus & Dundee	Primula Garden at Reswallie, Reswallie, Forfar
East Lothian	Humbie Dean, Humbie
East Lothian	Longwood, Humbie
East Lothian	Shepherd House, Inveresk, Musselburgh
East Lothian	Stobshiel House, Humbie
Fife	Gardener's Cottage, Crombie Point, Shore Road, Crombie
Perth & Kinross	Bradystone House, Murthly

Friday 10 June

Ayrshire & Arran	NEW 29 Scaur O'Doon Road, Ayr

Saturday 11 June

Ayrshire & Arran	NEW 29 Scaur O'Doon Road, Ayr
East Lothian	Dirleton Village, Dirleton
Edinburgh, Midlothian & West Lothian	NEW Broomieknowe Gardens, Lasswade
Perth & Kinross	Cloan, by Auchterarder
Perth & Kinross	The Bield at Blackruthven, Blackruthven House, Tibbermore

Sunday 12 June

Angus & Dundee	The Doocot, Kinloch, Meigle, Blairgowrie
Ayrshire & Arran	NEW 29 Scaur O'Doon Road, Ayr
Ayrshire & Arran	Barrmill Community Garden, Barrmill Park and Gardens
Dumfriesshire	NEW Craigieburn, Craigieburn House, by Moffat
Dumfriesshire	Cowhill Tower, Holywood
East Lothian	Dirleton Village, Dirleton
Edinburgh, Midlothian & West Lothian	NEW Broomieknowe Gardens, Lasswade
Edinburgh, Midlothian & West Lothian	Rivaldsgreen House, 48 Friars Brae, Linlithgow
Fife	Pittenweem: Gardens in the Burgh, Pittenweem
Glasgow & District	12 Chatelherault Avenue (The Good Life Garden), Glasgow
Inverness, Ross, Cromarty & Skye	Field House, Belladrum, Beauly
Kincardine & Deeside	Kincardine Castle, Kincardine O'Neil
Kirkcudbrightshire	Seabank, The Merse, Rockcliffe
Peeblesshire & Tweeddale	West Linton Village Gardens, West Linton
Perth & Kinross	Cloan, by Auchterarder
Renfrewshire	Wraes, Corseliehill Road, nr Houston
Wigtownshire	Castle Kennedy and Gardens, Stranraer

Monday 13 June
Ayrshire & Arran   NEW 29 Scaur O'Doon Road, Ayr

Tuesday 14 June
Angus & Dundee   Primula Garden at Reswallie, Reswallie, Forfar
East Lothian   Shepherd House, Inveresk, Musselburgh

Wednesday 15 June
Fife   Gardener's Cottage, Crombie Point, Shore Road, Crombie
Peeblesshire & Tweeddale   Laidlawstiel House, Clovenfords, Galashiels
Peeblesshire & Tweeddale   The Potting Shed, Broughton Place, Broughton, Biggar

Thursday 16 June
Angus & Dundee   Primula Garden at Reswallie, Reswallie, Forfar
East Lothian   Shepherd House, Inveresk, Musselburgh
Fife   Gardener's Cottage, Crombie Point, Shore Road, Crombie
Perth & Kinross   Bradystone House, Murthly

Friday 17 June
Angus & Dundee   Balhary Walled Garden, Balhary, Alyth, Blairgowrie

Saturday 18 June
Angus & Dundee   Balhary Walled Garden, Balhary, Alyth, Blairgowrie
Angus & Dundee   Torwood, Milton of Ogilvie, Glenogilvy, Glamis by Forfar
Ayrshire & Arran   NEW Dundonald Village Gardens, Dundonald, Kilmarnock
East Lothian   NEW A Blackbird Sings, 20 Kings Park, Longniddry
East Lothian   Inveresk Village, Inveresk, Musselburgh
Kincardine & Deeside   Dallachy, Logie Coldstone, Aboyne, Aberdeenshire
Wigtownshire   Woodfall Gardens, Glasserton

Sunday 19 June
Aberdeenshire   Heatherwick Farm, Kintore, Inverurie
Angus & Dundee   Torwood, Milton of Ogilvie, Glenogilvy, Glamis by Forfar
Argyll & Lochaber   Braevallich Farm, by Dalmally
Ayrshire & Arran   Barnweil Garden, Craigie, near Kilmarnock
Dumfriesshire   NEW Garden Cottage, Knockhill, Lockerbie, Dumfries
Dunbartonshire   NEW 4 Cairndhu Gardens Plant Sale, Helensburgh
East Lothian   Inveresk Village, Inveresk, Musselburgh
Edinburgh, Midlothian & West Lothian   89 Ravenscroft Street, Edinburgh
Edinburgh, Midlothian & West Lothian   Meadow Place, 19 Meadow Place
Edinburgh, Midlothian & West Lothian   Moray Place and Bank Gardens, Edinburgh
Glasgow & District   NEW The Gardens of Milton of Campsie, Milton of Campsie
Inverness, Ross, Cromarty & Skye   Old Allangrange, Munlochy
Kincardine & Deeside   Dallachy, Logie Coldstone, Aboyne, Aberdeenshire
Kirkcudbrightshire   NEW Clonyard Farm, Colvend, Dalbeattie
Lanarkshire   Dippoolbank Cottage, Carnwath
Renfrewshire   NEW No 14 – A Village Garden, 14 Taylor Avenue, Kilbarchan
Wigtownshire   Woodfall Gardens, Glasserton

Tuesday 21 June
Angus & Dundee   Primula Garden at Reswallie, Reswallie, Forfar
East Lothian   Shepherd House, Inveresk, Musselburgh

Wednesday 22 June
Fife   Gardener's Cottage, Crombie Point, Shore Road, Crombie
Peeblesshire & Tweeddale   The Potting Shed, Broughton Place, Broughton, Biggar
Renfrewshire   Craig Hepburn Memorial Garden, Stirling Drive, Linwood

Thursday 23 June

Angus & Dundee	Primula Garden at Reswallie, Reswallie, Forfar
East Lothian	Shepherd House, Inveresk, Musselburgh
Perth & Kinross	Bradystone House, Murthly
Renfrewshire	Craig Hepburn Memorial Garden, Stirling Drive, Linwood

Saturday 25 June

Ayrshire & Arran	Underwood Lodge, Craigie, Kilmarnock, South Ayrshire
East Lothian	Gullane House, Sandy Loan, Gullane
Edinburgh, Midlothian & West Lothian	19 Gardiner Road, Edinburgh
Fife	The Tower, 1 Northview Terrace, Wormit
Fife	Willowhill, Forgan, Newport-on-Tay
Wigtownshire	NEW Aldouran Wetland Garden, Kirkland Bank, Leswalt

Sunday 26 June

Aberdeenshire	NEW Hatton of Fintray Village Gardens
Aberdeenshire	Altries, Maryculter, Aberdeenshire
Aberdeenshire	Heatherwick Farm, Kintore, Inverurie
Angus & Dundee	NEW Brechin Gardens in June, Locations across Brechin
Ayrshire & Arran	Underwood Lodge, Craigie, Kilmarnock, South Ayrshire
Berwickshire	Ruthven House, Coldstream
East Lothian	Gullane House, Sandy Loan, Gullane
East Lothian	Tyninghame House and The Walled Garden, Dunbar
Edinburgh, Midlothian & West Lothian	5 Greenbank Crescent, Edinburgh
Edinburgh, Midlothian & West Lothian	NEW Claremont, Redmill
Edinburgh, Midlothian & West Lothian	Even More Gardens of the Lower New Town, Edinburgh
Fife	Balcarres, Colinsburgh
Fife	Boarhills Village Gardens, Boarhills, St Andrews
Fife	Newburgh – Hidden Gardens, Newburgh
Fife	The Tower, 1 Northview Terrace, Wormit
Glasgow & District	Strathbungo Garden, March Street, Glasgow
Inverness, Ross, Cromarty & Skye	House of Aigas and Field Centre, by Beauly
Kirkcudbrightshire	NEW Four Gardens in Anwoth, Anwoth, Gatehouse of Fleet
Lanarkshire	NEW Lindsaylands, Biggar
Moray & Nairn	Gordonstoun, Duffus, near Elgin
Moray & Nairn	Haugh Garden, College of Roseisle

Monday 27 June

Fife	Willowhill, Forgan, Newport-on-Tay

Tuesday 28 June

Angus & Dundee	Primula Garden at Reswallie, Reswallie, Forfar
East Lothian	Shepherd House, Inveresk, Musselburgh
Lanarkshire	NEW Little Sparta, Stonypath, Dunsyre

Wednesday 29 June

Peeblesshire & Tweeddale	The Potting Shed, Broughton Place, Broughton, Biggar

Thursday 30 June

Angus & Dundee	Primula Garden at Reswallie, Reswallie, Forfar
East Lothian	Shepherd House, Inveresk, Musselburgh
Fife	Gardener's Cottage, Crombie Point, Shore Road, Crombie
Perth & Kinross	Bradystone House, Murthly

JULY

Saturday 2 July

Angus & Dundee	NEW The Old Schoolhouse, Kilry
Ayrshire & Arran	NEW Carbieston House, Coylton, Ayr
Perth & Kinross	Blair Castle Gardens, Blair Atholl

Sunday 3 July

Aberdeenshire	Bruckhills Croft, Rothienorman, Inverurie
Angus & Dundee	NEW The Old Schoolhouse, Kilry
Ayrshire & Arran	NEW Carbieston House, Coylton, Ayr
Berwickshire	Netherbyres, Eyemouth
Dumfriesshire	Dunesslin, Dunscore
East Lothian	Stenton Village, Stenton, Dunbar
Fife	Craigfoodie, Dairsie
Fife	Earlshall Castle, Leuchars
Glasgow & District	Horatio's Garden, Queen Elizabeth University Hospital, Glasgow
Kirkcudbrightshire	Southwick House, Southwick
Roxburghshire	NEW Morebattle Village Gardens, Kelso
Stirlingshire	NEW Tillicoultry Parish Church Community Garden, Dollar Road

Monday 4 July

Inverness, Ross, Cromarty & Skye	Torcroft, Balnain, Glenurquhart

Tuesday 5 July

Ayrshire & Arran	Dougarie, Isle of Arran
East Lothian	Shepherd House, Inveresk, Musselburgh
Lanarkshire	NEW Little Sparta, Stonypath, Dunsyre

Wednesday 6 July

Fife	Gardener's Cottage, Crombie Point, Shore Road, Crombie
Peeblesshire & Tweeddale	Portmore, Eddleston
Peeblesshire & Tweeddale	The Potting Shed, Broughton Place, Broughton, Biggar

Thursday 7 July

Angus & Dundee	Inchmill Cottage, Glenprosen, near Kirriemuir
East Lothian	Shepherd House, Inveresk, Musselburgh
Fife	Gardener's Cottage, Crombie Point, Shore Road, Crombie
Perth & Kinross	Bradystone House, Murthly

Friday 8 July

Aberdeenshire	Easter Ord Farm, Easter Ord, Skene, Westhill
East Lothian	NEW Gifford Bank, Gifford
East Lothian	Broadwoodside, Gifford

Saturday 9 July

Aberdeenshire	Easter Ord Farm, Easter Ord, Skene, Westhill
East Lothian	NEW Gifford Bank, Gifford
East Lothian	Broadwoodside, Gifford
Fife	Crail: Gardens in the Burgh, Crail
Inverness, Ross, Cromarty & Skye	2 Durnamuck, Little Loch Broom, Wester Ross
Inverness, Ross, Cromarty & Skye	NEW 7 Braes of Conon, Conon Bridge
Lanarkshire	Old Manse Wild Garden, Old Manse, Wanlockhead, Biggar

Sunday 10 July

Aberdeenshire	Easter Ord Farm, Easter Ord, Skene, Westhill
Angus & Dundee	The Doocot, Kinloch, Meigle, Blairgowrie
Berwickshire	Coldstream Open Gardens
Fife	Crail: Gardens in the Burgh, Crail
Glasgow & District	Milton Community Garden, Liddesdale Square, Milton, Glasgow
Inverness, Ross, Cromarty & Skye	NEW 7 Braes of Conon, Conon Bridge
Kincardine & Deeside	Douneside House, Tarland
Lanarkshire	Old Manse Wild Garden, Old Manse, Wanlockhead, Biggar
Wigtownshire	Woodfall Gardens, Glasserton

Monday 11 July

Inverness, Ross, Cromarty & Skye	Torcroft, Balnain, Glenurquhart

Tuesday 12 July
East Lothian   Shepherd House, Inveresk, Musselburgh

Wednesday 13 July
Fife   Gardener's Cottage, Crombie Point, Shore Road, Crombie
Peeblesshire & Tweeddale   Portmore, Eddleston

Thursday 14 July
East Lothian   Humbie Dean, Humbie
East Lothian   Longwood, Humbie
East Lothian   Shepherd House, Inveresk, Musselburgh
East Lothian   Stobshiel House, Humbie
Fife   Gardener's Cottage, Crombie Point, Shore Road, Crombie
Perth & Kinross   Bradystone House, Murthly

Saturday 16 July
Angus & Dundee   Arwin House, 17 Renny Crescent, Montrose
Ayrshire & Arran   Whitewin House, Golf Course Road, Girvan
Caithness, Sutherland, Orkney & Shetland   Auchlea, Balnapolaig Muir, Dornoch
East Lothian   NEW A Blackbird Sings, 20 Kings Park, Longniddry
Peeblesshire & Tweeddale   NEW Carolside, Earlston
Wigtownshire   Amulree, 8 Mill Street, Drummore, Stranraer
Wigtownshire   Damnaglaur House, Drummore, Stranraer
Wigtownshire   Rawson Garden, 1, High Drummore Cottages, Stranraer

Sunday 17 July
Aberdeenshire   5 Woodlands Gardens, Cults, Aberdeen
Angus & Dundee   Arwin House, 17 Renny Crescent, Montrose
Ayrshire & Arran   Whitewin House, Golf Course Road, Girvan
Caithness, Sutherland, Orkney & Shetland   NEW Old Granary Quoy and The Quoy of Houton, Orkney
Dumfriesshire   Whiteside, Dunscore
Edinburgh, Midlothian & West Lothian   NEW Claremont, Redmill
Fife   NEW Coul House, Coul House, Maree Way, Glenrothes
Glasgow & District   Kamares, 18 Broom Road, Newton Mearns, Glasgow
Inverness, Ross, Cromarty & Skye   Kiltarlity Gardens, Kiltarlity
Moray & Nairn   Glebe House, Main Street, Urquhart
Moray & Nairn   Gordon Castle Walled Garden, Fochabers, Moray
Peeblesshire & Tweeddale   Glen House, Glen Estate, Innerleithen
Wigtownshire   Amulree, 8 Mill Street, Drummore, Stranraer
Wigtownshire   Damnaglaur House, Drummore, Stranraer
Wigtownshire   Rawson Garden, 1, High Drummore Cottages, Stranraer

Monday 18 July
Inverness, Ross, Cromarty & Skye   Torcroft, Balnain, Glenurquhart

Tuesday 19 July
East Lothian   Shepherd House, Inveresk, Musselburgh

Wednesday 20 July
Fife   Gardener's Cottage, Crombie Point, Shore Road, Crombie
Peeblesshire & Tweeddale   Portmore, Eddleston

Thursday 21 July
East Lothian   Shepherd House, Inveresk, Musselburgh
Fife   Gardener's Cottage, Crombie Point, Shore Road, Crombie
Perth & Kinross   Bradystone House, Murthly

Saturday 23 July

Ayrshire & Arran	Whitewin House, Golf Course Road, Girvan
Caithness, Sutherland, Orkney & Shetland	42 Astle, Dornoch
Caithness, Sutherland, Orkney & Shetland	Skelbo House, Skelbo, Dornoch
Fife	Willowhill, Forgan, Newport-on-Tay

Sunday 24 July

Ayrshire & Arran	19 Waterslap, Fenwick
Ayrshire & Arran	NEW 25 Stoneyholm Road, Kilbirnie
Ayrshire & Arran	Whitewin House, Golf Course Road, Girvan
Caithness, Sutherland, Orkney & Shetland	42 Astle, Dornoch
Caithness, Sutherland, Orkney & Shetland	Skelbo House, Skelbo, Dornoch
Edinburgh, Midlothian & West Lothian	9 Braid Farm Road, Edinburgh
Edinburgh, Midlothian & West Lothian	NEW Pentland Crescent Gardens, 2 Pentland Crescent, Edinburgh
Edinburgh, Midlothian & West Lothian	Craigentinny Telferton Allotments, Edinburgh
Glasgow & District	NEW Braehead House, 20 Braehead Road, Thorntonhall
Inverness, Ross, Cromarty & Skye	NEW Ar Dachaigh, Redhill Farm, Allanfearn, Inverness
Kirkcudbrightshire	Crofts, Kirkpatrick Durham, Castle Douglas
Moray & Nairn	Haugh Garden, College of Roseisle
Peeblesshire & Tweeddale	Kailzie Gardens, Kailzie Gardens

Monday 25 July

Fife	Willowhill, Forgan, Newport-on-Tay
Inverness, Ross, Cromarty & Skye	Torcroft, Balnain, Glenurquhart

Wednesday 27 July

Fife	Gardener's Cottage, Crombie Point, Shore Road, Crombie
Peeblesshire & Tweeddale	Portmore, Eddleston

Thursday 28 July

Fife	Gardener's Cottage, Crombie Point, Shore Road, Crombie
Perth & Kinross	Bradystone House, Murthly

Saturday 30 July

Aberdeenshire	Parkvilla, 47 Schoolhill, Ellon
Angus & Dundee	Easter Cammock, Glenisla, Blairgowrie
Ayrshire & Arran	Whitewin House, Golf Course Road, Girvan
Caithness, Sutherland, Orkney & Shetland	Amat, Amat Lodge
Kincardine & Deeside	NEW The Old Farmhouse, Milton of Logie, Dinnet, Aboyne
Moray & Nairn	Cuthberts Brae, 84 Seatown, Buckie

Sunday 31 July

Aberdeenshire	Parkvilla, 47 Schoolhill, Ellon
Angus & Dundee	NEW Brechin Gardens in July, Locations across Brechin
Ayrshire & Arran	Whitewin House, Golf Course Road, Girvan
Berwickshire	Marlfield Gardens, Coldstream
Caithness, Sutherland, Orkney & Shetland	Amat, Amat Lodge
Caithness, Sutherland, Orkney & Shetland	Langwell, Berriedale
Inverness, Ross, Cromarty & Skye	House of Aigas and Field Centre, by Beauly
Kincardine & Deeside	NEW The Old Farmhouse, Milton of Logie, Dinnet, Aboyne
Kirkcudbrightshire	Kings Grange House, Castle Douglas
Moray & Nairn	Cuthberts Brae, 84 Seatown, Buckie
Moray & Nairn	Glenrinnes Lodge, Dufftown, Keith, Banffshire
Peeblesshire & Tweeddale	Gattonside Village Gardens, Gattonside
Perth & Kinross	Cloan, by Auchterarder

AUGUST

Wednesday 3 August

Peeblesshire & Tweeddale | Portmore, Eddleston

Thursday 4 August

Angus & Dundee | Inchmill Cottage, Glenprosen, near Kirriemuir
Perth & Kinross | Bradystone House, Murthly

Saturday 6 August

Angus & Dundee | Angus Plant Sale, Logie Walled Garden, Kirriemuir
Ayrshire & Arran | Whitewin House, Golf Course Road, Girvan
Fife | Willowhill, Forgan, Newport-on-Tay

Sunday 7 August

Ayrshire & Arran | Whitewin House, Golf Course Road, Girvan
Dumfriesshire | Dalswinton Mill, Dalswinton, Dumfries
Edinburgh, Midlothian & West Lothian | NEW Claremont, Redmill
Edinburgh, Midlothian & West Lothian | Hunter's Tryst, 95 Oxgangs Road, Edinburgh
Kincardine & Deeside | Glenbervie House, Drumlithie, Stonehaven
Perth & Kinross | Drummond Castle Gardens, Muthill, Crieff
Perth & Kinross | Mount Tabor House, Mount Tabor Road, Perth
Roxburghshire | West Leas, Bonchester Bridge
Stirlingshire | 60 Greenhead, Alva, Clackmannanshire

Monday 8 August

Fife | Willowhill, Forgan, Newport-on-Tay

Wednesday 10 August

Peeblesshire & Tweeddale | Portmore, Eddleston

Thursday 11 August

East Lothian | Humbie Dean, Humbie
East Lothian | Longwood, Humbie
East Lothian | Stobshiel House, Humbie
Perth & Kinross | Bradystone House, Murthly

Saturday 13 August

Ayrshire & Arran | Whitewin House, Golf Course Road, Girvan
East Lothian | NEW A Blackbird Sings, 20 Kings Park, Longniddry
Fife | Willowhill, Forgan, Newport-on-Tay

Sunday 14 August

Ayrshire & Arran | Whitewin House, Golf Course Road, Girvan
Kirkcudbrightshire | Cally Gardens, Cally Avenue, Gatehouse of Fleet
Stirlingshire | Ault Wharrie, Ardnablane, Dunblane

Monday 15 August

Fife | Willowhill, Forgan, Newport-on-Tay

Wednesday 17 August

Peeblesshire & Tweeddale | Portmore, Eddleston

Friday 19 August

Aberdeenshire | Easter Ord Farm, Easter Ord, Skene, Westhill
Angus & Dundee | Balhary Walled Garden, Balhary, Alyth, Blairgowrie

Saturday 20 August

Aberdeenshire	Easter Ord Farm, Easter Ord, Skene, Westhill
Angus & Dundee	Balhary Walled Garden, Balhary, Alyth, Blairgowrie
Angus & Dundee	Hospitalfield Gardens, Hospitalfield House, Westway, Arbroath
Fife	Willowhill, Forgan, Newport-on-Tay
Inverness, Ross, Cromarty & Skye	2 Durnamuck, Little Loch Broom, Wester Ross
Moray & Nairn	55 South Guildry Street, Elgin
Moray & Nairn	An-Grianan, Rafford, Forres

Sunday 21 August

Aberdeenshire	Easter Ord Farm, Easter Ord, Skene, Westhill
Berwickshire	Duns Open Gardens, Volunteer Hall, Langtongate, Duns
Dunbartonshire	Glenarn Plant Sale, Glenarn Road, Rhu, Helensburgh
Fife	NEW Coul House, Coul House, Maree Way, Glenrothes
Moray & Nairn	An-Grianan, Rafford, Forres
Peeblesshire & Tweeddale	Quercus Garden Plants, Whitmuir Farm, West Linton

Monday 22 August

Fife	Willowhill, Forgan, Newport-on-Tay

Wednesday 24 August

Peeblesshire & Tweeddale	Portmore, Eddleston

Saturday 27 August

Fife	Willowhill, Forgan, Newport-on-Tay

Sunday 28 August

Kincardine & Deeside	Glensaugh, Glensaugh Lodge, Fettercairn, Laurencekirk

Monday 29 August

Fife	Willowhill, Forgan, Newport-on-Tay

Tuesday 30 August

Edinburgh, Midlothian & West Lothian	Whitburgh House Walled Garden, Pathhead, Midlothian
Lanarkshire	NEW Little Sparta, Stonypath, Dunsyre

Wednesday 31 August

Edinburgh, Midlothian & West Lothian	Whitburgh House Walled Garden, Pathhead, Midlothian
Peeblesshire & Tweeddale	Laidlawstiel House, Clovenfords, Galashiels
Peeblesshire & Tweeddale	Portmore, Eddleston

SEPTEMBER

Thursday 1 September

Angus & Dundee	Inchmill Cottage, Glenprosen, near Kirriemuir
Inverness, Ross, Cromarty & Skye	Dundonnell House, Little Loch Broom, Wester Ross

Sunday 4 September

Aberdeenshire	Heatherwick Farm, Kintore, Inverurie
Caithness, Sutherland, Orkney & Shetland	NEW Old Granary Quoy and The Quoy of Houton, Orkney
Dunbartonshire	James Street Community Garden Plant Sale, Helensburgh
Kirkcudbrightshire	3 Millhall, Shore Road, Kirkcudbright

Tuesday 6 September

Lanarkshire	NEW Little Sparta, Stonypath, Dunsyre

Thursday 8 September

East Lothian	Humbie Dean, Humbie

Sunday 11 September
Inverness, Ross, Cromarty & Skye

Old Allangrange, Munlochy

Saturday 17 September
East Lothian

NEW A Blackbird Sings, 20 Kings Park, Longniddry

Sunday 18 September
East Lothian

Fairnielaw, Athelstaneford, North Berwick

Fife

Greenhead Farmhouse, Greenhead of Arnot, Leslie

Stirlingshire

Coldoch, Blairdrummond, Stirling

Friday 23 September
Angus & Dundee

Balhary Walled Garden, Balhary, Alyth, Blairgowrie

Saturday 24 September
Aberdeenshire

Tarland Community Garden, Tarland, Aboyne

Angus & Dundee

Balhary Walled Garden, Balhary, Alyth, Blairgowrie

Fife

NEW Coul House, Coul House, Maree Way, Glenrothes

Sunday 25 September
Dumfriesshire

Drumpark, Irongray

Friday 30 September
Edinburgh, Midlothian & West Lothian

Silverburn Village, 23 Biggar Road, Silverburn

OCTOBER
....

Sunday 2 October
Argyll & Lochaber

Benmore Botanic Garden, Benmore, Dunoon

Fife

SGS Plant Sale at St Andrews Botanic Garden, St Andrews

Sunday 9 October
Peeblesshire & Tweeddale

Dawyck Botanic Garden, Stobo

Peeblesshire & Tweeddale

Stobo Japanese Water Garden, Stobo Farm, Stobo

Saturday 15 October
Angus & Dundee

Westgate, 12 Glamis Drive, Dundee

Sunday 16 October
Angus & Dundee

Westgate, 12 Glamis Drive, Dundee

DECEMBER
....

Sunday 11 December
Edinburgh, Midlothian & West Lothian

Moray Place and Bank Gardens, Edinburgh

Index of Gardens

PRE-ORDER YOUR SCOTLAND'S GARDENS SCHEME GUIDEBOOK FOR 2023!

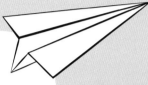

PLEASE SEND ME _____ COPY / COPIES OF THE SGS GUIDEBOOK FOR 2023, PRE-ORDER PRICE £7.50 PLUS £3.00 UK P&P AS SOON AS IT IS AVAILABLE.

I ENCLOSE A CHEQUE / POSTAL ORDER MADE PAYABLE TO SCOTLAND'S GARDENS SCHEME.

NAME

ADDRESS

POSTCODE

SCOTLAND'S GARDENS SCHEME,
23 CASTLE STREET, EDINBURGH
EH2 3DN

Scotland's
GARDENS
Scheme
OPEN FOR CHARITY

COPIES OF OUR GUIDEBOOK MAY ALSO BE PURCHASED ON OUR WEBSITE:
SCOTLANDSGARDENS.ORG

THANK YOU FOR VISITING

Check our website scotlandsgardens.org before setting out in case of cancellations or changes to published listings.

Drumpark © Stewart Littlewood

Field House

Parkvilla © Andy Leonard

Pitcurran House © Camelia Hudema

Kincardine Castle